D1298548

# THE SISTERS OF MERCY IN THE CRIMEAN WAR

# THE SISTERS OF MERCY IN THE CRIMEAN WAR

*By*

EVELYN BOLSTER, M.A., Ph.D.

THE MERCIER PRESS
4 BRIDGE ST., CORK

FIRST PUBLISHED IN U.S.A.
AUTUMN 1964
© EVELYN BOLSTER

MADE AND PRINTED IN IRELAND BY
CAHILL AND COMPANY, LIMITED,
PARKGATE PRINTING WORKS, DUBLIN

*A Thighearna, tabhair gnósa dom an saothar so do dhéanamh,
chum do Ghlóire-se, chum leasa m'anma agus
do réir mar atá orduighthe Agat-sa.*

*(An old Irish prayer said before commencing work.)*

*To*
*My Parents*
*and*
*in memory of*
*Ven. Archdeacon T. F. Duggan*
*who died in*
*Lima, Peru,*
*17 December, 1961*

# CONTENTS

# LIST OF ILLUSTRATIONS

# ACKNOWLEDGEMENTS

To-day, after a lapse of more than a century, the Crimean War still fascinates the historian. Raglan sleeves, cardigans, balaclavas —all derive their origin from personages or place-names of the Crimea ; as does also the legend of the Lady with the Lamp. That Florence Nightingale was an administrator of no mean ability cannot be denied, yet her methods of dictatorship, intrigue and personal vendetta have unhappily bespattered the early days of nursing reform. Only now is it becoming clear that Sir John Hall and the Sisters of Mercy whom she so grossly misrepresented were no more the black sheep of the Crimea than she was herself the white angel.

Of course, if the end justifies the means, there can be no criticism of Florence Nightingale. If, on the other hand, one believes that totalitarianism is never justified, there is much in Florence Nightingale's administration which calls for criticism. Viewed from this angle, history calls for a new approach to certain aspects of the Crimean campaign and for a vindication of the Sisters of Mercy.

The need for such a vindication was impressed on me some eight years ago by the late Archdeacon Thomas F. Duggan, at that time Parish Priest of Kinsale. Without his inspiration, encouragement and support this book would never have been attempted. Any good therefore achieved through the medium of my pen, derives ultimately from him.

I have been fortunate in receiving considerable help from various other sources. Firstly, I wish to record my indebtedness to the late Professor James Hogan, D.Litt., University College, Cork, who proved an expert guide and whose friendship was my mainstay during the years of research which have gone into the compilation of this history. I am sorry he did not live to see the book in print.

I should like to thank Rev. Mother M. Imelda of Kinsale, for giving me access to the historic archives of her convent. The contents of these archives, *viz.*, the *Bridgeman Diary* and a collection of unpublished official correspondence, are enough in themselves to throw an entirely new light on the experiment of female nursing introduced into the British Army in 1854. A study of these documents has enabled me to assemble what I believe to be a true and accurate account of the actual nursing done in the military hospitals of the Crimea. Publication of such unpublished documentary evidence should fill an obvious gap in all current histories of the Crimean War and go far towards counteracting the distorted version of the nursing experiment with which the general reader is all too familiar.

I should also like to thank the Superioresses of the Convents of Mercy in Cork, Charleville, Dublin, Carlow, Limerick, Gort, Liverpool, Hertford and Bermondsey for the use of materials from their archives. Sister M. Malachy, community archivist in Charleville, and Sister M. Imelda of Carlow deserve a special word of thanks for their patient compliance with my requests over the years.

My respectful thanks are expressed to His Grace Most Reverend J. C. McQuaid, D.D., Archbishop of Dublin, for permission to consult and quote from the Cullen Papers preserved in the Archiepiscopal Archives.

I am indebted to Monsieur l'Abbé Alphonse Chapeau, D. ès L., of the Catholic University, Angers, France, for the use of the Manning papers of which he is the custodian.

I have permission from Sir Zachary Cope to quote from his book, *Florence Nightingale and the Doctors*. Mr. Cuthbert Fitzherbert, on behalf of his son Nicholas, has allowed me to reproduce certain extracts from Henry Clifford's *Letters and Sketches from the Crimea*. Mr. James Avery Joyce has permitted me to quote from his *Red Cross International and the Strategy of Peace*.

From Sir Shane Leslie who was perhaps the first to realise the historical import of the Kinsale archives and to evaluate the work of the Sisters of Mercy in the Crimea, I have permission to use ' Forgotten Passages in the Life of Florence Nightingale ' as published in *The Dublin Review*, 161, October, 1917.

Mr. Donald H. Simpson of the Royal Commonwealth Society has furnished me with information I could not otherwise have come by, and for which I thank him. I convey a similar tribute to the late Rev. Canice Mooney, O.F.M.

I wish to thank Mr. J. E. Gaffney, Librarian, Cork City Public Library ; the Librarian, University College, Cork ; the Librarian and staff of the Students' Library, Mount Street, Dublin ; Mr. D. P. O'Neill of the National Library ; Basil O'Connell, Q.C., of the Genealogical Office, Dublin Castle ; Mr. Eamonn Ambrose of *The Cork Examiner ;* Commdt. Brendan Daly, Collins Barracks, Cork ; Mr. Noel Blakiston, Public Records Office, Chancery Lane,

London ; the officials of the British Museum and War Office ; and finally the War Office Librarian.

Rev. T. J. Walsh, M.A., was of considerable help to me in the initial stages of assembling materials. The assistance given me by Professor Denis Gwynn, D.Litt., is incalculable. Out of his wide experience, Professor Gwynn suggested many deletions and improvements in my original manuscript. The work in its present form owes much to him.

I should here like to thank Rev. J. Good, D.D., D.Ph., for reading and checking proofs with me and for preparing the manuscript for final publication.

To my superioress, Mother M. Oliver, I express my gratitude for helps too numerous to mention, such as provision of time, convenience for work and ever-ready understanding and encouragement. My Mistress of Schools, Sister M. Bonaventure, by lessening my educational commitments has also contributed in a very real sense to this book. Nor must I forget the many friends, at home and abroad, whose prayers, good wishes and constant interest made me feel that my research would one day be worthwhile.

Finally, the help received from countless minds and pens in compiling this book is gratefully acknowledged by the inclusion of their works in the Bibliography.

E. B.

St. Maries of the Isle, Cork.

# INTRODUCTION

A confidential letter, dated March 5, 1855, and directed to Scutari Barracks Hospital, concluded thus:

> " The real mistake we made in the selection of these ladies (between ourselves) is that they are *Irish*.* You cannot make their lax minds understand the weight of an obligation."[1]

The writer of the above was Sidney Herbert. The recipient was Florence Nightingale, Lady Superintendent of the British Military Hospitals in Turkey. The " ladies " were fifteen Sisters of Mercy who on the collapse of the British Army Medical Department had volunteered their services as nurses in the Crimean Military Hospitals. Sidney Herbert, one-time Secretary at War in the Aberdeen Ministry, accepted that offer, and despite a subsequent change of heart in their regard, his was the main responsibility for the appointment of Catholic Sisters to the Crimean hospitals.

Mr. Herbert's sentiments represent clearly the bitterness characteristic of current Anglo-Irish relations and arise right out of the heart of the spirit of the times. It is well to remark at the outset, however, that though this attitude was not entirely shared by the Crimean officials (Medical Officers and Protestant Ministers), it nevertheless must be kept in mind as a necessary background to the present work, and it goes far towards explaining the difficulties which militated against the Irish Sisters from the very inception of their mission.

The appointment of the Sisters to the military hospitals is not at all surprising in view of the part taken by the Sisters of Mercy in relieving and reforming social abuses and hospital conditions in early nineteenth-century Dublin. A brief glance at the social and economic history of the period will best illustrate how essential it was that such a reform should have been inaugurated in Ireland.

Mary Catherine McAuley, foundress of the Congregation of Our Lady of Mercy, and born in Dublin in 1781, grew to womanhood in what, perhaps, was one of the most unsettled eras of

---

*Italics are the author's.

Ireland's troubled history. Religious disabilities were heavy and severe. Tithe war was intermittent. Agrarian crime and White-boyism were rife. Remedial measures on the part of the government were confined to coercion acts, insurrection acts, suspensions of *Habeas Corpus,* and other such exceptional legislation. Sporadic relief measures, passed from time to time, had somehow punctuated this campaign of repression and given hope of a better future, but such hopes were forever dashed by the legislative Union of 1800 which sent the country headlong into calamity.

Ireland had then an iniquitous land code. Her small tenantry, steeped in poverty, were clad like beggars, housed like beggars, and fed like beggars. Rents were high; agricultural wages were low; and the bulk of the peasantry being mere tenants at will, had no other means of redress against landlord oppression save alone recourse to violence. After 1815 their status deteriorated alarmingly. During the wars with Napoleon the prices of cattle and corn had risen prodigiously. With peace they fell thirty per cent; but the rents did not fall. Then followed the drift to the towns and further misery, for the town-dwellers, finding the struggle for existence intensified by the influx from the country, sank along with the peasantry. Manufacture dwindled; hundreds were thrown out of work; bread was dear, and the meagre savings of the people were swallowed up in levies imposed upon them to defray the cost of England's foreign wars. And during all this time Ireland's population was steadily increasing: an indigent population living in the shadow of a powerful Ascendancy party.

Emancipation in 1829 was not to prove the long-awaited " Open Sesame " to fuller and more comprehensive liberties for the Catholics. The forty-shilling freeholders were disfranchised; evictions became more common; hatred of the Irish continued to be an outstanding feature of the administration; and though the country was reasonably prosperous in the late 1820's, its wealth was confined to the Ascendancy and to the comparatively few Catholic families who had managed to weather the storm of penal legislation.

Poor Law Relief was unknown in Ireland until 1838, when it was introduced in a form which gave alms but no employment, and extended to this country the degrading workhouse system recently established in England. By requiring the destitute to take up their abode in a Workhouse, those who might be only in need of temporary relief, to enable them to tide over a bad season, would be rendered paupers forever. Their homes would be broken up; their possessions sold; their family connections severed and their liberty lost forever. Neither Catholics nor Protestants were willing to accept relief on such terms. They preferred to live on in poverty—even to beg in the streets—rather than seek admission into the hated Houses of Industry from which there appeared to be no escape but the emigrant ship or the pauper grave.[2]

Economic distress, agrarian discontent, military repression—such, in outline, was the situation in Ireland when, in 1827, Catherine McAuley opened a house for the relief of the poor in Baggot Street, Dublin, on a plot of ground of which Sidney Herbert was landlord. A homeless orphan at the age of eleven, Catherine McAuley had drunk deep of the cup of poverty. An heiress at sixteen, and the legal ward of wealthy non-Catholic relatives, she went to live in Coolock House, County Dublin, where her manner of distributing her newly-found wealth showed that she inherited from her father, James McAuley, his own great attribute of charity. This, his spiritual and only legacy to her, urged her into the homes of the Coolock villagers, whose destitution convinced her of the need for some form of social service directed to the benefit of the sick poor. The Callahan thousands which she inherited from her benefactors in 1823 enabled her to purchase the Baggot Street property where, with a small group of associates, she launched a work of charity that was to be world-wide in scope, and which to-day continues to express itself in an ever-increasing variety of activities undreamt of by those early pioneers.

Mother McAuley's three-fold plan included visitation of the sick, the instruction of youth, and the protection of poor girls of good character. The institute she envisaged was purely secular; but a greater architect improved upon her plans, and Baggot Street House when completed was undeniably conventual in style. Archbishop Murray of Dublin, recognising, in this unwonted turn of events, evidence of the finger of God, encouraged the growth of the young organisation, which in 1830 was approved by the Holy See, and was dedicated to Our Lady of Mercy in the following year. Thus it happened that Catherine McAuley, the social worker, became foundress of an institute vowed to the "service of the poor, sick, and ignorant." Stressing the importance of the visitation, she herself led the way into the back streets and slums of Dublin where, with gentleness as her creed of service and the love of God as her only motive, she endeavoured, while relieving temporal distress, to minister also to the spiritual mal-nutrition of the poor. Poverty confronted her at every turn:

poverty as exemplified by the young newsboy whose dinner usually consisted of a crust of stale bread and the smell from the Gresham Hotel.

During the next ten years (1831-1841), Mother McAuley, at the request of the Irish Bishops, extended her congregation to the provinces, and in 1839 made her first English foundation at Bermondsey in the diocese of Southwark. Built on the ruins of an old Benedictine Abbey, this convent has a dual significance as the first religious house to be erected in England since the Reformation,[3] and the first also to furnish a group of volunteer nurses for the Crimea.

An epidemic of Asiatic cholera in 1832 gave the " Baggot Street Ladies " an opportunity of proving their title as Sisters of Mercy. Existing social conditions favoured the spread of the disease, but wild rumours that doctors and nurses were killing off their patients deterred the people from availing themselves of such hospital services as were provided. The rumours were not without some element of truth. Hospitals in the early nineteenth century had a somewhat sinister reputation, and nursing was regarded as a disagreeable and repellent form of domestic service undertaken only by those who failed to find employment in other spheres of usefulness. A nurse then was a coarse old woman, ignorant, dirty, intemperate, often brutal, sometimes immoral and with no trace at all of anything approaching a vocational spirit. Degeneration was such for a time that an eminent London surgeon was known to have declared that if he could get a sober set of women it was about as much as he could hope for.

Hospital conditions were appalling, especially in English-speaking countries, and more particularly in England itself where nothing constructive had replaced the spoliation wrought in Reformation times. Religious nursing orders, both Catholic and Lutheran, had supplied this need on the continent, but there was no parallel development in England until well into the nineteenth century. Thus one finds that even in places like Guy's Hospital (founded in 1725) and the London Infirmary (founded in 1740) conditions were unhygienic and dirty, with " fifty or one hundred patients crowded together in semi-darkness . . . in small dismal wards . . . deprived of all comforts and even of necessaries."[4] Whiskey was the panacea for all ailments in these institutions. There was no definite regulation as to its distribution. A patient might get none, or he might get a quart a day. In either case, recovery was doubtful.

The foregoing facts explain the attitude of the people to the

Dublin cholera hospitals which were classic examples of such maladministration and abuse. Persuasion having failed to remove prejudice, the Dublin Board of Health appealed to the Sisters of Mercy to help in the recently-opened depot in Townsend Street. The appeal met with a ready response. Within a short time popular fear gave way to confidence, the fever was gradually brought under control, and by the time it had spent itself the " Walking Nuns " were ministering in several other Dublin hospitals, notably Sir Patrick Dun's, Mercer's and Madame Spencer's. Mother McAuley's wish to have a hospital administered entirely by her own Sisters was not realised until after her death, but she went to her reward in November 1841 secure in the knowledge that her spiritual daughters had already won general recognition as nurses, and that her great scheme of reform was beginning to bear fruit.

Shortly after her death came the tragedy of the Great Famine with its complement of disease, starvation and death. Hungry people lay down on the roadside and died. Whole families perished in their wretched cabins. These, and the thousands swept off by famine fever illustrate but too well the fact that Lord John Russell and his colleagues dealt with the crisis from a purely English point of view, and without any consideration of the special circumstances of Ireland. But failure on the part of the government gave private charity its opportunity; and here the Sisters of Mercy stepped in. Late and early they were to be seen in the teeming workhouses and in the overcrowded slums, relieving pain, consoling the afflicted, and lavishing upon all with whom they came in contact those exercises of mercy they had so well learned from Catherine McAuley. In the years following the famine they became an integral part of Irish life, and when the call came for nurses in 1854, the emergency found them ready and willing to encounter even the dangers of the battlefield in fulfilment of their vocation of mercy.

Hospital reform in England during these years is necessarily associated with the name of Florence Nightingale. A lady of gentle birth and cultured upbringing, Miss Nightingale, though hampered by parental opposition and Victorian convention, succeeded in focussing public, parliamentary and royal attention on the condition of the English hospitals. Her one ambition in life was to be a nurse; but she realised that she could never nurse as she wished without some definite training. The problem was how to go about securing it. The situation in England being moribund, circumstances led her to certain continental hospitals administered by

Catholic Sisterhoods and Lutheran Deaconesses, where the information she acquired equipped her in no small measure for the reorganisation she later effected in her own country.

Her continental experiences included an observation of the renowned Roman hospitals of Trinita dei Monti and Santo Spirito; a period under the Lutheran Pastor Fliedner at Kaiserwerth on the Rhine; and a close study of the organisation of the Sisters of Charity in the Maison de la Providence, Paris. Winter holidays abroad were a further asset in promoting her desire for training; yet her search was not altogether confined to the continent.

The year 1852 saw her in Dublin where she hoped, through the influence of Henry Edward Manning, to be accepted by the Sisters of Mercy and be given the training of a nursing Sister. Her idea —a secret shared only by Manning and the Superioress—was to assume the habit of the Sisterhood and follow the routine of convent life while still remaining a Protestant. This she made clear to Manning when she asked him to inquire " whether they would take me in the hospital of St. (*sic.*) Stephen's* on the Green of Dublin (which is served by the Sisters of Mercy) for three months *as I am.*"

Negotiations fell through. The convent was undergoing repairs, and in any case, the scheme was not feasible on religious grounds. Later in the same year, however, Miss Nightingale was admitted into the Maison de la Providence, but personal illness and family interference brought this effort also to nought.

Florence Nightingale's attitude to the Catholic Church at this particular date was perhaps more practical than devotional. She saw it as a potential training-ground for nurses and envied the Catholic Sisters the advantages they undoubtedly possessed.

> " For what training is there compared with that of the Catholic Nun? Those ladies who are not Sisters have not the chastened temper, the Christian grace, the accomplished loveliness and energy of the regular nun. I have seen something of different kinds of nuns, and am no longer young, and do not speak from enthusiasm but experience." [5]

So she wrote to Manning in July 1852, when destiny had already

---

*Though Miss Nightingale here made the common error of confusing the Sisters of Mercy and Charity, contacts with the former were a constant and paramount factor in her life.

shaped a course of events which brought her into closest personal contact with the Sisters of Mercy during the Crimean War.

At the outbreak of this war British medical arrangements were chaotic, with nursing services devolving entirely upon orderlies and pensioners. Untrained and unskilled, they were never left long enough in the hospitals to be of much use, and were, in general, unreliable, uncouth, unkind, drunken and not above consuming the food intended for their patients. Female nursing, as yet unknown in the British military hospitals, was quite the fashion in France, where for many years the Sisters of Charity had formed an important feature of the country's war milieu. Here was one of the many advantages denied to the British soldiers, who had to pay dearly for the fact that nuns had no place in England's scheme of war administration. Yet the day came when a frenzied appeal was voiced for the services of Catholic Sisters in the British army.

The no-popery campaign of 1850 and the prolonged bitterness engendered by the Oxford Movement gave a strange and unusual background to this appeal. Stranger still was the willingness of English ministers of state to accept the services of Irish Sisters. That Irish Sisters were permitted to serve a government which had so often endeavoured to suppress all manifestations of Catholic religious life in Ireland, was more unusual again. But perhaps the most extraordinary feature of all was the fact that Irish ecclesiastical superiors permitted their Sisters to mingle in an expedition of this nature, aware as they must have been of the reputation and character of the nineteenth-century nurse. And yet, it was no blind providence which urged the acceptance of the mission, for the Sisters who went to the Crimea soon discovered that Irish soldiers formed roughly one-third of the army they undertook to serve.

Emigration was then a permanent feature of Irish life, encouraged on the one hand by the " push " of economic distress, and on the other, by the " pull " of foreign enterprise. In the early nineteenth century this great exodus flowed mainly towards England and the continent, until with the collapse of the Repeal Movement, the abortive rebellion of 1848 and the destitution consequent upon the famine, a change of direction set in. From now on America was the goal—the land of sunshine where there was bread and work for all; but for the thousands who managed that passage, there was a corresponding quota of others who for

the sake of a meal and a shilling bartered their liberty to the
English recruiting sergeants. A contemporary ballad, The Kerry
Recruit, talks of this shilling enlistment:

> " So I buttered my brogues and shook hands with my spade,
> And I went to the fair like a dashing young blade;
> When up comes a sergeant and asks me to 'list:
> ' Arra, sergeant, a ghrá, put the bob in my fist.' "

When the Crimean War broke out, about ten thousand had been
enlisted in this manner. The war, originating in a quarrel over
possession of the Holy Places, naturally aroused interest in Ireland
where for three centuries back every conflict had been coloured
with the religious issue. It was only natural too, that since the
country in 1854 was in a state of political lethargy, there should be
a great awakening of interest in the achievements of the British
Army in the Near East where so many Irish hearts beat beneath
English uniforms.

Passing over the fact that General de Lacy,* an Irish Catholic,
was mainly responsible for first capturing the Crimea under the
Empress Catherine, Irishmen figured conspicuously in every important engagement during the campaign of 1854-'56. The list of
those killed in the attack on the Redan reads like the census
return of a parish in Munster. Of the fourteen hundred killed at the
Alma, seven hundred and fifty were Irish soldiers who led the van;
and when the colours of the 4th Regiment were taken from an
English soldier, they were later discovered wrapped about the
body of an Irish ensign. This man, Daniel Sullivan, left his ranks
to recover the flag, but fell dead, pierced with seven balls, just at
the moment of regaining his comrades. It was an Irishman, John
London of Carrick-on-Suir, who sounded the cavalry charge at
Balaclava; the son of an Irishman, Captain Nolan, who bore the
fatal order for the charge; and an Irish general, Lord Lucan,
who had command of the Light Brigade on that memorable day.
It is generally known that the Earl of Cardigan entered the fray

---

*Peter de Lacy, a native of Rathcahill, near Killeedy, in south Limerick,
described by the Russians as " our greatest soldier of the 18th century."
It was recently proposed that he should be honoured by the erection of a
memorial hospital near Riga, the Latvian capital. Commenting on which,
The Limerick Leader, April 4, 1959, stated that as he " caused the
world's first military hospital to be built in the Russian Crimea, it is
fitting that the new monument to his memory should take the form of a
hospital."

with the words: "Here goes the last of the Brudenells!"; but nobody bothered recording that an Irish trooper hearing him followed with "And here goes the last of the Murphys!" None of this valour was recognised, much less rewarded: all glory went to the Highland and other brigades. Finally, in the slaughterous engagement in the Inkermann gorges, the Irish regiments were again in the thickest of the fight; and when their ammunition failed, the gallant Eighty-eighth, the Connaught Rangers, charged a nine-gun battery with fixed baynots, accompanying the charge with the already famous war-cry, "Faugh-a-Ballagh!"[6]

Warfare in those days, in spite of its sordidness, had nevertheless an element of glamour, a personal element which is somehow altogether eliminated in our modern age which boasts of submarines and jet planes, nuclear weapons and megaton bombs. Because of the absence of such a personal element, modern battles are seldom commemorated in song. It was otherwise during the Crimean War, when gestures of bravery on the battle-field were brought to life again in rousing verses, especially in places where local interest in army affairs was encouraged by circumstances which in any way tended to militarism.

For Cork people the Crimean War had a manifold significance. Cork was then an important army depot, Victoria (now Collins) Barracks being the centre of military command for Munster, and Ballincollig, with its powder mills, providing a parallel with the modern Woolwich. The area around Cork—reputed to be the richest field for recruitment in the United Kingdom—was ideal for the training of armies for overseas service. Many Corkmen, too, having taken the Queen's shilling, were drafted to the army serving in the East. A Cork ship, the s.s. *Cormorant,* built in 1853 for the Packet Company, and captained by one Edward Byrne of Cork city, was chartered by the English Government for Crimean service.

Priests from the diocese went as chaplains to the seat of war. Seven of the fifteen Sisters of Mercy who served in the military hospitals were from convents in Cork city and county. The leader of the Bermondsey Sisters had been for some time superioress in the Rutland Street Convent (transferred in 1852 to St. Maries of the Isle); and Bishop Thomas Grant of Southwark, who first offered the services of Sisters to the government, lived for some years in Cork, while his father, an officer in the 71st Regiment, was stationed in the Victoria Barracks.

Finally, the Cork-born poet, Michael Joseph Barry, by publishing in *The Daily Reporter* his "Lays of the War", kept alive in the people an awareness of the happenings on the distant battle-fields. Hence, ballad singers on the Coal Quay drew interested audiences around them when they sang:

" Attention! and hould ye'er breath awhile—
for they walloped the Russians at Inkermann,
The boys of the Emerald Isle."

Neither performers nor audiences then realised that behind that " walloping " there lay a story written in blood, telling of the incredible sufferings of a gallant and heroic army, and the irresolution and incapacity which presided over the councils of its chiefs.

## CHAPTER 1

# THE CRIMEAN WAR

ON March 27, 1854, a message from Napoleon III to the Senate, and a simultaneous message from Queen Victoria to both Houses of Parliament announced a state of hostilities between the allied governments of France and England and the Empire of Russia. Thus began the Crimean War, the slowest war in modern history; a war which was slow to come and which in time staggered to an inglorious conclusion. The military part of the war may be forgotten now, for it was a sluggish campaign, lacking in military finesse, and having in the Balaclava Charge its only approximation to anything like epic proportions. It could be classified as an unnecessary war. It was certainly inconclusive. But for all that, it was not without features at once novel and significant. It brought about the first large-scale introduction of chloroform; it marked an epoch in the history of modern journalism; it produced Florence Nightingale and the idea of a military nursing service just as the battle of Solferino a few years later produced Henri Dunant and the International Red Cross; and it will always stand out on the page of history as a classic example of an ill-conducted British campaign in which the incompetence, the ineptitude and the lethargy of the War Department brought the army to the verge of annihilation. The immediate cause of the catastrophe was the collapse of all medical and transport arrangements at the seat of war. Its remote causes stretched back through long years of peace and carelessness in England; and in the inquiries which followed it was clearly shown that the evil was, in reality, the worst of all evils—one which has been caused by nothing in particular and for which no one in particular is to blame.

In the first place, the organisation of the war machinery was incompetent and out of date. From Waterloo to Balaclava the doctrine of "Responsibility" which Wellington had infused into the British system had taken such a grip on the minds of army officials that it was difficult, even impossible, to obtain independent action in an emergency. According to the testimony of Kinglake, the historian *par excellence* of the Crimean War, the decision to invade Russia was taken when most of the Cabinet members were asleep! Thus 45,000 British subjects and nearly half a million foreigners were condemned to death. Nor was that all. A second official doctrine, that of " Economy " had undermined the entire administration of the War Department. There was an extraordinary overlapping of authorities and an incredible parsimony and neglect in the matter of maintaining and officering England's standing army. The *personnel* of the army had been cut down; its *materiel* was allowed fall into decay. The staff and regimental officers were as untrained in the practice as they were unversed in the theory of war. The rank and file were equally unprepared; and there were no reinforcements. To enter upon war with such limited resources was plainly courting disaster. England had nothing to gain by participating in the Crimean War; but the English people were bored by peace and they welcomed this new campaign expecting, like Charles Kingsley that it would " sweep away at once the dyspeptic unbelief, the insincere bigotry, the effeminate frivolity which paralyses our poetry as much as it does our action."

From the start the organisation of the War Department led to confusion. The nominal control of the army rested with the Secretary of State *for* War, who in 1854 happened to be Colonial Secretary as well. Most of his time was devoted to administrative work which had no connection with the campaign. Control of army finances was under a Secretary of State *at* War, who received his orders, not from the Secretary for War but from the Commander-in-Chief. Add to this that the Ordnance was under a Board, the Commissariat under the Treasury, the militia under the Home Office, and that the Secretary of State for War exercised no direct authority over any of these departments.

The ramifications of the army medical services were equally confusing.[1] The Commissariat, the Purveying Department and the Medical Department were collectively responsible for the health of the British Army and the organisation of its hospitals. At the outbreak of the Crimean War each of these departments was understaffed. Mr. Ward, the seventy-year-old Purveyor, had but two clerks and three messenger boys as assistants. The Commissariat, hopelessly ill-equipped to cope with the problems of supply and transport, was headed by a civilian, a Mr. James Filder, who was called out of retirement to run it. Dr. Andrew Smith, Director-General of the Army Medical Service, had only a staff of twelve with which to execute the entire administration of his vast department. None of these bodies had any standing. They were subject, in varying degrees, to the Secretary of State, the War Office, the Horse Guards, the Transport Office and the Treasury. The system was likened to "a clumsy rickety machine, with a pin loose here and a tooth broken there, and a makeshift somewhere else, in which the force of Hercules might be exhausted in needless friction and obscure hitches before the hands could be got to move."[2]

The Commissariat were the general carriers for the army, charged with the delivery of provisions, forage, fuel and general stores. Special "extra diets"—arrowroot, rice, sago, port wine and milk—were supplied by the Purveyor, who, in turn, obtained them on requisition from the Commissariat Department. But while the Purveyor was responsible for the preparation and distribution of these extra diets, he had no authority over their purchase, nor could he reject them if unsuitable. Where the duties of the Commissariat ended and those of the Purveyor began, nobody seemed to know—neither the officials themselves nor the heads of the departments at home.

A similar obscurity existed between the Purveyor and the doctors, a prescription for a patient depending entirely on whether or not the Purveyor honoured a requisition. To be valid, every requisition had to be checked and countersigned by two doctors, one of whom had to be a senior surgeon. Where these signatures were lacking, "regulations" forbade the issue of goods. It was not altogether the fault of the Purveyor that he was the very embodiment of red tape and sealing wax. He was just another slave to an out-dated system of requisitions, memos and dockets which amounted to endless work on paper but provided no co-ordination among departments; and while the scribes were busy the army perished.

Once an official had seen to his own particular duty, he was unconcerned as to the possible miscarriage of his arrangements. Thus, for instance, a member of the Ordnance Department might order and arrange the packing of supplies for the army; but there his responsibility ended. He never bothered to enquire if these goods were ever shipped from England. *That* was the business of the Admiralty! A natural and unavoidable consequence of such ambiguity of services was an appalling carelessness in transport arrangements. A few examples will illustrate this point.

On one occasion a much-needed supply of boots was despatched to the Crimea—only to be found on inspection that they were all *left* fitting. Iron bed-frames were unloaded at Scutari: the legs were put on another vessel and sent on to Balaclava. Huts arrived without delivery notes and were left on board the transport ships which on the night of November 14, 1854, were lost in one of the worst hurricanes within living memory. Anything salvaged from this wreckage could only be used as firewood. Hence the ultimate fate of the huts, while the soldiers for whom they were intended shivered and died in pea jackets on the heights above Sebastopol.[3] Perhaps the most ridiculous blunder of all was the consignment of wooden legs delivered to the army at the rate of *four per man*; " which just showed," observed Lieutenant-Colonel Steevens of the Connaught Rangers, " what donkeys our government took us to be."[4]

Artillery and hospital stores were usually shipped as one cargo, and so arranged that it was almost impossible to extricate them. More often than not they were never unloaded, and so " the medicines which would certainly have done good, and the guns that might have done harm, were left to neutralize each other . . . . or else go together to the bottom."[5] Hospital supplies were often carried several times to and fro across the Black Sea before reaching their proper destination. Then what was wanted in Sebastopol was found to be at Varna and what was wanted in the Crimea was in Constantinople.

" This bureaucratic blunder," wrote Delane of *The Times,* " cost at least five hundred lives; but the government which denied that there was any want of stores will now, of course, maintain, that it was in pursuance of a wise and far-seeing policy that the medicines and the sick, the lint and the wounded, were kept three hundred miles apart."

Most of the supplies unloaded at Scutari literally vanished in the Turkish Customs House, described by Florence Nightingale as " a bottomless pit whence nothing ever issued of all that was thrown in." Other cargoes were similarly swallowed up in the government stores. The heads of departments in London might claim that these stores were better filled than all the granaries of Europe, but such flaunted abundance little availed the starving troops who were soon to be reduced to a diet of raw pork and green coffee. It took Miss Nightingale to reveal the actual state of affairs. In her *Notes on Matters affecting the Health, Efficiency and Hospital Administration of the British Army,* she cites a number of instances where even the most essential supplies were withheld from the troops because of the stringency of "service regulations" which discouraged initiative on the part of officials and forbade the issue of goods except through recognised channels. Unfortunately, Florence Nightingale became as much a slave to this system as were the officials whom she condemned. Because of such strict adherence to antiquated regulations, vast quantities of preserved foods, bales of warm clothing and large consignments of medical and surgical supplies were left unissued, while the army reduced to starvation rations and with nothing but jam pots from which to drink was ravaged by dysentery, scurvy and enteric fever—evils which were shortly aggravated by cholera, typhus and frostbite. Regulations were in fact carried so far that in January 1855 a whole cargo of cabbages was toppled into the harbour of Balaclava because nobody would dare incur the responsibility of issuing them.

The army which embarked for the Crimea in June 1854, chose as its destination the insalubrious sea-port town of Varna in Bulgaria, where nothing worthy of note was accomplished, but where an outbreak of " Varna fever " later recognised as cholera, played havoc with the health of the troops. Sebastopol, the main Russian naval base, was the next objective, but so inadequate were the transports provided for the journey thither, that all military kit and medical equipment had to be abandoned. On arrival in the Crimea on September 14, the troops discovered that the Purveyor's " warrants " did not extend to articles coming under the head of military kit. The most he could supply them with were tin or pewter cups and crockery-ware plates. Cutlery, shirts, toilet requisites, were not his concern.

A week later (September 20) the battle of the Alma was fought and won. As yet the weather was fine and the Indian summer gave no hint of the rigours of the coming winter; but cholera hung over the camp and the immolation of the British forces had begun. By October the army was an army of skeletons, faced with the prospect of a winter campaign in the Crimea, with no supplies and no clothes other than what they carried on their backs. Compelled to remain in the trenches for thirty-six hours at a stretch, these men had no better shelter than mud-logged canvas tents,* where they lay uncovered and unprotected, and bearing the full blast of the Boreas wind which howled over the Chersonese and which it was stated " would have effectively deprived any number of rats of their whiskers." Well might they be described as victims of the parsimony and incompetence of the War Office. Deaths were estimated at not less than sixty a day; those disabled by fever and disease were reported as no fewer than a thousand a week.

" Anything would have been better than such a melancholy

---

*It could be argued that trench conditions were even worse than this during the two World Wars; improved transport and medical arrangements however, obviated many of the more hideous miseries suffered by the troops in the Crimea.

waste of brave men, who would have died cheerfully in battle, but who could not go to the trenches without *tears in their eyes.*" [6]

So ran an article in *The Times.*

Inter-army communication was as chaotic as overseas transport from England. The approach to Balaclava was one vast sea of mud overstrewn with piles of human limbs and trunks. Further up on the highland, the carcases of horses were utilised as signposts, as may be inferred from the directions given by a Cockney sailor to a relief company that had gone astray. "Keep straight on," he said, "till yer comes to a dead 'orse on one side and a 'orrid smell on the hother, and then turn to yer right." [7] All of this was literally true. So hopelessly indeed did the transport system collapse that it was quite the normal thing for the unfortunate trooper in the Crimea to do the work of his own broken-down horse. Henry Clifford, V.C., writing in the early stages of the campaign when, as yet, the situation had not become chronic, remarked that

> " *Some one* is much to blame that so fine an army has been landed, without proper means of transport, in an enemy's country, where there are no resources, no help to hope for from the natives, only a few miserable ox-wagons, seized on landing in the Crimea, now broken down, and which had the Cossacks been more alert would never have fallen into our hands at all. Well might a French Officer exclaim on seeing a train of these miserable ox-vans going a mile an hour in the finest weather and under most favourable circumstances ' *Quelle Equipage Militaire*!!!!' The French have provisions of every description in *the centre of their camp* for their immense army for three months!!!" [8]

Scutari, a small town facing Constantinople from the Asiatic shore of the Bosphorus, was the medical headquarters of the British Expeditionary Force to the Crimea. Here an enormous Turkish Artillery Barracks and hospital was handed over by the Sultan to the British. At first it was assumed that the hospital, known as the General Hospital, would be adequate: the war was going to be of short duration. Events of unforeseen gravity shortly put paid to such wishful thinking. A cholera epidemic swept through the ranks, an unending procession of casualties kept drifting in from Balaclava, the medical organisation was thrown into disorder and a total administrative collapse followed. The conversion of the barracks into a hospital did not ease the situation; it only made the inadequacy of the administration stand out in ever sharper relief.

Empty, dilapidated and neglected, the word "hospital" was a misnomer for these shells of buildings which without forethought or preparation were set aside as the chief shelter for the victims of war. The Barracks Hospital contained a radical defect. Huge sewers underlay it. Filth of every description abounded in its corridors, the floors were so rotten that they could not be scrubbed, moisture oozed from the walls, and on the testimony of Florence Nightingale, "the vermin might, if they had unity of purpose, carry the four miles of bedding on their backs and march with them to the War Office."[9] Not alone that but there was a sad deficiency of even the commonest objects of hospital use. There were no beds, properly so called—just straw sacks thrown upon the rotten, unwashed floors and so crushed together that there was scarely room to pass between them. The sheets thrown upon these straw pallets were of coarsest canvas; there was no bedroom furniture of any kind—no trays, no ware, no soap, no brooms, no cutlery, no plates and empty beer bottles formed a sorry substitute for candlesticks. There were neither surgical nor medical appliances—no morphia, no lint, no medicine. There was no kitchen in which to prepare food. Water was scarce. The laundry was a farce. There were no nurses.

Not infrequently it happened that men admitted into these hospitals were left untended for days. " I am now in Scutari Barracks, the hospital of which is full," wrote a young soldier in October 1854. "We are lying here like so many pigs—hundreds lying in the passages. Very seldom you see a doctor, they have so much to do cutting off hands and legs."[10] Only the strongest survived those first days in hospital. Those who died were thrown upon an araba, or rough Turkish cart, drawn by a pair of oxen, and so carted to the bleak hillside for burial. Here a party of men, enfeebled themselves, awaited them, nominally as a firing party, but they never fired a volley. There was injury to the living; no honour to the dead. No wonder then that the heart of the strong sickened at the sight and the souls of the weak fled, as it were, to a better country for peace.

Medical conditions at the front were more appalling still. One reads of amputations without anaesthetics; screaming patients laid out upon old tubs for operations performed in semi-darkness or by moonlight; no bandages, no splints, no sterilisation. Then followed a four-hundred-mile journey across the Black Sea in conditions recalling in all their hideousness the worst days of the slave trade. In normal times this was a voyage of about four or five days; but the times were no longer normal, and now a good three weeks elapsed between departure and arrival. The "hospital ships" chartered for the conveyance of the sick were ordinary transports, the medical equipment of which was totally inadequate to the requirements of the existing crisis. The number of surgeons on board these transports was ill-proportioned to the overflow of patients. Red tapeism forbade the employment of civilian doctors in a military capacity; and though numbers of young and competent medical officers volunteered their services, they were rejected, with consequences which led *The Times* to declare that it was obviously considered "more economical to let wounds fester and brave men die in excruciating agony than employ a sufficient medical staff."

The slow voyage to Scutari was for all concerned a more agonising experience than anything hitherto endured in the trenches. Men, covered with putrefying wounds, men in the clutches of cholera and dysentery, men who had recently undergone the amputation of limbs, were left day and night on the open deck, uncovered save for threadbare blankets saturated with blood and ordure. Others were packed into the holds of the vessels where they lay exhausted and untended, their strength oozing out through their undressed wounds. Food, when available, consisted of the ordinary salt rations of ship diet and water was so stored as to be out of reach of the weak. Under such circumstances the sick were tended by the sick; the dying were left to die. For many months deaths occurring on this voyage averaged seventy-four in the thousand. The dead, laid out as they died, were left side by side with the living, the latter presenting "a spectacle beyond all imagination, with their thigh and shoulder bones perfectly red from rubbing against the deck of the vessel which had brought them from the Crimea."[11]

Journey's end brought added torture. At Scutari, the rickety landing stage, constructed with oriental ingenuity, could only be negotiated with difficulty in fair weather, or not at all. The human cargo from the ships was first lowered into caiques, or small rowing boats, to be afterwards transferred to the jetty when the choppy waters of the Bosphorus permitted. The last lap was, perhaps, the hardest of all. Worn out men dragged their weary way up the hill to the hospital. Those who had legs assisted their less fortunate comrades. Stretcher cases, left to the care of orderlies and pensioners, were so roughly jolted over the uneven path that many of them died on the quarter-mile stretch between the wharf and the hospital. The journey accomplished, the survivors were swallowed up in the dilapidated makeshift building which was the principal base hospital of the army. "I could well enter," wrote the Honourable and Reverend Sidney Godolphin Osborne, "into the feelings of one officer, who himself lying on a stretcher, seemed so disgusted with the whole scene that he exclaimed, 'Do cover my face for me.' It was indeed a trial of any man's nerves to see the way this important part of the public service was misconducted."[12] Within the hospital there were moments and there were places where the strongest hand was struck with trembling, and the boldest eye would turn away its gaze.

Back in England there was general exultation at news of 'that twentieth of September, when the Alma's heights were won'. Nothing was yet known of the administrative collapse and the resultant immolation of the troops. People were slow to believe the first whispered rumours that began to be circulated; they preferred to rely on the 'truth' of the guarded reports from Whitehall. The subsequent disillusionment made their reaction all the more hysterical.

Sidney Herbert, as Secretary at War, was held to be primarily responsible for the catastrophe. To a certain extent he was, but his position was an unenviable one. In those days of imperfect communication he was completely dependent on reports received from the heads of the medical department, who notwithstanding the awful calamity at Scutari, protested that the hospital organisation of the army was adequate. To Lord Stratford de Redcliffe, the British Ambassador at Constantinople, they were coldly officious. Departmental rivalry proved to be the death of co-operation between them and him. Lord Stratford was a member of the Foreign Office; the doctors were attached to the War Office, and because relations between these two departments were at the time notoriously difficult, the doctors refused to take the Ambassador into their confidence. Rather, they misled him as to the true nature of things. Dr. Menzies, senior medical officer at Scutari, gave him to understand that all deficiencies had been already remedied, that the hospital stores were excellently stocked, that the soldiers were in want of nothing. Information to this effect was duly issued from Whitehall; but gradually, steadily, distressingly, news of the actual state of affairs began to filter in from unofficial sources, and there sprang up from day to day and from hour to hour, whispered rumours of the sufferings to which the army was exposed: rumours which at length deepened not into a cry but into a roar of disapproval expressed by the entire press of the country.

The Crimean War marks the first occasion on which a 'Special

Correspondent' was permitted to accompany the army into battle. The step was a radical innovation, and as the new profession had not yet come into its own, no means as to its regulation had so far been formulated. Censorship was unknown, nor had the correspondent as yet mastered the art of wording his despatches in the manner least calculated to give offence to the home government or information to the enemy. Ignored, as were all civilians who insinuated themselves into military affairs, he was nevertheless given free access to all regiments and to all sections of the camp. William Howard Russell, special correspondent to *The Times,* then a radical newspaper under the editorship of Delane, availing himself of such *carte blanche* facilities, was the individual most responsible for awakening the British public to a realisation of events in the Crimea. An Irishman, with an Irishman's hatred of injustice, and a Celtic capacity for indignation, Russell was a keen observer and a brilliant writer, and he could convert into powerful and striking narrative events which to a less keen onlooker might appear casual, trivial, or unimportant. He had an abundant sagacity, was highly skilled, and his written accounts had the novelty of being first-hand and totally different from the officially-worded army communiqués. He also enjoyed the unique advantage of being able to give eye-witness accounts of the hopeless administrative incompetence that was then involving the army in disaster. And because he did not hesitate to reveal the miseries to which the troops were subjected, he stands out as the correspondent *par excellence* of the Crimean War.

*The Times* published Russell's articles in full and uncensored. By so doing it stirred the country into great undertakings, it paved the way for the downfall of the Aberdeen Bureaucracy, it saved " the remnant of an army ", and it gave momentum to an invigorating direction of one of the strangest campaigns in which England ever engaged. It proclaimed the end of a corrupt regime and the departure from an antiquated practice which in the Crimea had contributed to involve the army in many disasters. Military promotion at that time was assessed on a basis of blue blood and broad acres; merit availed but little. So far did discrimination go that the officers chosen to lead the army in 1854 were high-born veterans of the Peninsular War, courageous certainly, but not at all equal to the task confronting them. The early disasters and the degrading spectacle of administrative collapse made imperative a radical overhaul of the entire war machinery of England, but before this change was finally effected it became necessary for *The Times* to direct attention more than once to the fact that the army was reduced to the verge of ruin by a hideous complication of fatal neglects.

The nation was thunderstruck. Charges of neglect towards the sick and wounded raised a feeling of resentment against the authorities, resentment which was lashed to fury when on October 12, 1854 *The Times* published the following report from its special correspondent.

" It is with feelings of surprise and anger that the public will learn that no sufficient preparations have been made for the proper care of the wounded. Not only are there not sufficient surgeons—that, it might be urged, was unavoidable; not only are there no dressers or nurses—that might be a defect of system for which no one is to blame; but what will be said when it is known that there is not even linen to make bandages for the wounded? Can it be said that the Battle of the Alma has been an event to take the world by surprise? Has not the expedition to the Crimea been the talk of the last four months? And yet, after the troops have been six months in the country, there is no preparation for the commonest surgical operations! Not only are the men kept, in some cases, for a week without the hand of a medical man coming near their wounds; not only are they left to expire in agony, unheeded and shaken off, though catching desperately at the surgeon whenever he makes his rounds through the fetid ship; but now, when they are placed in the spacious building, where we were led to believe that everything was ready which could ease their pain or facilitate their recovery, it is found that the commonest appliances of a work-house sick ward are wanting, and that the men must die through the medical staff of the British Army having forgotten that old rags are necessary for the dressing of wounds. If Parliament were sitting, some notice would prob-ably be taken of these facts, which are notorious and have excited much concern; as it is, it rests with the Government to make inquiries into the conduct of those who have so greatly neglected their duty." [13]

*The Times* accompanied the above letter by a leading article, appealing to its readers to render such help as might be possible to the soldiers in the Crimea. A *Times* Fund was opened by Sir Robert Peel, and a *Times* official, a Mr. MacDonald, was sent to Scutari to expend the proceeds on supplies and comforts for the sick and wounded. Once again official quarters took offence. Lord Stratford de Redcliffe frowned at the idea of utilising private money for government purposes. In his eyes, such subscriptions were a slur on the administration of the country. He accordingly suggested that Mr. MacDonald might dispose of his money by building a badly-needed Protestant Church in Pera! Private charity and benevolence however would not be denied. The collapse of the medical organisation in the Crimea swept away official prejudice to such an extent that help was welcomed from any and every quarter and departmental rivalries were buried in the general effort to restore the national reputation.

Meanwhile, Russell continued to chant England's dirge. On October 13 he wrote that

> " it is impossible for anyone to see the melancholy sights of the last few days without feelings of surprise and indignation at the deficiencies of our medical system. The manner in which the sick and wounded are treated is worthy only of the savages of Dahomey . . . The worn-out pensioners who were brought as an ambulance corps are totally useless. Here the French are greatly our superiors. Their medical arrangements are extremely good, their surgeons more numerous, and they have also the help of the Sisters of Charity who have accompanied the expedition in incredible numbers. These devoted women make excellent nurses." [14]

These scathing attacks quickly changed the mood of the country. There is no direct evidence that Russell was hinting that the services of Sisters in England should be sought; but his readers were so rabidly indignant at the unfavourable contrasts he drew, that on the following day, October 14, a letter was published in *The Times* asking: "Why have we no Sisters of Charity? There are numbers of able-bodied and tender-hearted Englishwomen who would joyfully and with alacrity go out to devote themselves to nursing the sick and wounded, if they could be associated for that purpose, and placed under proper protection."

" Why have we no Sisters of Charity? "

## CHAPTER 2

## THE APPEAL FOR NURSES

THE angry outburst from the anonymous contributor to *The Times* paved the way for the first tentative step towards the introduction of female nurses into the British Army. It was instrumental also in partially suppressing the violent outbreak of bigotry and religious animosity still simmering as a result of the restoration of the English Hierarchy in 1850. Old prejudices were momentarily forgotten, and England, despite her rooted aversion to every manifestation of Catholic life, openly expressed her urgent need for the services of Catholic Sisters in her army. An interested spectator of this phenomenal development was Thomas Grant, Bishop of Southwark, who saw in the crisis an opportunity expeditiously afforded of advancing the work of Catholic Sister-hoods, and who determined that his own diocese should at once furnish its due contingent of helpful self-devotion to the troops.

There was one snag: the Sisters of Charity had then no convent in England, nor indeed, until well after the period of the Crimean War. Nothing deterred, Bishop Grant applied to the Convent of Mercy, Bermondsey. This Irish convent, domiciled in London, and founded from Cork in 1839, was to enjoy, through the personality of its Irish-born Superioress, a certain prominence during the ensuing war years. Dr. Grant's purpose in applying to Bermondsey was two-fold. He hoped, while providing skilled medical care for the troops, to calm thereby the storm of opposition recently aroused against nuns in England by the bigots of Exeter Hall notoriety. " Let the nuns who are so fiercely assailed," he said, " proceed at once to the battlefield. There their daily life, seen by the whole world, and their devotedness to the cause of charity, will be the best answer to the vile calumnies uttered against them." [1] To Dr. Grant goes the credit of taking the initiative following *The Times* appeal, and to the Sisters of Mery from Bermondsey the honour of being the first nurses to set out for the Crimea. This latter point is one of the unappreciated facts of history.

Late on Saturday, October 14th, 1854, Bishop Grant in a visit to Bermondsey, informed the community that the government might require their services as nurses in the military hospitals. The

Superioress, Mother M. Clare Moore, immediately offered herself
and three of her Sisters for the mission. Deeply touched by the
spontaneity of this offer, Dr. Grant deemed it unnecessary to
deprive Bermondsey of its Reverend Mother as he had already
written to Ireland for volunteers. Further consideration, however,
led to a change of plan. On the following Monday a letter from the
bishop requested Mother M. Clare and four of her Sisters to be
ready for Turkey next morning. The haste was prompted by a
desire on the part of Dr. Grant that the Sisters selected to serve
in the war hospitals should, if possible, precede the secular nurses.
The government being indifferent in the matter, the money necessary to finance the journey was provided by Lord Arundel and
Surrey; but a subsequent change of heart at the War Office
entailed that the Sisters' expenses from Paris to the Crimea would
be defrayed by the authorities.

In the early hours of Tuesday, October 17, 1854, this pioneer
group of Sisters of Mercy embarked bravely on the first stage of
their unusual mission. Unaccustomed to foreign travel, ignorant
of their itinerary, they only knew they were going to Turkey and
hoped their guardian angels would be kind enough to take care
of them and lead them safely to their destination. On arrival in
Paris they succeeded, after many disappointments, in securing
accommodation at the Hotel Clarendon. Next morning a telegram
from Dr. Grant advised them to remain in the French capital
until further orders. A letter, dated October 19, explained the
delay.

The government had decided to send an officially organised
nursing expedition to the Crimea; a decision which was encouraged
by a small group of philanthropists then keenly interested in
experimenting in the field of military nursing. Florence
Nightingale, the most prominent member of the group, was already
a celebrity in London as a champion of hospital reform. Her
colleagues included, among others, Sidney Herbert, the Secretary
at War; his wife Elizabeth (Liz), and Mary Stanley, daughter of the
Bishop of Norwich and sister to Canon Arthur Penrhyn Stanley of
Canterbury, later Dean of Westminster. Also associated with this
circle of eminent Victorians was the illustrious convert, Henry
Edward Manning, former Archdeacon of Chichester, and for many
years personal friend and confidant of Miss Nightingale. The party
first met in Rome during the winter of 1847, a time when the
Oxford Movement was shaking the Anglican Church to its
foundations. All five belonged to the reforming High Church or
Puseyite party. All were interested in the same schemes of social
welfare; in addition to which Manning was hoping while in Rome

to solve his religious doubts, under stress of which his health had become seriously impaired. Though as yet the Archdeacon was impervious to the claims of Catholicism, grace eventually conquered and his submission to Rome in 1851 delivered one of its heaviest blows to Anglican prestige generally. Two lady members of this group followed Manning into the Church: Mary Stanley during the Crimean War, and Liz Herbert after her husband's death.

Catholicism likewise exerted a profound influence upon Florence Nightingale, but unlike her friends " who had left the arms of one Church to go to those of another, a more faithful mother," she failed to reach the goal. Her religion, which she inherited from her parents, was that of the Anglican Church, but Anglicanism never satisfied her. It was her firm and avowed conviction that " the Church of England could not have stood in any other country but England because she is such a poor historian. I have always thought that the great theological fight has yet to be fought out in England between Catholicism and Protestantism. In Germany it was fought out three hundred years ago. They know why they are Protestants. I never knew an Englishman who did; and if he enquires he becomes a Catholic." In 1852 she admitted in confidence to Manning that " if I do not reach the Church of the Catholics, I have no Church; for the Anglican has long since melted away into a ghost. I cannot find her . . . I have a precipice behind me."[2]

Denominational claims, however, left her unmoved. Her attraction was for the organisation rather than the doctrines of the Catholic Church. It is possible that at one period she may have considered that submission to Rome would solve her personal difficulties: " If you knew what a home the Catholic Church would be to me!" she wrote to Manning. " All I want I should find in her. She would give me ' daily bread '." Beyond this rather vague though pious aspiration, however, she was not prepared to go. " I often wish it had pleased God to let me be born a century later," she complained. " I often tell Him that these times are too difficult for me, and say to Him in shame and sorrow that I am not up to them and find my task too much for me."[3] Notwithstanding which she resisted all the efforts made by her friends to convert her. She felt that Catholic tenets conflicted with her own ideas of freedom of conscience and freedom of thought. Submission in the accepted Catholic sense was abhorrent to her. Strong-willed, competent and enthusiastic as she was, the conversion of her dynamic personality to the Catholic Church would have demanded a supreme and novel sacrifice of all she held dear; and this she was not prepared to make.

Her correspondence with Manning over a period of years would seem to indicate that she came at one time to the very threshold of the Church. Manning was convinced of her sincerity until he discovered that she was at the same time formulating a new ideology of her own, quite at variance with Catholic doctrine. Her ideas as eventually expressed in a privately published book (1859) entitled *Suggestions for Thought to the Searcher after Truth among the Artizans of England,* reveal her as a free-thinking deist. The book was a failure; but its theme was enough to convince Manning that Florence Nightingale was lacking in the essential predispositions to Catholicism, and he refused to accept her as a convert.

Miss Nightingale has left on record that her attraction to Catholicism vanished in 1852 consequent upon a visit to Dublin. She mentions " a terrible lesson learned in Dublin ", but as there must have been some more fundamental reason for this complete change of heart, it appears that when she seriously considered the question of conversion she hesitated, wavering between her own mind, her parents' opposition, and the world's attitude to the Catholic Church. Conviction—which alone might have overcome her pride—was lacking, and this was the main factor which prevented her from submitting to the Church which had so much to offer her and whose clergy were the only ministers she deemed worthy of the name *Pastors.*[4]

After 1852 Florence Nightingale so concentrated all her energies on nursing that when the collapse of the medical arrangements in the Crimea became publicised she was the obvious refuge of the authorities. Manning expressed well the popular sentiment in her regard when he wrote to Mary Stanley asking " Why will not Florence Nightingale give herself to this work?" But Florence Nightingale did not wait to be asked. Keenly alive to the possibilities of the situation, she wrote to Liz Herbert on October 14, announcing her intention of going to Constantinople, and asking advice on several points of procedure from the Secretary at War. The letter crossed one written by Sidney Herbert on the 15th, in which he formally asked Miss Nightingale to undertake an official nursing expedition to the military hospitals. Her appointment as " Superintendent of the Female Nursing Establishment of the English General Hospitals in Turkey " was the outcome of this correspondence. Everything relating to the distribution of nurses, their hours of duty, their allotment and selection was under her control, subject to the sanction and approval of the Chief Medical Officer of the Army. Her position was clearly to be that of an administrator. As such, her appointment, at Sidney Herbert's request, was sanctioned by the Cabinet. The date was October 19, and the Bermondsey Sisters were still in Paris awaiting further orders from Dr. Grant.

It was decided that Miss Nightingale's party should not exceed forty. Volunteers were to be interviewed at Herberts' house in Belgrave Square by a special selection committee of which Mary Stanley was a member. A rush of applicants was expected; but few came, and of these only fourteen could be considered as suitable. Certain Anglican Sisterhoods were next approached: St. John's House in Blandford Square, a High Church establishment; the Protestant Institution for Nurses in Devonshire Square, an Evangelical body; and the Sellonites of Devonport. The guardians in Devonshire Square refused point blank to submit their nurses to Miss Nightingale's control. A similar objection was voiced by the authorities in St. John's House, but they proved open to persuasion. Six of their number and eight Sellonite Sisters eventually represented the contribution from Anglican Sisterhoods to the government expedition.[5]

Realising that the Catholic body was the one which gave the most spontaneous support to the venture, the government decided to increase the number of Sisters to ten. The decision proved embarrassing for Bishop Grant. So far, his appeal to Ireland had been unsuccessful; and as it was impossible to withdraw any more Sisters from Bermondsey, his chances of filling up the required number seemed hopeless. But Dr. Grant was not easily daunted. He laid his case before the Sisters of the Faithful Virgin who ran an orphanage at Norwood and who helped him out of his dilemma by offering themselves as candidates. That these Sisters were not nurses did not worry Bishop Grant. He had secured ten Sisters for the government, and that was all that mattered. He was later given ample opportunity to repent of his impetuosity.

On Saturday, October 21, the Norwood Sisters left London in Miss Nightingale's entourage, accompanied by the six High Church Sisters, the eight Sellonites and the fourteen nurses who constituted England's response to the government's appeal for nurses. Within a few days Miss Nightingale, armed with plenary powers, contacted the Bermondsey Sisters in Paris, and on the 27th the party sailed from Marseilles in the *Vectis,* a mail-boat bound for Constantinople. A Mr. and Mrs. Bracebridge who accompanied Miss Nightingale brought the party up to its original complement of forty. They arrived at Scutari on November 4, the eve of the battle of Inkermann.

Before leaving England each nurse had to sign an agreement placing herself unreservedly under the direction of the Lady Superintendent.[6] Florence Nightingale made it clear that the authority vested in herself should be supreme and unquestioned. This urge towards absolute power was the keynote of her attitude all through the war. She pursued it ruthlessly, caring little for the rights or objections of others, riding rough-shod over the claims of medical officers, and not hesitating on occasion to make representations and misrepresentations to the War Office. Her determination to wield this supreme power was fostered, wrote Sir Edward Cook, by the knowledge that she had " both the ear and confidence of ministers and the interest and sympathy of the court." That was her trump card, and she produced it on every possible occasion. In the daily routine of administering the chaotic conditions of the Crimea, clashes of view and interest were inevitable. Florence Nightingale's manner of dealing with such contingencies was apt to become equally uncomfortable for friend and foe alike.

In her appointment as Lady Superintendent Florence Nightingale was certainly honoured as no woman had ever before been honoured; and in discharging the duties of that appointment she effected much that was praiseworthy and benevolent. Still, she was anything but a plaster saint. She was neither the Santa Filomena of Longfellow's poem, nor the gentle Lady of the Lamp celebrated in Charlotte Yonge's *Book of Golden Deeds,* whose name became a household word in the palace, the mansion and the cottage, and who became a legendary figure even in her own lifetime. The real Florence Nightingale was a woman of disconcerting contrasts, with a violent temper, a tongue that could blister and an inexhaustible repertoire of nick-names. She respected no one, and any threat, real or imaginary, to her authority over the army nurses was enough to throw her into a passion. Naturally wilful and censorious, she was reluctant to bestow praise or approval on any others in the Crimea apart from herself, two doctors and the Bracebridges. All others she classed as incompetent and incapable, and she protested vehemently against the employment of any other lady but herself in a position of authority in the military hospitals.[7] The obedience she demanded from her nurses was absolute: her own behaviour towards the medical officers was anything but submissive. She defied rather than obeyed the doctors, and was from the start heartily disliked by them. It is not surprising then that Florence Nightingale's vaunted devotion to duty gave rise to paradoxical situations and accentuated the tendency to personal animosities in the management of the army medical services.

The authority claimed by Miss Nightingale over the nursing personnel was taken by her to apply to the Catholic Sisters as well. Unlike the Anglican authorities, Dr. Grant saw no reason to object to this arrangement. He actually sanctioned the measure by signing an agreement on behalf of the Bermondsey Sisters. Henceforth, the Sisters through the action of their Bishop, were servants of the government, distinguished only from the secular nurses in that their services were to be unremunerative. The document drawn up by Dr. Grant for their guidance stated that as the government had appointed Miss Nightingale to be superintendent of the nurses' department of the army, the Sisters were to be under her sole direction in all matters pertaining to hospital routine. They were to have a Religious Superior of their own through whom the Lady Superintendent would communicate with them, and it was to be understood that they were to regard themselves free to introduce religious topics *only* with persons of their own faith. On the latter point the Bishop counselled the greatest caution, stressing at the same time that the religious character of their position must never be lost sight of. He added that if denied free communication with Catholic patients the Sisters should not hesitate to return home.[8] Whether they liked it or not, the Bermondsey Sisters had no other option in the matter but to follow the course mapped out for them by their Bishop.

Here it is imperative to stress the fact that the five Sisters from Bermondsey signed no contract with the War Office. The arrangement entered into by Dr. Grant was concluded after their departure. The implications of their new situation were unknown to them until Florence Nightingale presented herself at the Hotel Clarendon with an explanation. The Sisters, she maintained, were to take orders from her and not from their Superioress; the Superioress was to defer to the wishes of the Lady Superintendent rather than to the prescriptions of her Bishop.[9] Such was Florence Nightingale's interpretation of her own powers *vis-à-vis* the Bermondsey Sisters. One should hesitate however before convicting Dr. Grant of wilfully embarrassing the Sisters. It may have been that he failed to foresee the possible outcome of his action; after all, he did not know Miss Nightingale. It could have been that he hoped to secure more favourable terms when opportunity presented itself. The fact remains that the party set out for the Crimea under such forbidding auspices.

In the event, the arrangement worked out smoothly enough

as far as concerned the Bermondsey Sisters. Their Superioress, Mother M. Clare Moore, became one of Miss Nightingale's dearest friends, and when through ill-health she was obliged to return to England, she was assured in no uncertain terms of Miss Nightingale's esteem and affection:

> " What you have done for the work no one can ever say. . . . My being above you was my misfortune, not my fault. My love and gratitude will be yours, dearest Reverend Mother, wherever you go . . . I do not presume to give you any other tribute. The gratitude of the army is yours." [10]

Incidentally, the gratitude did not mean much. For forty years the Bermondsey Sisters were ignored in England. Like all other labourers in the military hospitals, they were eclipsed by the imposing figure of Florence Nightingale to whom were given all the honours of having served in the Crimea.

This group of Sisters went originally to the war as an endeavour in private charity. They did not mingle with the later and larger mission which followed, though both groups worked simultaneously in the military hospitals and for an almost equal period of time.

From the beginning, the constitution of Florence Nightingale's party provoked adverse criticism among English Protestants who objected to the undue percentage of Catholics and High Church Anglicans it contained. Catholic circles, both ecclesiastical and secular, in Ireland and England were equally alarmed when Dr. Grant's part in the transaction became known. To place nuns under the superintendence of a Protestant lady, to invest that lady with arbitrary powers of selection, distribution and dismissal, to deny a Religious Superioress the due exercise of the rights of her office, was considered a breach of Ecclesiastical Law, and Bishop Grant was heavily censured for having endorsed it. One English priest, in a letter published in *The Tablet*, asked,

> " What must Catholic Europe, and especially our brave allies on the other side of the channel, think of the wisdom of our politico-ecclesiastical arrangements?" [11]

From another source came the query that if nuns were to be thus placed under obedience to any Protestant lady whom the government might choose to patronise, how could Catholics resist that government when it should propose to subject the Priests to the Anglican Ministers? [12] The writer's fears were subsequently realised, when in the course of the Crimean War an attempt was made to extend the authority of the Chaplain-General of the Forces over the Catholic chaplains; but the latter, being less conciliatory than Bishop Grant, refused to submit to the indignity entailed in the attempted legislation.

In Rome, Archbishop Cullen was horrified that Dr. Grant had not provided better safeguards for the Sisters. The Archbishop's disapproval was not directed against Miss Nightingale personally; he merely expressed his regret at a decision which placed Catholic Sisters under the supervision of any Protestant Superintendent, and quoted the Pope as saying that " such a thing ought not to be."[13] The logical outcome of these representations was a decision that if other Sisters were to be enlisted as military nurses it would be imperative to make modifications in their arrangements with the War Office.

It may be mentioned in passing that Dr. Grant, in his efforts to meet the needs of the Government by a policy of conciliation, received little thanks and less courtesy from that same government for all his trouble. His investiture as Bishop of Southwark should not have offended Anglican sensibilities: after all, Southwark had never been an Anglican See. Yet so far did bigotry go that whenever official correspondence from Government departments was directed to Dr. Grant, he was always addressed impersonally as *Sir*. Had he, in the present instance, proved himself less ready to temporise in political matters, he might have succeeded in winning more favourable working conditions for the Sisters. A great deal of the later difficulties and misunderstandings might possibly have been thereby obviated.

On arrival in Scutari Florence Nightingale received no welcome from the medical authorities. The hospital organisation, already on the brink of collapse, was threatened with total paralysis by the non-stop arrival of casualties from Balaclava where the Light Brigade had made history ten days previously. Confronted with a crisis so imminent, the doctors, over-worked, understaffed and fighting a losing battle against overwhelming odds, were understandably exasperated by what they considered the high-fangled notions of Sidney Herbert and his colleagues in foisting a band of uninitiated nurses upon them. They objected, in no unmeasured terms to " this monstrous regiment of women "; but they were forced to swallow their anger and annoyance at the discovery that the ' Nightingale power ' was not to be easily overlooked.[14] Prejudiced and antagonistic though they were, they had no other option but to admit Miss Nightingale into the Barracks Hospital, though for the time being they refused to employ her in its wards.

The nurses were accordingly introduced to a gloomy, squalid, dilapidated building, one glance at which was enough to convince them that the reports current in England were true. At every step they saw ample evidence to justify their coming out, even though the doctors, bent on preserving the last shreds of professional pride, still denied their usefulness. The ensuing deadlock was of short duration. The arrival of the first casualties from Inkermann on November 9 created a crisis of such immediate urgency that for the moment personal resentments were forgotten. Miss Nightingale and her colleagues were not only accepted, they were actually welcomed into the wards of the Barracks Hospital. The experiment of female nursing was now definitely on trial.

The accommodation offered to the party was in keeping with the general condition of the hospital. Six apartments were allotted to the entire group. Fourteen nurses were given the largest room. A somewhat smaller apartment was allotted to the ten Sisters. The rest of the party was distributed in the remaining four rooms. The secular nurses were shortly housed under happier conditions, but Miss Nightingale found it convenient to overlook the Sisters until a more distant date when she was finally compelled to give them consideration. The difficulties confronting Miss Nightingale in her position as Lady Superintendent at Scutari were admittedly great ; her responsibilities correspondingly onerous ; but circumstances required that she should have secured better accommodation for the Sisters (whom she professed to value so highly) than one " sordid room opening into a thoroughfare of dirt and confusion."[15]

Five beds lined each side of this room in which the only division between the Bermondsey and Norwood communities was that afforded by a soiled white calico screen placed mid-way between the beds. The whole aspect of the apartment bespoke squalor, destitution, desolation. Its only furniture apart from the beds was a backless chair which, recalling another and more celebrated antique, contrived the ' double debt to pay ' of a seat and a table. Broken window panes offered unlimited scope to the icy blasts then blowing. There was neither fire, light, nor comfort of any kind. There was not even covering on the beds.

Food was even worse than accommodation. The daily fare consisted of sour bread and tainted meat so prepared and presented as to deter even starving mongrels from sampling it. The first meal served to the Sisters on arrival was indicative of the general menu. A private from one of the regiments volunteered to provide some tea for them, the very thought of which at that precise moment was enough to make them forget the discomforts and fatigues of their long and weary journey. Alas for their hopes! A can of warm water on which were floating as many tea-leaves as could be counted on one hand made its appearance. Milkless and sugarless, this insipid beverage was presented to each Sister in a copper basin, together with a morsel of coarse military bread. Food was as scarce as it was unpalatable, and the Sisters, reduced to a choice between sickness and starvation, were on occasion obliged to go on duty fasting and to trudge ankle-deep in snow from hospital to hospital with never any hope of a hot drink or a decent meal to sustain them. Yet not once did they complain. Neither did they seek redress as did other members of the party. Meeting all difficulties and privations with cheerful acceptance, they were an example of patience and resignation to the sick whose sufferings were even more grievous than their own, and to whom they afforded no small consolation in those unforgettable early days in Scutari.

The mortification caused by uncleanliness was the only point on which the Sisters were ever known to murmur. For six weeks after their arrival a drink of pure clean water was an unheard-of luxury. As for washing purposes: so lacking were all conveniences that they had to take turns at the same basin, being careful to spare the water afterwards for laundering. Drying facilities were equally primitive, any Sister caught in the rain having no other alternative but to go to bed for a few hours while an orderly held her wet garments over the kitchen fire.

The Sisters had neither an oratory for devotional exercises, nor any private apartment to which they might retire when not engaged in the wards. When they sought such opportunities of religious retirement, Miss Nightingale's objections prevailed. Her complaints against her nurses had already begun—they were to become an increasing headache to Sidney Herbert as time went on. But Miss Nightingale praised the Bermondsey Sisters for their submission: " The only trouble *they* have given is that they want to separate from the rest of us."[16] The folly of Bishop Grant's action was even then apparent.

Privations and inconveniences to the contrary however, Scutari had also its consolations for the Sisters. Respect and esteem were accorded to them by persons of all ranks and persuasions, and not least by the soldiers whose enthusiasm went to the extent of sharing their own slender rations with them and among whom a healthy rivalry developed as to the best method of helping and serving ' their Reverend Gentlewomen '.

" Everybody here treats us with kindness and consideration," wrote one Sister to Bermondsey. " The men are respectful, reserved and delicate. The doctors looked coldly at us the first day, were civil the second, and amiable afterwards. The nurses seem to take pleasure in doing everything to oblige us. Even the fleas and their horrible relations have lost no time in making our most intimate acquaintance!"[17]

And so in scorching heat and bitter cold, amid scenes of famine, disease and death, these Sisters continued to exercise their work of charity. That Florence Nightingale valued their services cannot be doubted: her final tribute to Mother M. Clare Moore was that "You were far above me in fitness for the general superintendency, both in worldly talent of administration, and far more in the spiritual qualifications which God values in a superior."[18] Notwithstanding the eulogy, one finds it hard to understand why Miss Nightingale never allowed Mother M. Clare any scope for the exercise of those qualities she so admired in her.

After the departure of Miss Nightingale and her contingent of nurses it only remained for Sidney Herbert to await news of their reception in Scutari. On November 8 he was gratified to hear from Mr. Bracebridge that all was well. Florence Nightingale's letter of the 14th also carried a hopeful note. "We are very lucky in our medical heads," she wrote. "Two of them are brutes and four are angels ; for this is a work which makes angels or devils of men and of women too."[19] Her general attitude was one of friendship towards the doctors; as yet she had little censure to pass upon them. Later, her letters contained nothing but recriminations and invectives; but it is only fair to state that her highly-coloured pictures are not fully corroborated by the testimony of others coming from the same hospital. Mary Stanley's letters, for instance, the tone and temper of which form a refreshing contrast to those of Miss Nightingale, tell a different and probably truer story. She fully recognises the humanity and efficiency of many of the medical men and the willing help of several others in authority in the military hospitals.

A second communication from Mr. Bracebridge on November 28, dispelled Sidney Herbert's remaining doubts. Certain phrases of Mr. Bracebridge indicated that Miss Nightingale's position in Scutari was secure; that female nurses had already proved a boon to the soldiers; that their employment in military hospitals was both practical and useful, and that further assistance in that line would be welcome. Considerations nearer home carried equal significance. Public opinion in England was focussed on Scutari. It was generally urged that the number of nurses should be increased. Newspaper announcements drew daily attention to the growing list of hospital admissions. Under the circumstances, Sidney Herbert thought it perfectly reasonable to arrange for a second party of volunteer nurses for Scutari. He could see but one obstacle to be surmounted.

Previous to Florence Nightingale's departure it had been agreed that no other nurses were to be sent to the military hospitals except at her request and upon her recommendation. Sidney Herbert's decision to organise a second band could obviously be construed by her into a breach of this agreement; but Mr. Herbert thought otherwise. In his opinion, the agreement, published in *The Times,* was aimed principally at the exclusion of troublesome outsiders, but did not at all prohibit the War Office from implementing the personnel of the nursing staff. No misgivings as to the reception awaiting the newcomers at Miss Nightingale's hands crossed the mind of the Secretary at War. " I am full of hope for the future," he confided to Mary Stanley when requesting her to supervise the selection of the second party.[20] It was understood that Miss Stanley would conduct the nurses to Scutari, hand them over to Florence Nightingale, and return at once to England.

Sidney Herbert was anything but prepared for what followed. Great was his dismay when the mail arriving on December 24 revealed to him that the step which he had taken—as he supposed in accordance with Miss Nightingale's wishes—only incurred her most vigorous denunciation. The following pages while endeavouring to unravel the strange sequence of ensuing events, endeavour also to make reply to the unfounded charges imputed to certain members of the second party of nurses. And though the Lady with the Lamp loudly upbraided Sidney Herbert for despatching the second contingent of nurses to the military hospitals, time was to prove the wisdom of his choice, for Mary Stanley and her companions did angels' work among the sick and fever-ridden troops in Scutari and Koulali. On Miss Stanley's return to England, some of her party remained on in Koulali and later extended the benefit of their ministrations to the inmates of the General Hospital at Balaclava.

## CHAPTER 3

## THE IRISH RESPONSE

THE apparent rejection of his proposal by the Irish Hierarchy was no small set-back for the ambitious project outlined by Bishop Grant for nursing Sisters in the British Army. He had expected nothing less than an immediate reply, failing which he indulged a lingering hope that a contingent of Sisters of Mercy would arrive in London not later than October 21, just three days after his own telegraphic despatch. But the Irish Bishops were not so precipitate in their arrangements as was his lordship of Southwark. Neither were they disposed to emulate him in his reliance on the good-will of the English Government. That government had too often proved perfidious in its dealings with the sister country, where the scars caused by prolonged religious persecution were not yet entirely healed.

The ungraciousness which characterised the granting of emancipation in 1829 could not but give rise to grave misgivings in the minds of all who realised that English statesmen in framing the measure had yielded rather to necessity than to justice, civil war being the only alternative to concession. Theoretically, the term " Catholic Emancipation " implies the removal of all degrading disqualifications imposed upon Catholics as such, but the restrictive measures which accompanied the Act of 1829 made this theory impracticable, for England had neither abandoned nor even modified her traditional attitude towards Irish affairs. The administration of Ireland remained in Protestant hands. The Church of the Catholics continued to be impoverished and its ministers despised, while the scanty earnings of the Catholic population went to maintain an alien Church establishment which they abhorred, from which they accepted no services and which was officered and endowed beyond all proportion to its duties. It was indeed " a hard trial for the Irish to be thus obliged to pay the clergy and build the churches of the gentry while their own clergy and churches were sharing the decay of the time ".[1] Between 1831 and 1848, the first decades consequent upon the Emancipation Act, Ireland, to quote Benjamin Disraeli had " a starving population, an absentee aristocracy and an alien church." Religious orders throughout the country continued to labour under many and grave disabilities, and to aggravate the general unrest, the anti-Catholic campaign of 1850 was extended to Ireland where it manifested itself in a storm of hysterical bigotry.

Against such an overcharged background the cautious attitude of Irish ecclesiastical and religious superiors needs neither clarification nor explanation. Everything considered, it was obvious that safeguards would need to be secured before Irish Sisters would be permitted to give their services to the English Government. It was accordingly decided that all necessary arrangements for such an undertaking would be concluded on application from the proper authorities to the parent house of the Sisters of Mercy, St. Catherine's, Baggot Street, Dublin.

Legislative and disciplinary measures connected with Irish ecclesiastical affairs necessitated Archbishop Cullen's prolonged absence in Rome at this particular period. Preparations for the forthcoming definition of the dogma of the Immaculate Conception on December 8 required that Cardinal Wiseman should also be in Rome. In their absence the administration of their respective dioceses devolved upon their Vicars General, Very Reverend William Yore of Dublin and Very Reverend Robert Whitty of Westminster, who therefore transacted all arrangements relative to the mission of the Irish Sisters of Mercy to the Crimea. Henry Edward Manning, then urging the provision of Catholic chaplains for the army, proved himself a willing and indefatigable advocate of the Sisters. His conversion to Catholicism, though it severed his friendship with Gladstone, had not really impaired his prestige in England. With the Herberts, Mary Stanley and others he was still intimate; if anything their dependence upon him was more pronounced than before. Thus it was that in his own person Manning bridged the gulf between Anglicanism and Catholicism and was the obvious go-between when Bishop and Convent and War Office needed a linking together. At the same time he managed to keep the absent Cardinal and Archbishop in touch with the progress of his negotiations.

Manning's hopes for the success of the new enterprise were based on securing a sufficient number of Sisters. He asked for at least twenty, and confided to Mary Stanley his belief that " we shall not do well to take any seculars—if we can find (and we can) enough religious—save only in the case of someone extraordinarily efficient if she should be found ".[2] Convinced as he was of the usefulness of religious in the military hospitals, Manning left no stone unturned at the War Office. For this reason the acceptance of the final arrangements by all parties was largely due to him.

The application to the Irish convents was made through Monsignor Yore, V.G., who, in turn, had been informed by

Monsignor Whitty, V.G., that the War Office had made arrangements with the Bishop of Southwark to send out Sisters as nurses to the Crimea. It happened that Mother M. Vincent, the reigning superioress in Baggot Street, was a sister to the Vicar General of Westminster—a factor of no mean significance in expediting the transaction then under discussion. When on October 17 Monsignor Yore acquainted Mother M. Vincent with the contents of her brother's letter, she immediately wrote asking his formal permission to offer the services of the Sisters of Mercy to the Government. Her letter, dated October 18, reads as follows:

" Very Reverend Sir,

We have heard with great pain of the sufferings of our countrymen engaged as soldiers in the East in the service of the Queen. We know it must be difficult, if not impossible, to procure for them skilful nurses, speaking their own language and sympathising with their habits and feelings, and that care and attention in a strange land which could be so well supplied at home.

Attendance on the sick is, as you are aware, part of our Institute ; and sad experience among the poor has convinced us that even with the advantage of medical aid, many valuable lives are lost for want of careful nursing.

It has occurred to us that as the French Sisters of Charity have been found so useful and acceptable to their countrymen in the hospitals of Constantinople, we, too, might render similar services to our countrymen and help to mitigate their sufferings in the English hospitals.

We therefore, Reverend Sir, through you and with your permission, in the absence of the Archbishop, beg leave to offer our services to the proper authorities to act as nurses in the care of the sick and wounded, under the direction of the medical officers.

Our services must necessarily be gratuitous. Only let us be transported to the scene of our labours and be maintained there, and the survivors brought back to our own country.

Hoping to receive a favourable answer, I am, respectfully and sincerely yours in Jesus Christ,

Sister Mary Vincent Whitty,
Mother Superior."[3]

Dr. Yore forwarded the above to the War Office on October 20, adding that the proposal of the Sisters of Mercy had his " hearty concurrence," and that if the Government would accept it, he would be happy to give his " best services " in carrying it into effect.

"I do not anticipate that we shall be able at present to send more than from ten to twenty nuns," his letter concluded. " And it will be necessary that they be conveyed to the scene of their labours and maintained there, and that they be accompanied on their passage by a chaplain, who should continue during their stay and return with them, receiving the usual appointments of a chaplain."

On the same day, October 20, Dr. Yore brought to Baggot Street a copy of this letter, and requested Mother M. Vincent to organise a group of nursing Sisters, numbering between ten and twenty. Mother M. Vincent immediately circularised those Convents of Mercy with large communities, expressing the hope that one or two Sisters might be spared from each. Enclosing copies of her own letter of October 18 to Dr. Yore and of the latter's to the Secretary at War, she addressed the Superioresses as follows:

"My dear Reverend Mother,

Enclosed you will see our communication with the Government, which was dictated by one of our friends here, in order that there might be a written document for sending out religious, which, it is supposed, will be of service to the Catholic cause in Ireland hereafter.

The Government has virtually applied for Sisters and offered to defray their expenses ; and as there is no time to lose, I beg of you to send your candidates on Tuesday or Wednesday to St. Catherine's. If their services be not required they can return. The eyes of the whole world will be on the poor nuns : I know you will select those you think will give most glory to God. They will want a supply of clothing, etc.

Five Sisters from Bermondsey have gone to the war as a private charity. Let me have a line by return saying how many can come for certain. Give all the aid you can, and believe me, my dear Reverend Mother,

Affectionately yours in Christ
Sister Mary Vincent Whitty." [4]

At this stage in the negotiations a letter arrived from Archbishop Cullen urging that every precaution be taken on behalf of the Sisters' welfare. His Grace pointed out that the Irish Sisters, unlike the French Sisters of Charity, were totally unaccustomed to living in military surroundings, and would therefore need the assistance and protection of " a prudent priest ", should they decide to go to the war hospitals. The Archbishop disapproved of the arrangement made for the Bermondsey Sisters, and in his determination to save the Irish Sisters from a similar embarrassment, he withheld his consent to their going to the Crimea until it was arranged that they were not to be associated in their work with the paid nurses, or be subordinate to any save the medical officers.[5] He subsequently modified his opinion on the latter point on the assurance of Manning that the Sisters would find in Miss Nightingale a friend upon whom they could rely.

Convinced that a personal appeal would carry more weight than a circular, Monsignor Yore appointed the Reverend James Quinn D.D., to accompany two of the Baggot Street Sisters in a search for volunteers. Dr. Quinn had a long association with the Sisters of Mercy. As curate in the Parish Church of St. Andrew's, Westland Row, he had discharged over a period of years the offices of chaplain and confessor to the community. Later, as Archbishop of Brisbane, Dr. Quinn loved to relate to his listeners in the Antipodes how the Sisters took the initiative in seeking him out at his residence in Westland Row on Monday, October 23, 1854:

" One evening while sitting with a few agreeable friends I was informed that two ladies in a carriage outside wished to speak to me. I went immediately to ascertain who they were and what might be their business. I found they were two Sisters of Mercy, and after exchanging salutations, one said they would be obliged if I would get my hat and cloak and accompany them. I asked where to. She replied there was no time for an explanation—they were already in danger of being late for the train; they would tell me on the way.

It appeared that a number of Sisters of Mercy were wanted as nurses in the Crimea. The government had applied to Dr. Manning to obtain them and the two Sisters already mentioned were on their way to the south of Ireland to collect them. After travelling all night we arrived at Kinsale very early in the morning. Having seen the Sisters to their convent, I went to the Church to perform my devotions. I soon fell into a sound sleep where I knelt and so continued till aroused by the commotion of a number of persons around me. These good people looked perplexed and alarmed at seeing a stranger dressed as a priest in such a helpless, inexplicable condition. I felt bound to allay their concern by explaining how I came there, by which they seemed greatly relieved.

When the Reverend Mother had heard the business on which the Sisters had come, she sent to request that the Bishop would be good enough to come down from Cork to settle the matter. He arrived within a few hours, and the whole community, beginning with the Reverend Mother, begged on their knees to be allowed to join in the perilous expedition. The Bishop permitted the Superioress, Mother Mary Francis Bridgeman, with two of her Sisters to accompany us. . . .

One was a young lady of two-and-twenty. Her father, being absent, could not take leave of her; but a friend telegraphed and he met us at the railway station of Mallow. We were made aware of his presence by hearing him call the name of his daughter as he ran along the platform. Coming breathless to the carriage window, he enquired excitedly why she was leaving and where she was going. The conversation was short; he soon learned the facts of the case and declared that she had his full approbation and blessing; that he had given her to God and would never repent of it. A gentle voice said, ' Good-bye, Father; take care; the train is moving.' And we rolled on."[6]

It was Tuesday, October 24, feast of St. Raphael, patron of travellers.

On arrival in Baggot Street the Sisters learned that Mother M. Vincent's circular to the convents of St. Maries of the Isle, Cork, St. Joseph's, Charleville, and St. Leo's, Carlow, had met with as generous a response as had the expedition to Kinsale. They were not surprised. The very nature of the appeal made it impossible for Sisters of Mercy to disregard it. Were they not the vowed servants of " the poor, sick and ignorant "? Furthermore, the highly-coloured accounts filtering in daily from the Crimea enhanced the projected mission as an opportune short-cut to heaven. Those selected to go to the war hospitals were objects of special envy to their less fortunate companions who had perforce to satisfy themselves with a less spectacular though none-the-less important share in the venture. Borrowing and lending became the order of the day, the " Stay-at-homes " responding nobly to the situation. Each gave the best from her own scanty possessions to supply the needs of the travellers, contributions being so generous that like the young bride on her wedding morn, these Spouses of Christ were not a little amused to discover that each had on " something old, something new, something borrowed, something blue ". The " something blue," their most treasured possession, was the royal mantle of Mary, the Mother of Mercy, under whose protection and patronage they were undertaking this new mission.

The arrival of the Kinsale Sisters brought the number of volunteers to eleven. Three Sisters from Liverpool and one from Chelsea completed the party. A memorial tablet in the Convent of Mercy, Gort, County Galway, has preserved their names for us:

> Sisters M. Agnes Whitty and M. Elizabeth Hersey, Baggot Street; Sisters M. Paula Rice and M. Aloysia Hurley, Cork; Sisters M. Joseph Croke and M. Clare Lalor, Charleville ; Sisters M. Aloysius Doyle and M. Stanislaus Heyfron, Carlow; Sisters M. Elizabeth Butler, Winifred Sprey and Magdalen Alcock, Liverpool ; Sister M. Bernard Dixon, Chelsea ; and, from Kinsale, Mother M. Francis Bridgeman, Sister M. Joseph Lynch and Sister M. Clare Keane.

In listing the events of the Crimean War, most accounts from English sources dwell with special emphasis on the spectacular, if mistaken, Charge of the Light Brigade, and on the equally spectacular nursing activities of the Lady of the Lamp. Few, however, give even a passing recognition to the work of these Irish Sisters of Mercy who somehow came to be known as the ' Kinsale Nuns '. Even the encyclopaedias have no account of them. Generally speaking, their work has been practically overlooked by a forgetful world, the only records remaining being confined to unpublished private letters and unpublished official correspondence. Yet the usefulness of these Sisters in the English military hospitals cannot be gainsaid; nor can they any longer be denied their meed of praise. Their participation in the war of 1854 was an expression of the appeal which that war exerted upon people of all classes, creeds and shades of opinion throughout the countries of western Europe.

In Ireland the course of the Crimean War was followed with keen attention by a large and representative section of the population ; and this for many reasons. The country at the time was enjoying a comparative if uneasy peace. People were gradually recovering from the worst effects of the famine. Ballingarry was almost forgotten, and there was no great political movement in the offing. It was but natural then that a foreign war should arouse the interest of the Irish, a war moreover, which was regarded in some real sense as religious. In reality, the religious factor was negligible.

The causes of the Crimean War, as of all wars, may be divided into ' ostensible ' and ' real '. The real cause of the war was the ambition of Nicholas I of Russia to carry out a programme of territorial expansion worthy of and initiated by Peter the Great: to conquer Turkey and annex it to his empire. The ostensible cause was a quarrel between Greek and Latin Christians over the custody of the Holy Places. These Holy Places, as an organisation, were originally created by an act of Imperial authority at a time when the political seat of the Empire had already shifted from Rome to Byzantium. Liturgically speaking, this was a decisive factor in determining the prowess of the Church of Jerusalem in the fourth and fifth centuries, though the worldwide radiation of its influence was due rather to the sanctity of the Holy Places themselves and the consequent influx and efflux of devout pilgrims.

Following the Moslem conquests of the seventh century the Imperial organisation of the Holy Places broke down. This was but a temporary collapse, since the eleventh-century reconstruction of the building by an act of Byzantium was a legal and effective re-assertion of the continuity of Imperial jurisdiction over them.

Little direct good accrued to the Holy Places from the crusading movement; but the memory of the Crusades was an inspiration to Francis of Assisi—an inspiration which determined many significant trends in the history of the Middle Ages, for little by little the Friars Minor established themselves in the guardianship of almost all of the Holy Places. Gradually the western rite, which was to become a permanent element in the ensuing conflict, was introduced; but it is to be noted that this liturgical encroachment took place at a time when the political influence of Byzantium was at its nadir.

Matters continued thus until the sixteenth century when the Greeks began once more to re-assert themselves in the Holy Places. The old liturgical rivalry between Greeks and Latins was by this time complicated by profound theological differences; and the Greeks who succeeded, partly by force, partly by negotiation, in securing some sites and buildings from the Franciscans, and gaining a foot-hold in others as co-tenants, had behind them the government of Byzantium, the Ottoman Empire, which, from 1517, possessed the Holy Land by the same right of conquest as had entitled Constantine to organise the Holy Places twelve centuries before. Eventually, the Latins held their remnant of custody and worship from the Sublime Porte, and looked to the ' Most Christian King ' for the sanctions of international law.

By 1854 the Ottoman influence had declined to such a degree that when the Czar of Russia claimed rights and responsibilities in the Holy Places, the Sultan was powerless to resist. In his capacity of a Christian sovereign, more particularly as of the

Eastern Orthodox persuasion, Nicholas I regarded himself as more suitable for the title of Guardian of the Holy Places than the Grand Turk. So it happened that a particular act of brigandage against the Franciscans at Bethlehem, an incident in the cold war between Greeks and Latins that had been going on for centuries, served as the occasion for the Crimean War. The Greek clergy, under the aegis of Russia, encroached upon the territory of their rivals, and the step was resented by Napoleon III, for whom the dispute was mainly a matter of political power and prestige. Ever since the Crusades France had been considered as the protector of the Latin Christians in Turkey; but since the expansion of the Russian Empire threatened this position Napoleon seized the opportunity to engage France in a war which he hoped would firmly establish his dynasty among the great thrones of Europe by conciliating the French clergy, by humiliating Russia and by satisfying the national craving for victory and vainglory.

Nicholas I was equally sanguine. The Ottoman Empire was on the decline; the Sultan was the ' Sick Man ' of Europe; the time seemed ripe for an extension of Russian influence in eastern Europe. Matters moved to a crisis when the Czar, having announced the Sultan's inability to keep peace in the Holy Land, demanded that Russia be allowed the right to " protect " Orthodox Christians within the Turkish Empire. Napoleon III, seeing in this claim something more than a mere protective right, urged the Sultan to resist. Nicholas I was undeterred: he did not fear a Franco-Turkish alliance. England was his only worry.

To English eyes the immediate question at issue over the Holy Places seemed at first sight absurdly trivial and easy of adjustment. England was profoundly indifferent to the quarrels of Latin and Greek priests in the shrines of Palestine. In point of fact, the religious motive was purely incidental to French and English policy, which was directed solely towards defending the integrity of the Turkish Empire. Nicholas I, on the other hand, was intent on a war which he hoped would terminate by the expulsion of the infidels from Europe and the final settlement of the Eastern Question.

It was hoped in England that a general war might yet be averted. A letter written in February 1853 by Lord John Russell to Lord Cowley, the British Minister at Paris, declared the government's hesitation to enter the lists:

" We should deeply regret any dispute that might lead to a conflict between two of the great powers of Europe; but when we reflect that the quarrel is for exclusive privileges in a spot near which the heavenly host proclaimed peace on earth and good-will towards men—when we see rival Churches contending for mastery in the places where Christ died for mankind—the thought of such a spectacle is melancholy indeed." [7]

But the traditional British technique of diplomacy failed to produce a peaceful settlement of the question. In any case, the British Ministry as a whole had no firm mind on the matter; neither had Sir Stratford de Redcliffe, the Ambassador at Constantinople, who was ultimately responsible for England's participation in the Crimean campaign, for while the ship of state was drifting without clear direction, Sir Stratford grasped the tiller and steered the vessel right into the whirlpool of war. In June 1853 the Russians overran the Danubian principalities of Moldavia and Wallachia, thereby involving France and Russia in a struggle for predominance in the Middle East. The contest was one from which England could not afford to hold aloof. Russian expansion threatened the British route to India; hence it became a cardinal point of British policy to check this development and thus maintain the *status quo* in the eastern Mediterranean. At the beginning of February 1854 diplomatic relations between Russia and the courts of England and France were broken. War followed on March 27.

The Irish, with the religious issue foremost in mind, kept their attention focussed on the Crimea where England was depending in no small measure on the loyalty of Catholic hearts and the strength of Catholic arms to fight her battles for her. Knowing this, the desirability of having Catholic Nursing Sisters in the army was not lost on Sidney Herbert—least of all as Secretary at War—since it was currently estimated that one-third of the soldiers billeted in the Crimea were Irish Catholics.

Irish Regiments, properly so-called, were seven in number. There were three cavalry regiments of dragoons: the 4th Royal Irish Regiment of Dragoon Guards; the 5th, Princess Charlotte of Wales's Dragoon Guards; the 6th, the Inniskilling Dragoons. The 8th, or the King's Royal Irish Hussars, completed the cavalry regiments. Infantry regiments were the 18th Royal Irish Regiment; the 88th, or Connaught Rangers, and the 89th Regiment, later known as the Second Battalion Royal Irish Fusiliers.[8] In addition to these exclusively Irish Regiments, it is beyond question that the English regiments also contained large numbers of troops of Irish origin.

The rousing send-off accorded to the regiments on embarkation expresses eloquently the attitude of the Irish towards the war. With the 89th Regiment this was particularly emphasised as may be gathered from the following extract from *The Illustrated London News.* Describing an occasion when the troops were guests of honour at a banquet given by the Mayor and Council of Waterford, the paper relates that

> " in the Town Hall the Union Jack, the Tricolour and the Crescent blended over the Mayor's seat; and the fine apartment was decorated with flowers and evergreens. Soon after the arrival of the soldiers, the Mayor and High Sheriff, accompanied by the Bishop of Cashel and the Roman Catholic Bishop (who were meeting together for the first time) went down to the hall to receive the guests. A procession was formed, with the Mayor bearing his wand of office at its head, the officers and troops following . . ."[9]

Practically every Irish townland had some representative in the Crimea. The first reports to reach these districts were heartening; they announced the victory of the Alma on September 20, 1854. With this account came news of the prominent part taken by the Connaught Rangers in the battle, and Irish hearts were justly proud of the popular ' Yellow Regiment,' so-called from the yellow facings on the soldiers' uniforms. Under Colonel Shirley and Brigadier Pennefather the Rangers were that day lined up on the slopes of the Alma facing an array of Russian batteries drawn up across the river. To the command, " Up now, lads, over the wall and charge them!" the Rangers scaled the wall, tore through the vineyards, crossed the river and gained the opposite slope.[10] For nine long hours they remained under steady fire from the Russian guns, their only respite being an occasional pause during which they quenched their thirst with the grapes which grew in profusion in the area.

Stories of this nature seemed to augur that all was well, but the security was short-lived. The rude awakening that followed provoked widespread consternation, especially when the disclosures of the war correspondents and the daguerreotype reproductions of the press were supplemented by letters from the Crimea itself. Passed from house to house and from parish to parish, these letters told their own sad tale of hardships, privations, misery and, in several cases, despair. One pathetic story told of a young soldier on trench duty who endeavoured to while away the weary hours of his vigil by singing an Irish lullaby. A Russian bullet intercepted him, and he fell dead, his song unfinished. In another letter the writer gives an interesting sidelight on current black market prices charged by Turkish hawkers in Sebastopol :

> " Potatoes are a penny each; onions the same; sugar a shilling a pound; tea, two shillings; cheese, two shillings; soap, a shilling; pepper, two shillings. A two-penny loaf of bad brown bread is half-a-crown. Brandy and whiskey are seven-and-six a bottle. We pay 4½d per day for rations." [11]

Writing from Scutari Barracks on October 10, the chaplain, Father Michael Cuffe, complains of the spiritual privations of the Catholics :

> " My sentiments I cannot tell, but they are those of an Irish Priest. We have buried nearly three hundred since the 20th of last month. There are no such things as sick calls—we are left solely to our own consciences to seek or not to mind those who are in danger of death. All the calls we get are to attend funerals. Think therefore, the work I must have, to daily pass through so many hundreds to find out by my own prudence those who are in danger of death. Even to find Catholics is a difficulty, and then to administer the Sacraments."

Father Cuffe's observation is reinforced by a similar complaint from a young soldier whose letter home concludes on a pathetic note:

> " I have no more to say at present, but I wish I saw a priest." [12]

Other letters of a like nature drew attention to the services rendered by the Sisters of Charity to the French soldiers. The desire implied in the comparison was that the Irish soldiers also wanted to have Sisters of their own to look after them. There was already evident a widespread disapproval at the scarcity of Catholic Chaplains in the Crimea as compared with an overflow of Protestant Ministers. English statesmen were becoming increasingly aware of the fact that reports on the spiritual privations of the Catholics were causing consternation in Irish homes. The crisis eventually came to a head : England had to bow to the inevitable and ask for the services of the Irish Sisters of Mercy.

As we have seen, the Sisters chosen for the mission were assembled in Dublin by October 24, 1854, awaiting instructions to travel. An immediate departure was expected, but Sidney Herbert, wishing to ascertain how Miss Nightingale fared in Scutari, decided to make sure of the attitude of the medical staff of the military hospitals before further committing himself.

A second and more serious cause of delay arose on the question of a chaplain for the Sisters. In spite of Dr. Yore's stipulation that the Sisters should have a priest to accompany them, the War Office authorities refused to see why such an appointment should be necessary. The Bermondsey Sisters had gone without a chaplain, so why not the Irish Sisters also ? Manning alone was sympathetic, and felt that, in respect to the Irish Sisters, there was no other alternative to granting them their request. The question inevitably led to an impasse; October drew to a close without the issue being settled, and the problem eventually came to a head with Mother M. Francis Bridgeman's arrival in London on November 3.

In Dublin, other and equally important matters were under consideration. A code of rules was drawn up for the Sisters, by which they were to regulate their conduct for the duration of the war. We give them as follows:

" The Sisters shall attend to the spiritual and material needs of the Catholic soldiers in the hospitals; but to the material needs only of non-Catholics.

" They shall not discuss religious topics with those outside the Catholic Church. If a desire for knowledge of Catholic doctrine is evinced, they shall inform the chaplain.

" The silence ordered by our Holy Rule is to be strictly observed in the hospital, and the Sisters shall be very reserved and guarded in their dealings with the patients.

" The spiritual exercises and the horarium shall be arranged for the Sisters by their Superior.

"Any notable difficulties which the Sisters may experience in the discharge of their hospital duties, are to be mentioned to the Superior, who if she deems it expedient, shall refer the matter to the administrator of the hospital.

" The Sisters shall not be bound by the clause of the Rule which obliges to the daily recital of the Office. The local Superior will arrange their spiritual duties in accordance with the particular circumstances in which they are placed for the time being." [13]

The advantage of having all the Sisters under one superior was next discussed. Mother M. Francis Bridgeman was unanimously selected for the office, and the obedience of the Sisters was transferred to her for the duration of their term in the military hospitals. Her appointment was confirmed on November 24 by Dr. Yore : " As Vicar General of the Archdiocese of Dublin, in the absence of the Archbishop, I appoint Sister Mary Francis

Bridgeman, Mother Superior of the Sisters who leave Ireland for the East."[14]

Mother M. Francis was given to understand that she was not on any account to relinquish her charge until the return of the Sisters to Ireland. Her suggestion that she should place herself and her Sisters under Mother M. Clare Moore of Bermondsey was turned down by the other superiors present in Baggot Street, who made it clear that she, and she alone, was to be their representative in the Crimea. Henceforth it was as much her duty to rule as it was the duty of the Sisters to obey. Mother M. Francis therefore asked that she should be entirely free to act in all circumstances as she considered best. To this the Superioresses agreed.

The delay on the part of the War Office threw a temporary damper on the enthusiasm of the Sisters assembled in Baggot Street awaiting the order to travel. Nevertheless, they took advantage of the respite to collect the many essentials for their mission that had been overlooked in the first bustle of packing. Mother M. Francis thought it advisable at this stage to acquaint her Bishop, Dr. William Delany, with the details of her new appointment, to seek his approval and blessing and to discuss with him the difficulties that had already arisen. There is no extant copy of her letter to the Bishop, but the latter's reply, dated Cork, October 29, 1854, was to her at once encouraging and consoling:

" Dear Reverend Mother,
    I have just received your note and am quite charmed with its spirit. Your mission seems to me most manifestly the will of God, and there can therefore be no difficulty. A multitude of disappointments in details or arrangements should not weigh by a feather. I fear none however, on the score of chaplain; and were there reason to apprehend inconvenience, I would still say ' Proceed in the name of God '. So great a work for Charity and Religion is more than equivalent to an infinity of devotions."[15]

Acting on her bishop's advice, Mother M. Francis placed the future of her mission in God's hands, knowing that the solution of all the apparent difficulties would be safe in His keeping. It was eminently characteristic of this Sister of Mercy to take risks once her conscience was at rest. Previous to her present appointment she had in this manner proved her mettle in many spheres of activity on both sides of the cloister.

CHAPTER 4

## MOTHER MARY FRANCIS BRIDGEMAN

JOANNA, elder daughter of Lucy Reddan and St. John Bridgeman was born in 1813 at Ballagh, Ruan, County Clare.[1] Related on her mother's side to the O'Connell family,[2] she had a profound admiration for her illustrious kinsman, the Liberator, at whose house in Derrynane she was a frequent visitor in her young days, and from whom she seems to have imbibed in great measure her abiding love of faith and fatherland. Patriotism and determination were noted Reddan characteristics, and Joanna Bridgeman was amply endowed with both.

Her father's family, the Bridgemans, were of Norman extraction, possessing at one time vast estates in the counties of Limerick and Clare. Penal legislation however made such heavy encroachments on these estates that by the time of Joanna's birth the family fortunes had dwindled to a mere fraction of the original. Such reverses notwithstanding, Mr. St. John Bridgeman in 1813 was still a gentleman of means with all the extravagant tastes and habits of a gentleman. Delighting in the pleasures of the chase, he was an excellent horseman, a keen sportsman and an outstanding host whose house in Ruan had the reputation of being second to none in the lavishness of its hospitality. Lucy Bridgeman participated but little in the, to her, somewhat strenuous activities of her husband. A born home-maker, her life was devoted to the upbringing of her young family which by the year 1818 included two boys and two girls. Her tragic death, shortly after her fourth confinement, brought about unhappy changes in the Ruan household. The children were temporarily looked after by relatives, until a mistaken second marriage contracted by their father early in 1819 made life in the old home impossible for them. They eventually took up permanent residence at Scarriff with Joanna Reddan, a maternal aunt, who though still in her teens, proved a second mother to them. There soon developed a strong intimacy between the two Joannas; a bond destined to be sundered many years later when the younger of the two as a Sister of Mercy would send her namesake to the wilds of California to establish the first Convent of Mercy in the Far West.

Towards the end of 1819 Joanna Reddan disposed of her family property at Scarriff and moved to Limerick, the better to secure

Convent of Mercy, St. Maries of the Isle, Cork.

with my duties which they made several attempts to do, and the Purveyor, Mr Fitzgerald, was equally competent to conduct his own department — So that their labours were shorn of much of the newspaper éclat that had formerly attended them and that may have given dissatisfaction — Now I believe my first & greatest offence to the great lady was declining to ride round the Regimental hospitals on front in her train when she visited them in the summer of 1855 — She wrote me a note, on receipt today that it was her intention to visit them at a certain hour — and I replied that I was sorry my time was much occupied, but I had asked ___ kindly to accompany her! She was then at the zenith of her popularity and no wonder she was ___ after the abject homage that had been paid to her at Scutari. Pardon this digression — and believe me to remain

Sincerely Yours
J Hall

Thank God I am
getting well & strong again

Letter of Sir John Hall to Mother Bridgeman, March, 1858.
*vide* p. 263.

educational facilities for her young charges. Limerick was then a garrison town of doubtful morality, with an appalling disregard of virtue among the younger inhabitants. Disgraced women roamed the streets at night. By day they hid themselves in the squalor of back lanes and alleys. And though several attempts to reclaim these unfortunate wretches had been made, all such attempts proved abortive until Miss Reddan, shortly after her arrival, opened a Magdalen Asylum for them in Clare Street. Encouraged by the Bishop and clergy of Limerick, this asylum flourished and in time expanded into the larger institute which is to-day so capably administered by the Sisters of the Good Shepherd whom Miss Reddan was instrumental in bringing to this country from their convent in Angers.

The cholera epidemic of 1832 saw Joanna Reddan and her ' penitents ' applying themselves unflinchingly to the care of the sick in their homes and in the hospitals, a task in which the younger Joanna took an active part. Just nineteen, she was " attractive and noble in her bearing, dignified in her address and manners. It was a touching sight to watch her as she passed from bed to bed with a smile of heavenly hope on her face. For everyone she had a kind word, and sufferers in their direst extremity felt the balm of a new consolation when this young girl stood by their side. To the Protestant medical men she was a phenomenon. ' What singular taste that young lady must have! ' they more than once exclaimed . . . . Regarded by all as a child of benediction, her kindness earned for her the grateful prayers of those to whom she so unselfishly ministered."[3]

In a final effort to relieve the emergency the schools of the Christian Brothers, recently founded in Limerick by Edmund Ignatius Rice, were converted into wards, and for the ensuing six months' duration of the epidemic, aunt and niece were tireless in their devotion to the sufferers, the former in the City Barracks, the latter in the schools. Close observation of choleraic symptoms during these months enabled Joanna Bridgeman to evolve a system of treatment which, with but slight variation, still obtains to-day. Her method was the application of hot stupes or poultices to the patient's abdomen in order to relieve the severe muscular spasms which are the greatest torment of cholera. In modern times hot water bags and hot blankets have replaced the old time-consuming method of poulticing, but the basic principle underlying the treatment is unchanged. Joanna Bridgeman introduced her own system into the Crimean hospitals, where with the concurrence of the medical officers it was adapted to the new chloroform treatment being applied there.

Natural charm and amiability of manner early marked Joanna as one of society's favourites. Her friends, wishing to include her in their own gay circle, represented to Miss Reddan the disadvantages entailed for her niece by her association with the Magdalen Asylum. Miss Reddan, not wishing to compromise Joanna's future, sent her to live with other relatives in a more up-to-date quarter of the city. Here the ' charming girl from Clare ' became involved in a lively social whirl into which she threw herself with such zest and apparent enjoyment that before the year 1833 had run its course she was universally hailed as the belle of every ball in Limerick. But soon the novelty of this new life began to pall. The allurements of society lost their attraction. The young girl's heart grew restless. The more she considered it, the more she became convinced that her vocation lay not in the giddy whirl of worldly enjoyment but in the peace and tranquillity of the cloister. Realising that she was out of her element, she returned to her aunt's home in Clare Street, resumed her life of active charity and added to her former duties that of teaching in the poor schools of Limerick.

These schools were attached to an old convent where, owing to the ᵈdisturbed nature of the times, Poor Clares and Presentation Sisters had failed to take root. On the withdrawal of a second community of Poor Clares in 1831, two Sisters remained on and with the help of some charitable Limerick ladies, kept open a small school, into which they welcomed Joanna Bridgeman in 1834. The school, known as St. Peter's Cell, functioned until 1838 when a Convent of Mercy was established in the city. The site of the new convent adjoined that occupied by the school and enclosed part of an old Dominican Abbey.

" The house," wrote Mother McAuley, " is capable of being made a valuable institution if God will grant His blessing to our exertions. We are the third order who have made a trial. First, Poor Clares, then Presentation, and now Sisters of Mercy. God grant them the grace of perseverance."⁴ The Convent of St. Mary's, Limerick, was officially opened on September 24, 1838, the feast of Our Lady of Mercy, and the direction of the poor schools was confided to the Sisters of Mercy with whom the two Poor Clares affiliated.

The Limerick foundation was fortunate in enjoying for several months the personal supervision of Mother McAuley. On November 1 the foundress accepted Joanna Bridgeman and a companion, Ellen Potter, as postulants for the new community. Considering the subsequent achievements of Joanna's life, it was surely no blind or fortuitous circumstance which enabled her to receive her early religious training from the very source whence issued the Congregation of Our Blessed Lady of Mercy. In those early days before the final confirmation of the Rule, circumstances often demanded a shortening of the probation period of postulancy, in order to meet the appeals for new foundations and also to increase their stability by adding to the number of their professed members. Joanna Bridgeman's postulancy terminated on December 4, 1838, five weeks after her application to Mother McAuley. Known henceforth as Sister Mary Francis, she was professed on December 9, 1839.

Having served a profitable novitiate under her aunt's direction in Clare Street, Sister M. Francis found her years of experience in the medical and educational spheres a valuable asset in her religious life. She was shortly appointed assistant to Mother M. Vincent Hartnett in the schools. It was a timely appointment which helped to stifle the great loneliness entailed by separation from the aunt to whom she was so deeply indebted and so closely attached. To loneliness was added another, and not less painful trial, in the representations of thoughtless if well-meaning individuals who accused her of ingratitude to that aunt and of injustice to the penitent home by deserting both at a time when her assistance was sorely needed. It required a superhuman effort on the part of the young religious to conquer the temptation thus aroused, but with the sterling courage that was hers she won through in the end. The remaining years of her religious life in Limerick saw her engaged in the particular works of the Institute, *viz.,* teaching, nursing, visiting the sick, in the discharge of which she was such a source of universal edification that her appointment as superioress of the first convent affiliated to St. Mary's, Limerick, occasioned little, if any surprise.

Shortly before the death of Mother McAuley in 1841, a well-endowed widow, Mrs. Mary Anne Burke, was admitted as postulant to St. Mary's. Her object was to secure a Convent of Mercy for Kinsale where her brother, Very Reverend Justin Foley McNamara, was Parish Priest. The request was subsequently seconded by Most Reverend Dr. Murphy, Bishop of Cork, and a promise was given that the matter would receive attention after Mrs. Burke's religious profession. Sister Mary Anne was professed on December 12, 1843, and in the following April, five Sisters, accompanied by Sister M. Francis Bridgeman and Mother M. Elizabeth Moore, the Limerick Superioress, set out for Kinsale.

At the Bishop's request and on the invitation of Mother Mary Josephine Warde, they spent some days in the Convent of St. Mary's, Rutland Street, Cork. This convent (transferred in 1852 to its present site—St. Maries of the Isle) led the way to overseas expansion of the Congregation by undertaking a foundation to Bermondsey in 1839. The event entailed a heavy loss for the Cork Sisters by depriving them of their superioress, Mother Mary Clare Moore, who settled down permanently in Bermondsey after a brief return visit to Cork in 1841. For this reason the Bermondsey convent had a more than ordinary link with its Motherhouse; and as the English foundation was still young, memories of Mother M. Clare were vivid in Rutland Street when the Kinsale-bound Sisters visited there in 1844. A decade later, two members of the Rutland Street community, Sister M. Paula Rice and Sister M. Aloysia Hurley accompanied Sister M. Francis Bridgeman to the Crimea where they renewed their acquaintance with Mother M. Clare under circumstances which none could have foreseen in 1844.

On arrival in Kinsale in the early afternoon of April 9, the Sisters were met by the Reverend Justin Foley McNamara who conducted them to their new home, a private house which was to be their temporary residence pending the completion of the convent. Meantime there was work to be done. Economic life in Kinsale was almost at a standsill. Poverty, neglect, ignorance and apathy had become the hallmark of a once wealthy community. Proselytism was in the air, famine was in the offing, and the swelling tide of emigration was exacting its own heavy toll from among the inhabitants of Kinsale. Five Sisters of Mercy could hardly be expected to remedy a crisis of such astounding proportions; nevertheless, their arrival marked the opening of a new chapter in the history of this ancient town.

Mother M. Francis was at once inducted as superioress, with Sister M. Anne as assistant. Visitation of the sick commenced immediately, and as the Convent Schools were not yet ready, some Sisters were appointed to spend a few hours each day teaching in the National Schools. The opening of the Convent Schools on March 28, 1845, was followed shortly by the establishment of an orphanage and House of Mercy for the protection of poor girls of good character. The beneficial results of the Sisters' work were soon apparent among the town-dwellers of Kinsale who like most people all over Ireland had long been deprived of all external aids to a rich and abundant spiritual life.

The famine years of 1845-'46-'47 were years of prolific activity for Mother M. Francis and her Sisters. The increasing onset of famine fever and the determined campaign of proselytism that accompanied it made all other concerns for the time being insignificant. The opening of ' soup houses ' saw the beginning of a movement which unashamedly sought to make traffic out of the miseries of the poor who often had nothing to give in exchange for the necessities of life, but their faith. Not a few, in desperation, were prepared to barter anything in return for mere sustenance, intending, of course, to retract their errors when the times improved.

Mother M. Francis, in her efforts to combat the pernicious influence of the ' soup houses ', established first a dispensary and later an industrial department in connection with the Convent Schools. Her object was to safeguard the spiritual well-being of the women and young girls of the town, and at the same time to promote their temporal interests by providing them with useful employment. In this way she introduced them to several types of work, plain and ornamental, net making, hair work, muslin embroidery and point lace. Lace-making found ready devotees in Kinsale; and as Irish point lace became fashionable, orders came from many parts for this exquisitely delicate work. So it continues to-day. Kinsale Lace still retains its value and has lost nothing from competition with synthetic inferior imitations.

In May 1849 a fresh outbreak of cholera was detected in Kinsale, and Mother M. Francis, ever on the alert, took advantage of the crisis by securing permission for the Sisters to help in the Workhouse Hospital. The Protestant guardians of the institution who had hitherto opposed the admission of nuns into their wards, were now only too glad to accept them. The doctors too thawed out and came to place such implicit confidence in ' Mrs. Bridgeman ' that they eventually gave her a free hand in the hospital. So well did the Sisters acquit themselves of their duties during the epidemic that they were ever afterwards accorded free access to the Workhouse wards for purposes of instruction among the Catholic inmates. By degrees they were taken in as nurses and were in time entrusted with the entire administration of the hospital.

Famine pressure with its attendant miseries was scarcely relaxed in Kinsale when another project of greater moment claimed the immediate attention of Mother M. Francis, whose reputation as an organiser and administrator was by now firmly established throughout the Irish convents of her Congregation. In this case an application from the Right Reverend William Ullathorne for a Convent of Mercy in Derby was referred to Kinsale by the Baggot Street community. Mother M. Francis accepted the proposal, selected some of her best Sisters, and arrived in Derby on October 17, 1849.[5] The financial difficulties connected with this foundation, while keeping her in England for some six months, gave her none-the-less, ample scope for exercising to the best advantage that aptitude for making ends meet which was one of the most outstanding characteristics of her administrative ability.

In 1849, the year of the Derby foundation, Joanna Reddan sought admission as a postulant in Kinsale. Although now in her fiftieth year, she still hoped to realise an aspiration she had cherished since the day on which she presented her young niece to Catherine McAuley in 1838. Responsibilities did not then permit her to join the Sisters of Mercy. The Magdalen Asylum was still her charge, and she could not consider herself free to abandon it without making provisions as to its future. She accordingly remained at her post in Clare Street until 1847 when she was authorised by Bishop Ryan of Limerick to go to Angers for Sisters of the Good Shepherd. On her return the Bishop compelled her to become a member of the new community : "And if you do not," he threatened, " I will send them all back again to France." But a year's novitiate convinced Dr. Ryan that Joanna Reddan's vocation lay elsewhere. With his permission she withdrew from the Clare Street community and went straight to Kinsale.

Called in religion, Sister M. de Sales, Joanna Reddan found her true home in Kinsale, where under the patronage of the Saint of Geneva she became a model religious, edifying all by her simplicity, her sanctity and her sincere efforts to adapt herself to the unaccustomed routine of convent life. Some there were who rejoiced at the reunion of aunt and niece; there were also those who criticised, seeing no good reason as to why Miss Reddan chose to enter a convent where her niece was both foundress and superioress; unless of course she had personal motives in view. But the critics were soon silenced. Personal attachment for her niece had little to do with Joanna Reddan's decision to enter in Kinsale as the following events will prove.

In the autumn of 1854 Dr. Joseph Alemany, Archbishop of San Francisco, petitioned through Father Hugh Gallagher for a foundation of Sisters of Mercy in California.[6] The many difficulties confronting this mission to the west did not deter Mother M. Francis from accepting the proposal of the Archbishop, nor from selecting Sister M. de Sales from among those who volunteered their services. Selection of her aunt signified her acceptance of the greatest sacrifice that could have been demanded of her human affections; yet she made it unflinchingly. The choice was a fortunate one as far as concerned the missionaries. Sister M. de Sales, with years of experience behind her, proved indispensable to her young superior, Mother M. Baptist Russell, sister to the

Lord of Killowen. Despite the twenty-odd years that separated them in age and experience, these two, by some excellent team-work, steered the new foundation through its many initial diffi-culties in the Far West, where, we are told, "the indomitable courage of Sister M. de Sales, her brave spirit and unflagging energy were an inspiration to the younger Sisters". As might be expected she distinguished herself in the fever hospitals of San Francisco and in other Californian foundations of the Congrega-tion with the tireless energy that once was hers in the far-off days in Limerick. Ever an inspiration to those about her, she died unexpectedly on a missionary journey in November 1857 and was the first Sister ever laid to rest in a newly-consecrated cemetery in San Francisco.

Yet another and a heavier sacrifice was demanded of Mother M. Francis on her return to Kinsale after bidding God-speed to the missionaries. In October 1854 came the summons to the Crimea and her appointment as superioress. Even in well-established communities the office of directing others is a difficult one at best, presupposing on the natural level talents of more than ordinary calibre, and on the supernatural, acknowledged spiritual qualifications. When the question is one of giving cohesion to members of different communities, each with its own customs and observances, it is obvious that tact, discretion, and ability must be eminently characteristic of the person selected to rule. On the assumption that Mother Bridgeman (as we shall henceforth call her) was thus endowed, the superioresses from Cork, Charleville, Carlow and Dublin had no hesitation in trans-ferring their Sisters' obedience to her for the duration of the war. At the Bishop's bidding her post of superioress in Kinsale was to hold;* nobody expected the war to last very long.

Though reluctant to speak at any great length about the Crimean War, Mother Bridgeman embodied its main details, in so far as concerned the Sisters, in her diary. Sister M. Joseph Croke compiled a similar document, and several other Sisters catalogued their own private memoirs for their respective com-munities. But the Balaclava rats who were no respectors of litera-ture made short work of the memoirs, though through a possible surfeit of the Queen's English they refrained from sampling the diaries!

*Before leaving Kinsale, Mother Bridgeman signed a deed of resigna-tion which was to come into effect in the event of an absence exceeding one year. As things turned out, she was absent sixteen months in the Crimea, and the office of superioress in Kinsale devolved upon Mother M. Teresa Maher.

So it happens that two diaries, together with some letters from conventual archives, are the only traces left of a mission which for a time held the attention of western Europe. Supplemented by a lengthy correspondence exchanged between Mother Bridgeman and Florence Nightingale, the diaries make interesting reading as they unfold the intricacies of the not-so-delicate triangular dispute which involved Mother Bridgeman, Miss Nightingale and the War Office. Their contents go far towards revealing many facts which till now have been but imperfectly explained; and while casting new lights and darker shades on the military hospitals of the Crimea, they prove beyond a shadow of doubt that Mother Bridgeman and her Sisters deserved better at the hands of the English Government than to be despised because they were Irish and, as Cardinal Wiseman put it, "to be denied even the passing tribute of one generous word."[7]

## CHAPTER 5.

## THE WAR OFFICE

IN securing for Catholic soldiers the services of Sisters in the military hospitals of the Crimea Manning, as we have seen, was the driving force. As negotations proceeded, he had, of necessity, to make himself chief intermediary with the War Office; and when he, in turn, had to have a Dublin intermediary, of all people in the world, he appealed to Newman who had just been appointed head of the new Catholic University. Negotiations were at first retarded by a stiff no-popery attitude in English political circles, but by late October, Manning's representations were bearing fruit. The outcome of his exertions on behalf of the Irish Sisters may be seen from a letter he forwarded to Newman asking him to present it in his name to the superioress of the Baggot Street Convent. The substance of this unexpected communication between the future cardinals, and dated October 30, 1854 was as follows :

" My dear Newman,

The War Office has agreed with the Bishop of Southwark to the following arrangement :

i. That the Sisters proceeding to the hospitals in the East shall be under their own Superior in all matters out of the wards of the hospitals.

ii. That they shall, within the wards of the hospitals, be under the Medical Officers and the Superintendent of the Nurses in all matters of hospital regulations.

iii. That in all matters (except the details of nursing by the bedside of the sick where direct communication may be necessary) the Superintendent shall communicate with the Sisters only through their own Superior.

iv. That there shall always be a Priest to provide for the spiritual care of the Sisters; and that they could attach to the hospital, with this view, the Priest who should be selected as most fit for the assistance of the Sisters.

v. That the Government shall provide all expenses of going out, maintenance and return.

vi. I have, further, a written promise from those to whom the direction of all the household details is committed, to the effect that the Sisters shall form a separate community under their own Superior, in a house of their own, or a distinct quarter of any larger building.

vii. I have also a written promise that every care shall be taken of them, and any representations from them shall be gladly attended to."[1]

Even to the casual observer, the foregoing arrangements contain a detail of paramount significance. The War Office admitted the appointment of a distinct Mother Superior for the second band of Sisters going to the Crimea. This provided the basis on which from first to last Mother Bridgeman took her stand. And though there was a time to come when Florence Nightingale would maintain that the Sisters had no official status in the military hospitals, Manning's letter is irrefutable evidence that Mother Bridgeman was right in challenging that claim.

Miss Nightingale's persistence that the Sisters were interlopers in the military hospitals has been uncritically repeated by her many biographers. Not for an instant did anyone think of questioning the truth of her assertion. The fact however remains: Mother Bridgeman and her community had as much official sanction as had Miss Nightingale, and there was an equal amount of red tape lavished on their arrangements as on hers.

The Sisters from Bermondsey, on the other hand, had no official status, no autonomy as a community, no rights as individuals. The Irish Sisters had all three, and they enjoyed them within the terms of the Whitehall agreement. Failure to appreciate this fact has given rise to many and grave misrepresentations which detract from an otherwise epic saga of life in the military hospitals. Another point similarly unappreciated is that Florence Nightingale's original letter of appointment was so vague and ill-defined that her position in the military hospitals was constantly called in question and was not finally clarified until the Crimean War was practically over.

But to return to Manning. On the all-important question of securing a chaplain for the Sisters his best efforts had met with but partial success. The government shelved the matter. The letter to Newman continues:

" Now I would fain that Government would appoint and pay a special chaplain for the Sisters; and that they would send them as an independent body. But in as much as these two points have been again and again refused, our choice is the above arrangement or to refuse to go to the hospitals.

" Seeing in the arrangement no bar in point of duty, I have no hesitation as to what seems the right course. And I do not

know what would do us more harm or injustice than to be
backward at this moment."

It is evident that in Manning's eyes the rejection of any of the
War Office terms would be nothing short of disastrous. Having
taken the greatest trouble in drafting the document, he naturally
assumed it was sound, and failed to comprehend why *his* and the
government's proposals should not be considered satisfactory. His
one desire was to establish friendly relations between the contract-
ing parties, and he saw in the introduction of Sisters into the
army an opportunity for lessening the latent anti-Catholic
prejudices of the English. He saw it furthermore as a means of
proving that Catholicism was every bit as efficient as Protestantism
and tended more than any other religion to promote discipline, courage and loyalty in its adherents. For all that,
Manning's approach to the chaplaincy question was not yet
entirely Catholic. It was imbued with an Anglican and Victorian
attitude which prevented him from fully appreciating the Irish
difficulty. And on the chaplaincy question Irish ecclesiastical
authorities backed by their determined Archbishop, were particularly adamant in demanding that the Sisters must have a priest as
their director. Realising this, Manning's letter recorded that the
government had recently increased the number of Catholic
Chaplains from two to ten. Such a concession from the English
Government of the 1850's was regarded by many as extremely
generous; not so by the Irish in whose estimation it was but a
drop in the ocean. Ten priests for upwards of ten thousand
Catholic soldiers, as compared with an overflow of Protestant
Ministers! In the event, the actual number of Catholic Chaplains
at any given period during the Crimean War seldom exceeded six
as a subsequent chapter will prove. Protestant Chaplains on the
other hand, outnumbered them by eight to one.[2]

The letter to Newman concluded with a promise " to make
another attempt with the War Office on the subject of chaplain,"
but at the same time Manning confessed his fears that the " moot-
ing of the question " would probably put the government into an
attitude of objection to the entire proposal. None realised better
than Henry Edward Manning how delicate were negotiations on
the English side. To Newman alone he voiced his doubts, since,
like himself, Newman was another Janus-like figure on the stream
of thought between Catholicism and Anglicanism and would
consequently appreciate his dilemma. His final request to Newman
then, was to " give the Reverend Mother in Baggot Street his mind
on the matter," and to let him have " a few words in reply." And
he signed himself, "Always, Yours affectionately."

John Henry Newman did not answer this letter. It was answered in person by Mother M. Vincent Whitty and Mother M. Francis Bridgeman who arrived in London on Friday, November 3, and had their first encounter with Sidney Herbert at his Belgrave Square residence on the following day. Mr. Herbert's explanation that he could not authorise the departure of a second party of nurses without first hearing from Scutari satisfied them. If this was the only obstacle to their mission, then all was well; on the surface at any rate.

Matters were less easy of solution on the chaplaincy question but tactful diplomacy on Sidney Herbert's part produced a satisfactory, if temporary agreement. He formally promised that the priest appointed as director to the Sisters should travel in their party to the Crimea, though not ostensibly as their chaplain. Such an appointment could not be sanctioned in open court. None of the other groups had been so distinguished and the same course must be adopted now. Anglican prejudices must on no account be aroused by any apparent indulgence towards the Sisters of Mercy.[3] But Sidney Herbert's arguments were not at all watertight, for in his efforts to convince Mother M. Vincent and Mother Bridgeman he deliberately avoided the consideration that there was no immediate necessity to provide special chaplains for any group save that of the Sisters of Mercy. And he deliberately ignored the fact that the Crimea was even then swarming with non-Catholic ministers while the Catholic Chaplains were restricted to six or seven.

All such inconsistencies to the contrary, Mr. Herbert finally succeeded in winning over Mother Bridgeman and her companion. The arrangement he suggested appeared feasible enough to them. They therefore expressed their acceptance of the terms contained in Manning's letter, and the interview ended on a note of friendship and understanding. The Sisters were getting their spiritual director. But the apparent calm was illusive. A storm, not of the Sisters' making, was already gathering, and for the remainder of November the weather steadily roughened.

On November 5, the Sisters were received by Manning at his residence, 78 South Audley Street. The account of this, as of subsequent interviews, is best ascertained from the Manning-Stanley correspondence, from which it appears that a mutual reticence on the present occasion led to some embarrassment. Mother Bridgeman found her host somewhat difficult, in fact " rather hard to deal with." Manning, in turn, regarded her as " an ardent, high-tempered and, at first, somewhat difficult person —but truly good, devoted and trustworthy ", and he declared himself " greatly pleased by her humility and readiness to yield everything but principle." He was elated at learning that the Sisters " found no difficulty in the terms ", and above all that they had modified their attitude on the chaplaincy question in order to accommodate Sidney Herbert.

" They do not insist on a ' chaplain '," he wrote to Mary Stanley, " but they do on a ' priest ', who may be a hospital chaplain, but charged also with the care of the Sisters."

Manning still hoped for twenty volunteer Sisters, but such a number would so increase the total of religious already in Scutari as to constitute " a large convent in itself ";[4] and the illustrious convert must have realised that the Church would nowhere allow such an institution to exist without an Ecclesiastical Superior, an Ordinary and an Extraordinary Confessor.

As far as concerned the appointment of an Ecclesiastical Superior, that office was conferred upon Mother Bridgeman in Dublin by Dr. William Yore, as representative of Archbishop Cullen. It was reaffirmed in London by the Vicar-General of Westminster, acting for Cardinal Wiseman. It was finally acknowledged by the War Office. Her position, thus sanctioned by the heads of Church and State, admitted of no misrepresentation, nor could it ever be called in question. But her jurisdiction at best was a delegated one, in the exercise of which she was bound by ecclesiastical regulations which stipulated that where circumstances made it impossible for a bishop to attend to the immediate direction of any community, a priest must be appointed as his representative there.* In the unusual circumstances attendant on the mission of the Irish Sisters of Mercy to the Crimea, such an appointment was essential, and Mother Bridgeman was only acting within her rights by insisting on it. She was at the same time merely following the advice of Archbishop Cullen and his Vicar-General who emphasised that a special director be appointed for the Irish Sisters.

As to the offices of chaplain and confessors, they are normally kept separate, and only in the most exceptional cases are the triple duties vested in the same priest. Such an exception was admitted in November 1854 when the appointment of a spiritual director in this three-fold capacity was sanctioned for the Sisters of Mercy. Thus after many struggles Mother Bridgeman had at last won her rights.

---

*Vide Canons 525, 526, et seq. in the codification of the Codex Juris Canonici (1917), when this position was clarified.

On her return to Dublin shortly after these first interviews Mother M. Vincent Whitty in a letter to Rome acquainted Archbishop Cullen with all particulars to date.

"Dr. Manning gives the highest character of Miss Nightingale," she wrote on November 18. "He has known her for years . . . I have only just returned from England and am trying to get Dr. Dooley to let us have one of his priests on whose prudence he can depend, to go with the Sisters, if they go. They will, I think, require more than human prudence, mixed up as they will be with soldiers, doctors and ladies of all ranks and persuasions. But I am sure our Blessed Mother will not let us go unless we really do well. I send a copy of the regulations we made for the Sisters during their mission . . . I wish they had your Grace's approval and correction, if the Sisters go."[5]

The Dr. Dooley above-mentioned was a secular priest of the Archdiocese of Dublin. Mother M. Vincent's application to him therefore, removes the charge commonly imputed to Mother Bridgeman in the Nightingale biographies of ' demanding ' and ' insisting ' on a Jesuit chaplain for herself and her Sisters.

The desirability of keeping in personal contact with Manning and Sidney Herbert urged Mother Bridgeman to prolong her stay in London with the Sisters of Mercy, Chelsea, one of whom, Sister M. Bernard Dixon, was to accompany her to the Crimea. Together they daily visited St. George's and other London nursing establishments in hopes of gaining information on matters of procedure as applied to military hospitals. The details of their mission being now public, they were everywhere treated with civility and were " even instructed by some of the London physicians." Mother M. Vincent's letter to Archbishop Cullen laid special emphasis on the fact that " the Sisters appeared in their religious dress in the wards of these Protestant institutes; a circumstance that would have provoked a serious outcry a few years back."

At Sidney Herbert's bidding Mary Stanley was meanwhile engaged in organising and enlisting extra volunteer nurses. Applicants were many but former disappointments were again renewed and no more than twenty-two could be selected from among this second group of callers at Belgrave Square. Money was the main consideration behind almost every offer of service. Some applicants were attracted by the lure of adventure. Others were confessedly in search of husbands. Many of them made no secret of the fact that they were going to the Crimea simply to escape from misery at home. On a comparison there was little to distinguish the hired nurses of Mary Stanley's party from those who accompanied Florence Nightingale, though the Nightingale biographers emphasise the fact that the second group were in general more demoralised and less reliable than the first.

Miss Nightingale was not long in Scutari before realising that her nurses would constitute her greatest difficulty. A few short weeks were sufficient to show her that these women, the carefully selected advance-guard of a future corps of military nurses, were untruthful, thoroughly disgraceful and absolutely unreliable. Florence Nightingale applied only one kind of test to a nurse : Was she a good woman and did she know her business ? To be good, intelligent and religious was not enough in itself. But there was one memorable occasion on which Miss Ninghtingale probably altered her opinion on this point and may well have wished that all her staff were Sisters bound by religious vows. The occasion was a certain morning when six of her nurses presented themselves before her with six sergeants announcing that they were to be married immediately.[6]

As a participant in the Crimean nursing experiment Mary Stanley's position was far less spectacular than that of Florence Nightingale, but for all that, she stands out as one of the ablest and most disinterested persons who appear on the scene. She had been twice appointed by Sidney Herbert to select the personnel of the nursing staff for the military hospitals. She was intimate with Florence Nightingale and keenly interested in promoting the scheme for female military nursing, but her ready compliance with the plans of Sidney Herbert in regard to the second group of nurses provoked criticism of her motives and character. Charges of insincerity and disloyalty to Miss Nightingale were levelled at her. She was accused of ambition, self-seeking and jealousy, and of endeavouring to concentrate on herself the limelight of public attention. Critics also said that she had not acted in good faith; that she knew of the existing arrangement concerning the despatch of extra nurses to the Crimea : none were to be sent except at Miss Nightingale's request. But public opinion on this issue meant little to Mary Stanley. Sidney Herbert's decision out-weighed all other considerations. To him alone as Secretary at War, did she consider herself amenable, and it was through her long-standing friendship with him that she agreed at all to the project. In any case it was with the express intention of transferring the nurses to Florence Nightingale that she agreed to accompany them to Scutari.

The idea of setting up a rival party never once entered her head. Neither had she any desire to focus on herself what has been termed "the fame and glory of the Scutari nurses." The understanding between herself and Sidney Herbert was that she should return to England immediately. The prolongation of her stay in the Crimea was due to events entirely outside her control.

Shortly before her departure for the seat of war in December 1854 Mary Stanley had decided to make an open profession of Catholicism. Sidney Herbert's request that she should conduct a second party of nurses to Scutari caused a temporary postponement of her plans. Her High Church views were already creating disfavour among her Anglican friends, and she felt that an open avowal of Catholicism just then would be likely to create further prejudice against the Sisters. She accordingly delayed the pronouncement of her Act of Faith until March 1855, the eve of her return to England. In the long run, however, and despite her best endeavours to avoid unpleasantness, she unhappily laid herself open to censure and involved the Sisters whom she loved in a charge of proselytism which greatly compromised their relations with the War Office.

A recent biographer of Miss Nightingale describes Mary Stanley as of " confused and unbalanced mind "; of being the victim of " unreliable fervour "; of being backed by the " easily persuaded emotionalism of Mrs. Herbert."[7] Nothing could be more removed from the truth. Mary Stanley's submission to the Catholic Church was not at all the outcome of impulse, haste, cr misdirected zeal. Her transition from Anglicanism was gradual, determined, logical; and her final decision was nothing less than a courageous yielding to convictions against, and almost in spite of, her inclinations which were as anti-Roman and anti-Papal as possible.

A summary of her life will conveniently serve a dual purpose, portraying at once the course of her conversion and absolving Mother Bridgeman and her Sisters from the charge of proselytism.

As daughter of the Bishop of Norwich, Mary Stanley was reared to the most orthodox and unbending Anglicanism, and was more sincere in her adherence to its tenets than the majority of those who criticised her for abandoning it. No doubts as to the possible errors of her father's religion assailed her until like so many of her contemporaries she became interested in the Oxford Movement of the 1830's. She could scarcely indeed have remained insensible to a movement which affected so intimately her brother Arthur who was a college don in Oxford at the time but who proved insensible to the spiritual revolution which ended in bringing Newman and many of his college-fellows to Catholicism.

On her brother's withdrawal from the Oxford Movement, Mary Stanley continued to follow with interest the path of John Henry Newman; and there cannot be the shadow of a doubt, considering subsequent events, that Mary Stanley at this period of her life, certainly knew her own mind. In 1847 she was in Rome, looking for that Church "whose builder and founder was God," for the Anglican Church had already failed her. Since its claims and traditions led no further back than three centuries, she was convinced that it could not be the Catholic Church of the early Fathers. The visit to Rome appears to have had a profound effect on Mary Stanley; nevertheless she hesitated from a step which she feared would cause a rift in her immediate family circle.

And so the years passed on; years in which Archdeacon Manning (whom she had met in Rome) was her constant adviser and friend. The Archdeacon's conversion in 1851 led him to a redoubled interest in her spiritual welfare. More than once he reminded her that her acceptance of Catholicism would occasion little surprise. Her friends expected it; her family also. To Florence Nightingale it was a foregone conclusion. As early as 1852 when she herself was toying with the idea of becoming a Catholic, she had written to Manning, " Convert Mary Stanley or there will be no Mary Stanley to convert!"[8] Measured against this declaration, Miss Nightingale cannot have been too ' horrified ' at Mary Stanley's eventual conversion.

Another person more than ordinarily acquainted with Mary Stanley's leanings towards Catholicism was Mrs. Herbert. For this reason, it is altogether improbable that her husband was ignorant of the matter, though the Woodham-Smith biography of Miss Nightingale maintains that he would not have placed Mary Stanley in such a trusted position over the nurses had he been aware of her intentions. Mary Stanley's decision was an ' open secret ' in November 1854 and it is not only possible but highly probable that Sidney Herbert knew about it. And it is unlikely that Florence Nightingale did not give him some inkling of it, since she herself was in possession of the information for so long.

The first meeting between Mother Bridgeman and Mary Stanley was arranged by Manning at the Convent of Mercy, Blandford Square* for Sunday, November 12. From the moment of introduction a friendship developed between these two, which was to deepen and mature with the advancing years. A mutual similarity of outlook and unity of purpose were of incalculable benefit to their undertaking more especially in the dark months immediately ahead when they were literally thrown on their own resources on the inhospitable shores of the Bosphorus. From the start Mary Stanley was disposed to defer in all matters to the decisions

---

*To-day, St. Edward's Convent of Mercy, Harewood Avenue.

of Mother Bridgeman; and in her subsequent contacts with the Mother Superior she could recall but one disagreement which however did not long ruffle the calm tenor of their happy relationship. The misunderstanding stemmed from the constantly recurring and apparently insoluble problem of the chaplaincy. Despite her known tendencies towards Catholicism Mary Stanley failed to appreciate Mother Bridgeman's insistence on the appointment of a special priest; yet when this appointment was finally sanctioned, Mary Stanley more than anyone else had reason to be grateful for it.

It will be recalled that Mother Bridgeman signified her assent to the proposal of Sidney Herbert that the priest accompanying the Sisters to the Crimea would not be recognised as an official chaplain. She was so far satisfied with the arrangement that on the strength of it she offered to increase her party from fifteen to twenty—the number on which Manning had set his heart. Her offer was prompted by a desire on her part to place more trained and experienced nurses at the disposal of the government and of the army. But her motives were misconstrued. Her generous offer provoked the suspicion that a certain amount of proselytism was involved. Officialdom was immediately on the alert, and Sidney Herbert in order to stem the rising tide of Anglican anger. violated his recently-pledged word by declaring that on no account was a priest to travel with the Sisters.[9]

Mr. Herbert's failure to keep faith with Mother Bridgeman, while scarcely inexcusable is, to a certain extent, understandable. Like all politicians he appreciated the importance of conciliating public opinion—in this case, Anglican opinion; and the fact that such an attempt at conciliation entailed distress for the Sisters of Mercy was to him a matter of somewhat little moment, considering the other issues at stake. *His* main interest was to provide nurses, not chaplains, for the army.

To say that Mr. Herbert's change of attitude took Mother Bridgeman by surprise would be stating the case far too mildly. She was momentarily dumbfounded. Then her Irish aggressiveness—and she could on occasion be very aggressive—flared up. There ensued several more visits to Belgrave Square, but matters had seemingly reached a stalemate. Sidney Herbert was adamant; Mother Bridgeman was nonplussed; Manning was distinctly worried. On November 27 he wrote to Mary Stanley :

"I made it my first duty this morning to see Mrs. Bridgeman. She was a good deal distressed at a misunderstanding as far from her thoughts as from yours. Her meaning, she states, was simply this : If Mr. Herbert in his official character cannot publicly sanction a chaplain going with the Sisters, I hope he will not feel bound to forbid his going at the same time, and by the same public conveyance; and in that case it need not be again proposed."[19]

The concluding paragraphs of the letter outlined Manning's responsibility for the tensions then existing, à propos of which his sympathies are entirely with the Sisters:

" The responsibility of sending for twenty is wholly mine and mine alone. One thing I must say: if the good Mother Superior seemed to be encroaching in wishing to send twenty instead of fifteen, let it be borne in mind that it is without reward or recompense on this side of the grave that they leave their homes and work for a service of Christian Charity. This is a spirit of encroachment with which I pray God we may be more entirely penetrated every day we live.

A little mutual misunderstanding has indeed arisen, as ever will, even among those who have the best and truest hearts."

A second letter bearing the same date explains that Manning had asked for twenty Sisters " for the most obvious reasons of prudence," seeing that it had been necessary to reject the majority of such hired nurses as were willing to accompany the expedition. That there was urgent need for more nurses he did not for a moment doubt, for, as he observed, allowing that " ten wounded be assigned to one nurse, which would be the hospital proportion (or ought to be), the wounded after the battle of the Alma at Scutari would have required two hundred nurses; and the number of nurses going or gone is under a hundred." He asks what will be the number of the wounded " in three weeks' time " and even though future prospects were doubtful at best, the letter ends with the determination that the second party of nurses is to proceed eastwards no matter what the obstacles to be surmounted.

Before Sidney Herbert's change of heart a chaplain had actually been appointed for the Sisters. It had been impossible to spare a priest from among the secular clergy of Dublin just then, and the choice had therefore devolved upon the Reverend William Ronan, S.J., who was at that time comparatively unknown but who later became a prominent educationalist in Ireland as founder and Rector of Mungret College, County Limerick. Manning approved of this appointment and even allayed Mary Stanley's fears of Jesuitry by assuring her that she would " like and trust Mr. Ronan." To address a priest as " Father " was anathema to the susceptibilities of mid-nineteenth-century England.

For this reason Catholic army chaplains in the Crimea were commonly listed on official dispatches minus their ecclesiasttical prefixes. Mother Bridgeman figured as "Mrs." on the same despatches.

The appointment of a Jesuit chaplain for the Sisters was effected by the Very Reverend Robert Whitty of Westminster. Subsequent events proved that the Ignatian ideal was even then exercising its magnetism on the Vicar General. Shortly after the Crimean War he renounced his Westminster preference, entered the Jesuit novitiate and in later years was elected English Provincial of the Society.[11] Father Ronan on his appointment as chaplain in November 1854 endeavoured, as did Mother Bridgeman, to please all parties in so far as such a thing was possible, and he agreed that all unfinished arrangements should still be conducted by Manning. Oddly enough, the next eruption had its source in Manning himself.

That Manning was all for giving the Sisters a chaplain of their own emerges with unmistakable clarity from his letter to Newman on October 30. The following letter to Mary Stanley, dated November 29, shows an entirely different frame of mind; it even places Manning quite definitely in the lists against Mother Bridgeman :

> " I have from first to last understood that the chaplain is not to travel with the Sisters. I have said so and written ten times. If power of mine can hinder it, it shall not be. Say this to Sidney Herbert in my name, and tell him I have borne many censures on this point, and will do so to the end for his sake."

Students of Victorian England will agree that Henry Edward Manning would never openly endorse any development likely to jeopardise his own immediate prospects in either religious or secular affairs. His withdrawal from the Oxford Movement is a case in point: the Archdeaconship of Chichester was in the balance at the time. Conversion to Catholicism did not lessen the vaulting ambition of his Anglican career; and though he could and did on occasion withstand public opinion on matters involving principle, he was nevertheless in this instance inclined to respect authority, especially that of Sidney Herbert whom he believed to be well-disposed towards the Sisters. But—paradoxically it would seem—he at the same time admitted that the Sisters also had a grievance. " I wish I could see you at five-thirty this evening, for I foresee danger," he wrote to Mary Stanley." They feel aggrieved that Mr. Herbert has gone back on his word as given in their interview with him."

The altogether unexpected turn of events placed Mother Bridgeman in a delicate situation. She was stranded, as it were, midway between Baggot Street and Whitehall. The decision pending was one on which the whole future of her enterprise was swinging. She must either choose to travel without a priest, on the promise of his being sent after them, or else abandon the mission on the very eve of departure when all were so eager to travel. How could she be certain that Sidney Herbert would not again break his word? He had already failed her on this important issue; he might do so again. Still, having given the matter prayerful consideration, she decided to take the chance and go.

" We chose this course," she wrote in her diary, " relying on God Who has never forsaken us or failed to raise up friends for us in the hour of need." [12]

Father Ronan endorsed her decision and " gave his word " to Manning that he would not travel with the Sisters. December 2 was then fixed as the day of departure, and Mother Bridgeman accordingly telegraphed to Dublin urging that the Sisters should come to London without delay. They arrived on November 30.

The departure of " the Sisters going to the war " caused something of a sensation in Ireland, and not least at the Dublin jetties where they were waved off with a " God bless you and bring you all back safely to us." As the boat plied its way out from Kingstown they could be seen on deck—a lonely group taking a fond and farewell glimpse at their fast-receding native hills. But they were hopeless travellers, unaccustomed to the channel and not a few were obliged to seek refuge in their cabins whence they did not again emerge until the captain announced the completion of their journey. At Liverpool they were joined by Sisters M. Elizabeth, Magdalen and Winifred, from the Mount Vernon Convent of Mercy, and on arrival in London they were met by Mr. Frederick Lucas, M.P. for Meath, who was a convert from Quakerism and editor of *The Tablet*. Mr. Lucas was distantly related to Mother M. Vincent Whitty. She had confided the Sisters to his care, and in accordance with her instructions, he deposited them, travel-stained and exhausted, at the convents of Blandford Square and Chelsea. All were safely settled in by midnight.

Next morning, December 1, they rejoined Mother Bridgeman whom as yet they hardly knew but who seems to have won the immediate admiration of all.

"I must say I don't think we heard half the good things about her," wrote Sister M. Aloysius Doyle to her community in Carlow. "She seems to have both head and heart; and the Sisters say she is a saint as well. With such a Superioress we shall, with God's blessing, have a holy and successful mission."[13]

But the road to success was once again paved with difficulties. Mother Bridgeman and her Sisters were ordered to attend at Herberts' house and there individually sign an agreement identical with that of the hired nurses in that it would place them under the unqualified control of Miss Nightingale. This was, of course, a direct violation of the terms agreed on for the Sisters who from the first were understood to have a separate superior of their own "in all matters outside the wards of the hospitals." Mother Bridgeman refused to countenance the new measure; nor was she in the least impressed at the discovery that apart from being introduced to the ladies and nurses who were to be her co-workers in the military hospitals, she and her Sisters "might also have the benefit of a lecture on union and charity from Mr. and Mrs. Herbert."[14] Manning, wishing that a clear differentiation be maintained between the religious and secular personnel of the second party of nurses, became once again Mother Bridgeman's advocate; and though he agreed that "when conscience allows we ought to do as the Government desires," he was vehemently opposed to the Sisters signing the nurses' document, of which the following is a copy.

"Memorandum of agreement made this 1st day of December 1854, between Miss Nightingale under the Principal Medical Officer at (Scutari) on the one part, and .X. on the other part. Female nurses being required for the sick and wounded of the British Army serving in the East, the Secretary at War has agreed to employ the said .X. in the capacity of nurse at a weekly salary of —; and also to provide board and lodging; also to pay all expenses attendant upon the journeying to or from the present or any future hospital that may be appointed for the accommodation of the sick and wounded of the said army; and to pay all expenses of return to this country should sickness render it necessary for the said .X. to return, save and except such return shall be rendered necessary by the discharge of the said .X. for neglect of duty, immoral conduct or intoxication; in which case the said .X. shall forfeit all claim upon the said Miss Nightingale from the period of such discharge. And the said .X. hereby agrees to devote her whole time and attention to the purposes aforesaid, under the direction and to the satisfaction of the said Miss Nightingale, the whole of whose orders she undertakes to obey until discharged by the said Miss Nightingale."[15]

When the above was presented for the Sisters' signatures, Manning reminded the authorities that the Bermondsey Nuns had signed no document, but had received their instructions already signed by Bishop Grant. He proposed that the same course be again adopted and drew attention to the fact that the Sisters had already signified their assent to the agreement he himself had drawn up for them with the War Office.

As for Mother Bridgeman, she emphatically refused to allow her Sisters to sign any documents individually. The War Office, she said, recognised her as Superioress of the Sisters going to the Crimea: it was therefore her duty alone to sign a community document, and she was quite prepared to sign the agreement entered into by her Ecclesiastical Superiors with the War Office, *but no other*. The issue between her and Sidney Herbert admitted of no compromise. She would never jeopardise her own and her Sisters' position by affixing her signature to the offending document. It was to be the agreement received at Baggot Street on November 1, or nothing. Mother Bridgeman won. Her rights were finally conceded to her, and in presence of Mary Stanley she signed the original document at Chelsea. She also endorsed an agreement similar to that prepared for the Bermondsey Nuns to the effect that the Sisters would not interfere with the religion of Protestant patients in the hospitals. With the Catholics, it was understood that they were to be free.

Manning approved, but made it clear that " the objection of Mother Bridgeman was not to the signing of *any* document," but to an arrangement which would place the Sisters under Florence Nightingale's absolute jurisdiction. That had been the contentious point all through. Manning's last word on the matter was that " Mrs. Bridgeman and the others have points of dissimilarity which I think it very inadvisable to overlook ".[16] By which he meant that the Bermondsey Sisters, by order of Bishop Grant of Southwark, were placed under the jurisdiction of Miss Nightingale, whereas the Irish Sisters, by order of the Irish Bishops, were to form a separate community of their own. From the start, the authority of Miss Nightingale over the latter was of a limited nature.

Mother Bridgeman's final acquiescence was for Manning a mighty diplomatic achievement. No wonder he expressed himself as "more than contented with the Reverend Mother and the Sisters, and consoled and overjoyed after all our troubles ". His pre-occupation with the welfare of Mother Bridgeman and her community, and their segregation from the nurses as regards status extended itself also to an investigation of the financial aspects of the situation. It will be recalled that Mother M. Vincent Whitty had offered the services of the Sisters gratuitously to the government, only stipulating that they be provided with all expenses of travel, maintenance and return. Manning decided that the less they accepted from the government the better. He insisted that "from first to last the mission of the Sisters was not from the Government, but from their own Ecclesiastical and Religious Superiors ", and he desired to maintain this distinction. But if his decisions were to prevail, it would be imperative to raise funds somewhere, if only enough to provide the necessary outfit for the Sisters. That they could not fully finance the venture themselves was obvious: the Congregation, still in its early twenties, had spread with such amazing rapidity, that the requirements of the new foundations dictated a reduction of extraneous expenditure to a minimum. It was here that Manning intervened and offered to make some attempt to meet the exigencies of the situation.

Mary Stanley was again his confidante. " If the Government will give £3 a head," he promised, " I will add another £3 or £5 as cash—you may judge. I have requested the Reverend Mother to make out a list of outfit and send it to you. If you have any objection, state them first to me. Only ask the barest and lowest sum necessary . . . for I am a bad beggar."[17] He need not have worried as to the Sisters' demands. They were only too well accustomed to living in slender circumstances, and Mother Bridgeman would yet demonstrate in the Crimea how best to make a little go a long way.

As a preliminary step in his unwonted role of mendicant, Manning applied to the Railway and Packet Company to lessen the normal charge of passage from Dublin to London. He then managed to raise (nobody knows where) a sum of £160, to which he added another £60 from his own personal account. In the event, the Irish Sisters of Mercy were therefore independent of the Government for all incidental expenses, and on December 6, a very self-satisfied Manning sent the following account to Archbishop Cullen in Rome:

"It seemed best that we should not ask the Government any money for outfit. And it seemed to me to be of great importance that a marked distinction should be maintained between our Religious and stipendiary nurses. They now go, giving themselves without reward for the love of God; and I believe that this visibly disinterested conduct has already produced, and will yet produce still more effect on this country."[18]

Late in the afternoon of December 1, the entire second party— a group of nine ladies, twenty-two nurses and fifteen Sisters of Mercy were duly assembled at 49 Belgrave Square, the ground floor apartments of which soon took on the appearance of a badly-managed haberdashery department. There were boxes, galoshes, umbrellas, cloaks, collars, bonnets and caps strewn everywhere ; not to mention the countless and useless odds and ends which the nurses insisted on bringing along. Departmental chaos in official circles even at the height of the emergency was insignificant when compared with the confusion attending the distribution of regulation uniforms ; but when all was quiet Sidney Herbert and his wife managed to get in a few words of advice. The volunteers were told of the great work already accomplished in Scutari by Miss Nightingale and her first associates. They were warned of hardships and discomforts awaiting them, for after all, they were going to a military hospital and not on a voyage of pleasure. Above all, they were cautioned as to the necessity of strict, unquestioning obedience in all their dealings with those placed over them.

" He begged us," wrote a lady volunteer, " to remember that we all went out on the same footing as hospital nurses, and that no one was to consider herself as in any way above her companions."[19]

The utopian plan seemed to be to raise the moral character of the nurses by placing them on an equality with the ladies ; but Mother Bridgeman was sceptical on this point. An entry in her diary states that " it did not need much foresight to conclude how ineffectual this experiment would prove, and what the result was likely to be ".

The party was to be accompanied by the Honourable Jocelyn Percy, M.P., and Doctor Meyer ; and they had two couriers. Mr Percy had developed an enthusiastic admiration for Miss Nightingale and was going eastwards to serve her. . . . One freezing interview however with the lady of his dreams put paid to his romantic aspirations !

No priest was listed with the group ; it was understood that he would follow on later at an official distance from the Sisters. Until such time then as Father Ronan S.J. would arrive in the Crimea, Mother Bridgeman was willing that she and her community be placed under the direction of Father Michael Cuffe, senior chaplain at Scutari.

The same procedure was followed with this party as with that of Florence Nightingale: they were assigned by Sidney Herbert to Dr. Cumming who was principal medical officer at Scutari. Unfortunately this arrangement led to most unpleasant complications with the Lady Superintendent.

Of the nine ladies comprising Mary Stanley's party, one—Miss Fanny Taylor—positively and negatively affords us evidence of major importance. Anyone who reads her *Eastern Hospitals and English Nurses* will find it quite impossible to come away with the Woodham-Smith simplification, *viz.*, that Florence Nightingale was a woman of consistently heroic proportions, and that Mother Bridgeman who so often opposed her, had for her main objective, not the alleviation of suffering, but sheer unadulterated proselytism.

Miss Taylor was, in several ways, akin to Mary Stanley, more particularly in her parentage, her religious struggle, and the circumstances of her conversion to Catholicism. In other ways she had her points of similarity with Mother Bridgeman ; and because she figures prominently in the story of the military hospitals at Koulali, she must be dealt with at some length here.

Fanny Margaret Taylor, born on January 20, 1832, was the tenth and youngest child of the Reverend Henry Taylor, at that time Rector of Stoke Rochford in Lincolnshire. After his death in 1842 the family moved to London where after many changes of residence they eventually took up permanent residence in St. John's Wood. While at Stoke Rochford the Taylor family had displayed a sympathetic attitude to the Oxford Movement: the removal to London resulted in a continuation of the work of spiritual development begun in the Lincolnshire Rectory. Though still in her teens, Fanny Taylor was by the year 1848 assailed by acutely distressing religious doubts. Still, she clung tenaciously to Anglicanism, was full of contempt for Catholicism, and felt keenly the ' defection ' of two friends, the Lady Georgiana Fullerton and the Reverend Mr. Dodsworth of Regent's Park. Both had gone over to Rome.

Characterised from her earliest years by a love for the poor, Fanny in 1849 joined Miss Sellon's Anglican Sisterhood at Devonport ; but the Sellonite way of life failed to satisfy her and she was home again within a year. From that time until the outbreak of the Crimean War she did social work among the London poor as Joanna Bridgeman had done two decades earlier in Limerick. Like her too, she taught for some years in what was called a " Ragged School ", established for the reformation of the young hooligans whose natural habitat was in the back-lanes of Piccadilly and its immediate neighbourhood. She was here employed when the emergency in the Crimea became acute.

Fanny Taylor did not respond to the first appeal for nurses; but no sooner had Florence Nightingale departed than she was struck with remorse of conscience and was among the first to apply to Mary Stanley in late October, begging in spite of her extreme youth to be accepted for the second expedition. Notwithstanding stringent regulations against juvenile applicants, Mary Stanley who was a good judge of character, made an exception in this case. She accepted Fanny Taylor but advised her to undergo some preliminary training until such time as her services would be required.

She went accordingly to St. George's Hospital where Mother Bridgeman and Sister Mary Bernard were already employed in ward duties. Here indeed was one of those meetings which are planned in heaven. The only Sisters of Fanny Taylor's acquaintance were the Sellonites. Mother Bridgeman and Sister Mary Bernard were the first Catholic Religious to cross her path; and it is surely no mean tribute to the Sisters of Mercy to say that the outcome of this divinely-arranged meeting between Fanny Taylor and her " beloved and wonderful nuns " was the establishment of a new congregation for women Religious in the Church.[20]

After the Crimean War Miss Taylor published anonymously the narrative of her experiences in the hospitals of Scutari and Koulali. A two-volume publication, the book which made its appearance in 1856, has a significant bearing on the present study. Though seldom quoted from (one might more truly say, though generally ignored), it is one of the most important and revealing eye-witness accounts of the British military hospitals on the Bosphorus, giving as it does, a careful analysis of the factors which combined to spell such hopeless disaster for the Army Medical Department in the Crimea between 1854 and 1856.

An outstanding feature of this little-known book is the high encomium Miss Taylor accords to Mother Bridgeman and her Sisters and the careful reticence she observes in her references to Florence Nightingale. That guarded and careful silence is more eloquent than any words.

In the preface to the first volume, the writer sets forth her intentions. She " ventures to lay before her countrymen some account of the . . . gradual improvements that were made in the (military) hospitals " and, realising that many persons took a deep interest in the proceedings of the nurses, she adds " a narrative of their domestic life and of the perplexities which so often beset them, as well as of the pleasing and amusing incidents which frequently varied the scene." But in recording these events, she also wishes it to be understood by all that her object was " to nothing extenuate or aught set down in malice."

The party in Belgrave Square dispersed towards midnight on Friday, December 1. Few of those concerned with the morrow's venture slept that night. Last things had to be attended to ; hasty farewells were to be made ; all were to be in readiness before day-break on the following morning. The hired nurses were full of eager expectation, but the lady volunteers were already somewhat dubious of the future. It was too late to make changes ; for better or for worse, they must now proceed as a body.

The Sisters did not see their beds at all that night; they spent the remaining hours in choir beseeching God's blessing and pro-tection for all that lay ahead. Next morning, after early Mass and Holy Communion, they faced the future with confidence. They were going to the war as nurses in the service of the Queen of England ; that, in itself, was something. But as Sisters of Mercy they were long since enlisted in the service of the Queen of Heaven, and that, indeed, was everything. This distinction, and the religious dress they wore, marked them off from all other nurses in the Crimea. Their independence of Miss Nightingale in all matters not pertaining to hospital regulations was another point of discrimination peculiar to them alone.

That they were to be independent cannot be over-emphasised. A letter to *The Tablet*, and published a few weeks after their departure, makes the position crystal clear.

" It should be understood," wrote the Reverend W. R. Gawthorne, " that the Sisters go not as individuals with the nurses, but as a body under their own head. They live in community ; they keep their Rule together, and are, in all that respects their religious life and character, solely under their own Superior."[21]

*And to all this Sidney Herbert gave his explicit concurrence.*

## CHAPTER 6

## SCUTARI

AMONG the few personal souvenirs which Florence Nightingale took with her to Scutari was a letter from Manning in which he commended her to the " Protection, Worship and Imitation of the Sacred Heart."[1] It was a short note, but she treasured it and it is still to be seen among the Nightingale papers. Manning had also a parting exhortation for the Sisters of Mercy. His letter to them, dated December 1, expresses so fully his appreciation of the difficulties attendant upon the new mission as well as of the character and vocation of those whom he addressed that it deserves to be quoted in full.

> " 78 South Audley Street,
> December 1/54

My dear Sisters in Jesus Christ,

It seems but right that a few words of encouragement should be addressed to you who have so generously offered to go on a new and difficult mission, in which many unusual and unforeseen trials may come upon you.

You will, however, always bear in mind for Whose sake you go forth, and to Whom your labours of consolation are rendered. This thought alone, without such words as I, at least, can write, will suffice to strengthen you and to cheer you under all you may have to endure.

Nevertheless, there are certain points on which you may not think a few words without their use.

And first, you may perhaps meet with many privations and inconveniences in leaving the quiet and order of your simple convent home to enter upon a life of travel, activity and labour ; sometimes it may be, with slender and bad provision for food or dwelling, and with rough fare even in the few things your ordinary life requires.

You will not, I know, let privations or hardships overcome you, or draw from you a word of complaining ; but as you said, you will bear all these things with a cheerful heart for His sake, who often had ' not ' time ' so much as to eat,'* nor had ' where to lay His head.'†

---

*St. Mark, ii, 20.
†St. Matthew, viii, 20.

Again, in conversing with many people, as you needs must, you cannot fail to meet with many trials from the ill-temper or ill-will of the evil ; the slights and injustice of adversaries ; the rudeness and censure of those who, in many ways, are good.

Prepare yourself for this mortification and offer it gladly to our Divine Lord who bore all manner of contradiction for you.

Another subject about which you will need to exercise yourselves in the spirit of patient and glad compliance will be the work of learning how to treat medical and surgical cases. All of you have probably had experience in nursing ordinary sickness; and that alone is enough to make you feel how much more will now be required of you than you have yet had opportunity to learn.

You are going, therefore, to the work as learners, with a spirit of exactness and humility; and you will receive, I well know, the directions of physicians, surgeons or nurses, be they who they may be, with a prompt and cheerful readiness. We need never be ashamed to learn : every lesson we acquire is a new gift which we may lay out again in the service of our Lord.

Begin your work, therefore, from the beginning, from the simplest rules of practice; and learn accurately everything which relates to the care of the sick, the dressing of wounds, the handling of special cases of medical or surgical treatment. Being already called to the grace of the more perfect life, be not content with an imperfect or ordinary knowledge and skill in the nursing of the sick and wounded ; but strive to be as perfect in this ministry of consolation as well as in the life of the Counsels.

The Daughters of St. Vincent de Paul, ' whose praise is through all the Churches,' will be near you on your field of work. Let them be your examples as they are also your Sisters in the love and labours of our Lord. If it be His will that you return, which may God grant, to your native land, you may be called by Him to a work of Mercy to His suffering members, which will inscribe your name on the heart of England and Ireland as the name of Sister of Charity is engraved on the love and gratitude of France. This hope will cheer you under any trials or mortifications in learning your new ministry of compassion, and will keep you from being disheartened or shaken in your perseverance by any humiliations or vexations you may have to bear.

Remember that these things are Crosses, and that Name will make them light, even precious, to you.

And lastly, be not discouraged at the change from the recollection and tranquillity of your cloister and choir to the ceaseless motion and publicity of the world of work in which you will have to live. God is able to make the hospital a cloister and your own heart a choir. His graces will be with you in the measure of your daily need. If you leave Him in the silence of your convent it is to find Him by the bedside of the wounded. You leave Christ for Christ; and wherever you go for His sake, He will be with you.

Many prayers will be put up for you without ceasing, and oftentimes the Holy Sacrifice will be offered for you, that you may ' spend and be spent ' with glad hearts for our dear Lord's sake, and receive from Him the reward of joy which is laid up for those who serve Him in the least of His brethren.

May His loving care bring you safely home again. If not, I trust there will be more crowns in heaven.

Forgive these words from one who has no worthiness to be your counsellor, and give me a place in your prayers. May the grace of God be with you all.

> Believe me, my dear Sisters in Jesus Christ,
> Your faithful and humble servant for His sake,
> Henry Edward Manning."[2]

Thus encouraged, the Sisters proceeded long before dawn on the morning of December 2, 1854, to London Bridge Station where they formed part of as curious a group as ever London witnessed. The ladies and nurses all wore the same uniform, and that an exceedingly ugly one, consisting of a grey tweed dress or "wrapper," a worsted jacket of the same colour, a plain linen collar and a thick white cap. A short grey woollen cloak and brown straw bonnet completed the outfit, while over the shoulders was draped a scarf of brown holland, described as "frightful", and on which the words " Scutari Hospital " were embroidered in red. The *tout ensemble,* with each figure clad fully or scantily according to the caprice of the fitter, was so ridiculously outlandish that Sister Mary Aloysius Doyle declared it to be " already a triumph of grace over nature " that ladies could be induced to venture forth in such attire.[3]

The fifteen Sisters of Mercy, each in her ' robe of darkest grain,' formed a refreshing contrast to this motley assemblage of womanhood. By special concession from the Government they were permitted to travel as Religious. As such, their black serge habits, their white coifs and guimps and their long flowing veils made them look (and possibly feel) quite regimental as befitting those *en route* for the battlefield. And certainly nobody can blame them for being glad to have escaped the grey worsted and its unbecoming accessories!

The command: "Nurses for Scutari, move on!" gave the final bizarre touch to the proceedings at London Bridge. There was a moment's silence, then all boarded the train—a gasping and overworked locomotive strikingly characteristic of the transport facilities then operating between England and the seat of war. The route followed was that already taken by Miss Nightingale, from London via Folkestone to Boulogne which was reached shortly after mid-day. Again, as in the case of the former group, the travellers received an ovation from the fishwives of Boulogne who insisted on carrying their luggage to the Hotel des Bains where lunch awaited them. Here the host and hostess, " quite beside themselves at having fifteen veiled nuns on the premises " refused point blank to accept any payment for the meal.[4]

The party left Boulogne in the early afternoon and reached Paris by nightfall where week-end accommodation had been secured for them in the Hotel des Princes. Next day, Sunday, December 3, while the secular party sought entertainment in the French capital, the Sisters assisted at Mass in *Notre Dame des Victoires*, where they placed the mission under the protection of Our Lady in honour of her Immaculate Conception and arranged to have a novena of Masses offered in the Lady Chapel for the success of their undertaking. In the evening they attended Vespers, again at Notre Dame. " A delightful service," wrote one of the Sisters. " The music was solemn yet varied, and never monotonous ; the harmony delightful. The preacher was young and very energetic. He thundered fearful anathemas against the unrepentant sinner, but spoke so very fast that only the natives could follow him to the lower regions. Being ardent and enthusiastic, he excited *my* devotion . . ."[5]

On Monday morning, December 4, the party travelled by train to Lyons and thence by steamer down the Rhone to Valence. They hoped to get to Marseilles that evening, but the boat struck a sandbank from which it took two hours to dislodge her, and they had to spend the night at Avignon. They arrived at Marseilles on December 6. The overland route thus completed, one of the Liverpool Sisters, a bad traveller and somewhat advanced in years, thanked God for a safe journey: she thought they had arrived in the Crimea!

Sufficient to defence our relative positions

Thank you for thinking of erecting a Cross over the remains of our dear Sister Winifred, but as I had already consented that another party might undertake this I shall not trouble you —

Believe me to be dear Madam

Very sincerely yours in

Sr M. F. Bridgeman

Miss Nightingale.

Extract from letter of Mother Bridgeman to Miss Nightingale.
*vide* p. 214.

P.S. I am informed here that your kind Services may very possibly be required at Galata &c. if it relieves you from your present difficulties. I should be glad to hear had been the case.

I remain

Madam.

Your faithful Servant

Sidney Herbert.

Letter from Sidney Herbert to Mother Bridgeman, January, 1855.

*vide* p.114.

For the ladies the journey had been far from propitious. The hired nurses were already proving true to type. They were querulous, vulgar, insubordinate and not a few suggested an immediate return to England. Their ' kerb-stone English ' was a source of mortification to their lady companions ; they were rudely disrespectful to the Sisters ; their table manners were appalling, and their general demeanour such that the waiters in the French hotels wrote them off as " a set of wild animals from whom anything might have been expected." What might be the outcome of their introduction to the rough and tumble of military life, none of the ladies dared imagine.

On the afternoon of December 7, the party embarked on the *Egyptus,* a rickety unseaworthy mail boat, which were it not for the existing shortage of troopships, would have been returned to the docks at least six months earlier.[6] On the present occasion, in addition to the nurses, it was conveying between two and three hundred French troops to the Crimea. One of the Sisters, commenting on the ill-assorted nature of this passenger list, did not think " there was ever such a medley in any ship as in the old *Egyptus* that memorable evening." They set sail at three o'clock. Government authorities had spared no expense in providing for the comfort of the volunteer ladies on this outward voyage ; in fact, they indulged them to the point of extravagance. Officialdom was far less considerate towards the Sisters of Mercy. Having travelled second-class through France, the Sisters found to their dismay that there were no saloon cabins available for them on board the *Egyptus.* Any cabins going had been allocated to the ladies ; and though Mary Stanley and Fanny Taylor did their utmost to prevent it, Mother Bridgeman and her Sisters had no other option but to travel steerage in the fore cabins with the nurses. They were furthermore expected to dine in common with the nurses and the soldiery. That part of the arrangement came to an abrupt end after a drunken brawl one evening when intoxicated nurses and soldiers had to be removed from the saloon on stretchers.[7] Mother Bridgeman withdrew from the saloon; henceforth, Angelo, one of the couriers who was devoted to her, arranged and served separate meals for the Sisters at an earlier, quieter and more convenient hour.

At Messina, the ladies took advantage of a few hours' delay and went on a sight-seeing expedition through the town. The Sisters were satisfied with what could be viewed from the ship. Fanny Taylor, realising that " they considered it contrary to their Rule to leave the vessel except on business," presented them, on her return, with bouquets of pleasant-smelling orange blossom gathered from the gardens of the Capuchin monastery on the hill.

On the night of December 12, the *Egyptus* ran into a violent storm which blew the top off the Sisters' cabin, washed away the engineer's hut, and bade fair to consign all on deck to a watery grave. Pandemonium ensued, until Mother Bridgeman with accustomed serenity took over and managed to communicate some of her own calm to her terrified fellow-travellers. And as they watched her standing there in mid-deck, this slender and stately Sister of Mercy prayed to Mary, Star of the Sea, for deliverance. Then because December 12 was the anniversary of Catherine McAuley's profession and the foundation day of the Congregation of Our Blessed Lady of Mercy, Mother Bridgeman also invoked the Mother of Mercy to deliver them all from the angry waves. She assured her Sisters " over and over again, that there was no need to fear ; that the Heavenly Father had certainly not taken them from their convent homes in order to leave them at the bottom of the Mediterranean ; that He had work for them to do, and that they were not going to win their crowns so easily."[8] *Memorares* were meanwhile recited ; medals were thrown into the heaving waters, and when at length the storm had spent itself, a veteran soldier was overheard to remark that " the devil raised that storm but the Mother of God calmed it."[9]

The greatest disaster accruing to the Sisters from the storm was to find their berths swamped, their trunks submerged in four feet of water, and their pillows afloat in their flooded cabins. The ' unforeseen trials ' of Manning's discourse had certainly begun in a deluge.

After a delay at Novarino for repairs, the *Egyptus* once again put out to sea, and arrived at Athens on December 15. A number of Athenians, dressed like Highlanders came on board; among them an Armenian priest, who on his return sent two French Sisters of Charity back to the ship with a gift of oranges and flowers for Mother Bridgeman. By a happy coincidence one of the ' French ' Sisters was Irish! The Sisters had no convent in Athens; they came daily from Smyrna to attend cholera patients in the city.

At sunset on Saturday, December 16, the *Egyptus* skirted the plains of Troy, entered the Dardanelles and anchored off Gallipoli for some hours. Two more French Sisters of Charity embarked at Gallipoli. They were bound for Galata, a suburb of Constantinople, where was situated the Mother House of their order in the east. Once on board they were appropriated by the French soldiers who treated them as their exclusive property for the remainder of the journey. Shortly after leaving Gallipoli, journey's end was sighted: on Sunday evening, December 17, the travellers caught their first glimpse of Constantinople, with its marble palaces and domes rising out of the placid waters of the Bosphorus into the lovely blue of an eastern sky. Owing to the delay at Novarino they were just two days behind schedule. The Nightingale biographies give December 15 as the date of arrival. This, of course, could be an oversight; but in view of subsequent developments it is imperative that the correct date, taken here from contemporary sources,[10] be kept carefully in mind.

As the *Egyptus* anchored off the Golden Horn, the eyes of all on deck were straining to catch sight of the military hospitals of Scutari,

"which we all believed," wrote Mother Bridgeman, "to be the scene of our future labours; and where we hoped that we should at least have a cordial welcome and abundance of the work we had come so far to do, and for which we had already suffered so many hardships and dangers."[11]

The long journey out had had its perils and discomforts for the Sisters ; but for Mother Bridgeman it had also its consolations. She had by this time won the admiration and affection of the lady volunteers without exception, and the respect of the hired nurses. " Indeed, anyone would like her," observed Sister Mary Stanislaus Heyfron, " she is so warm-hearted and motherly. Added to this she has a most captivating manner and address—things not to be despised when one has to make her way and win the good opinion of such high functionaries as the deputies of her Majesty's Government."[12]

It was decided that all should remain on board that night. Meanwhile Angelo was despatched to announce their arrival to Miss Nightingale. He returned shortly accompanied by Mr. Bracebridge who informed them without preamble that they were " not wanted " in Scutari ; that their coming out had been " a gross misunderstanding on the part of the War Office "; that there was neither employment nor accommodation for them in the hospitals and that they must seek temporary shelter in the summer residence of the British Ambassador in Therapia until further provision could be made for them. To this abrupt and peremptory message there was no alternative but obedience ; it goes without saying that the unexpected reception occasioned grave disquiet in the minds of the newcomers. Sister Mary Joseph Croke who had a lively and mischievous sense of humour was the only one who contrived to look for the silver lining in the cloud which overshadowed the

*Egyptus.* Her rhymed version of the Crimean mission describes their arrival as follows:

> But notes as from a ' Nightingale ',
>     In strains unknown to us before,
> Our coming plaintively bewailed,
>     And warbled ' Do not come ashore.'
>
> This bird of note so passing sweet—
>     In this eastern land, how strange to say—
> To all but nestlers at her feet
>     Has almost proved a bird of prey.

Florence Nightingale, it appears, was furiously angry. She had accidentally heard of the impending arrival of Mary Stanley's party through being shown a letter received by Mrs. Bracebridge from Liz Herbert. She was consequently most disagreeably surprised to learn that the zeal of the War Office in this particular had overstepped her own powers of arrangement. In other words, she concluded that Sidney Herbert had acted over her head. Writing at once to Lord Stratford de Redcliffe she asked him to provide temporarily for " the reception, lodging and maintenance of this party " which, she said, exceeded her " worst anticipations." The tone of the letter revealed unmistakably Miss Nightingale's determination to send the newcomers home again; but the idea appeared " so monstrous at a moment when fifteen hundred sick were just arriving from Balaclava" that the Ambassador "resolved to do all in his power to utilize their services."[13] It was thanks to his efforts that the ladies and nurses were temporarily provided for. But the storm was not yet over; in fact, it was only gathering momentum.

The gentlemen of the party put up in Pera where they endeavoured to find employment for themselves and—if possible—accommodation for the others. They were not over successful; for though Dr. Meyer was eventually staffed in the convalescent hospital at Smyrna, the sadly-disillusioned Mr. Percy " sneaked home " as Miss Nightingale put it. He realised, as did Mrs. Herbert that, after all " dear Flo was still a mortal, which we were beginning to forget."[14]

On December 18 Mary Stanley went with her ladies and nurses to Therapia where the equality plan duly collapsed. The nurses refused point blank to do their quota of the household chores. They came out to nurse soldiers and " make poultices," not to be employed as menials.[15] Their behaviour revealed only too well that they were all of a pattern with the nurses whom Miss Nightingale had with her and whom she described on more than one occasion as " wholly undisciplined."[16] Difficulties with and concerning these nurses were even then beginning to pile up around the Lady Superintendent. She was scarcely two months in Scutari, yet several of her staff had already been sent home in disgrace, and from the constantly recurring insubordination of their successors, it appears that Florence Nightingale never succeeded in effectively controlling the situation.

After Mary Stanley's departure to Therapia Mother Bridgeman sought and obtained temporary hospitality from the Sisters of Charity in Galata. Two French Sisters came over in a man-o'-war to conduct Reverend Mother and her stranded community from the *Egyptus* across the bay of the Golden Horn to Constantinople. A short journey through the city slums brought them to the Maison de la Providence where the Superioress greeted her fifteen unexpected guests " with as much affection as if they were her own children, while the community in their own kind and cheerful way did their best to make them feel quite at home."[17]

Linguistic barriers notwithstanding, the Irish Sisters settled down with comparative ease in their new surroundings. The ready hospitality that had been accorded them in the name of religion and the fact that between the members of two distinct religious orders there was obviously only " one heart and one soul in God " was not lost on Mary Stanley, but afforded yet another proof of the excellence and universality of that Church at the threshold of which she was already standing. She was happy too that her " dear fifteen " were at last comfortably housed. Fanny Taylor was similarly impressed at the promptitude with which the French Sisters " were able to spare a room in their generally well-crowded convent." The incident marks a turning point in Miss Taylor's life. From now on she began to evince a lively consciousness of all things Catholic.

As it was holiday time in Galata, the convent boarding school was placed at the disposal of the Irish Sisters who fully expected to vacate it again within a week. But Christmas came and went—

" And what a Christmas! " wrote Mother Bridgeman. " I believe that with all its anxieties and trials it was the best Christmas we ever spent; I mean the most replete with spiritual joys and conformity to Him who came unto His own and His own received Him not."[18]

In other respects, however, there was little of the peace and good-will of Christmas to be found in Galata, for three days previously—December 22, 1854—Mother Bridgeman had joined issue with Florence Nightingale in a brisk and lively correspondence initiated by the Lady Superintendent herself. Their letters, hitherto unpublished, provide many an interesting clue to the problems raised by the triple clash of temperament, principle and personality between them. And though the existence of these letters is unknown to the keepers of the Nightingale papers, their importance in the present connection cannot be over-emphasised; nor is it possible to regard their contents as anything but explosive of all that the Nightingale legend of the military hospitals entails. For a better appreciation of their import, however, it is advisable at this stage to defer their perusal in favour of a review of the conditions then obtaining on the Crimean front and in the base and field hospitals of the British Army. From practically every angle the situation was an unusually complicated one.

Militarily speaking, the major engagements of the war—with a few notable exceptions—were over, and the remainder of the 'ill-fated and ill-managed campaign' was to be spent in an atmosphere of uncomfortable anti-climax. The failure of the first assault upon Sebastopol on October 17, was for the allies an unwelcome realisation that the great fortress was not going to capitulate at the mere sound of French and English trumpets. In fact, the garrison, in true Russian tradition, was emulating the earlier stand of Moscow against Napoleon. A prolonged siege was inevitable; but it was to be a siege conducted by half-clad, half-starved and badly-armed troops who by December were dying like flies in the bitter cold of a Crimean winter. The diet was destructive. The rations were short. The want of the commonest precautions immolated thousands. Fuel was scarce; medicine was not available, and there was no clothing suited to the season or in any way equal to the emergency. There was still a sad deficiency not only of fresh meat, but also of fresh bread, the inevitable outcome of which was that the " wretched scurvy-afflicted troops, whose gums were sore and whose teeth were loose, were compelled to endure positive torture in order to satisfy the cravings of their hunger with the hard biscuit doled out to them."[19] Fatigue duty was the main employment of these famished troops who by the end of the year were well inured to the discomforts and privations of trench warfare.

Men and horses, we are told, were in the same sorry plight. The horses were " so thin that they could not be girthed up tight, and too weak to support the men struggling on their backs, clinging to the saddles, some of them strapped on in the height of delirium." [20] In the space of a few months death had reaped a plentiful harvest in the Crimea. Cholera, dysentery, frost-bite and typhus continued to exact their own dread toll; and with the prolongation of the siege under such steadily deteriorating conditions there resulted a constant stream of emaciated disease-ridden patients ready for immediate hospitalisation. It is a peculiar feature of the siege of Sebastopol that cholera, dysentery, typhus and enteric fever—the natural outcome of malnutrition and neglect—registered a greater mortality than did the shells and bullets of enemy guns.

Conditions in Scutari were chaotic. The unexpected emergency created a precedent with which red tapeism could not cope. The Purveyor was bewildered. The Medical Department was paralysed. Everybody knew what ought to be done; nobody could be got to do it, because a hopeless system of codes, corollaries and contradictions discouraged all initiative. Any suggestion of default or defect was resented as a personal imputation by the commissariat, the purveying and medical authorities who were more immediately responsible for everything relating to the internal arrangements of the hospitals. Feelings were already high when in November 1854 Miss Nightingale's arrival added to the prevailing confusion. Her appointment provoked the angry opposition of the medical officers and in less time than it takes to tell it converted the Barracks Hospital at Scutari into a house of conflict. The doctors regarded Miss Nightingale's appointment as a reflection upon themselves, and upon their methods. Another person in like circumstances would have endeavoured to pour oil on troubled waters by an unqualified obedience to these doctors. Unfortunately, Florence Nightingale was never a peacemaker, and her high-handed manner of acting so alienated the Scutari doctors that they came to consider her appointment as an unwelcome display of Whitehall officialdom.

They had, in reality, a two-fold objection to the Lady Superintendent. Firstly, she was an unwanted representative from the War Office, who in all probability was sent out to spy upon them and send back her reports to Whitehall. Secondly, and perhaps more significantly, to men like themselves who had served a long and laborious apprenticeship in the Medical Department of the army, she was in the anomalous position of deputy from the Department of Health minus the necessary health certificate.

Viewed from this angle, Miss Nightingale's actual qualifications require careful examination and clarification.

## CHAPTER 7

## THE LADY WITH THE LAMP

FEW characters of the nineteenth century have been surrounded by so much glamour and public adoration as has Florence Nightingale. Gifted as she was with outstanding qualities, Miss Nightingale possessed an energy and determination which would have made her eminent in any age. She was a woman with a mission in life, and the tenacity with which she clung to this sense of vocation enabled her to succeed where a less resourceful character would most certainly have failed. Everyone knows the popular conception of Miss Nightingale: the saintly, self-sacrificing woman who threw aside the pleasures of a life of ease to succour the afflicted, the Lady with the Lamp who glided through the horrors of the hospital at Scutari shedding radiance and comfort on the dying soldier's couch, and who at the close of the war retired into the seclusion of an invalid's chair whence she dispensed further good deeds to nurses, to hospitals, and to the cause of humanity. Such is the vision familiar to all. But the truth was different; and so it happens " that in the real Miss Nightingale there was more that was interesting than in the legendary one; there was also less that was agreeable."[1]

Born in Florence in 1820 of well-to-do parents, carefully nurtured and educated as befitting her position, at seventeen she revolted against the cramped and narrow environment of her home. She was a difficult child, subject to moods and tempers, and so independently individualistic that her mother, distracted by "dear Flo's" apparent idiosyncrasies, lamented that she and her husband were "ducks who had hatched a wild swan."[2] She was not far out, because Florence Nightingale was undoubtedly a rare bird, even in the Victorian aviary which boasted of so many prodigies. But Mrs. Nightingale underestimated the case. Her unpredictable daughter was something more than a wild swan : she was an eagle, as Lytton Strachey so aptly puts it. And as the eagle from its lofty eyrie outsoars the other fowls of the air, so did Florence Nightingale outsoar her generation.

As far as such a thing is possible, Florence Nightingale received her canonisation in this life. She attained to a measure of popularity surpassed by few, and seldom has any name become as familiar as the one she bore. Even in her lifetime stationers sold notepaper water-marked with her face. Rhymed broadsheets with rough wood-cuts of her features were on sale at street corners. Penny biographies were displayed in every bookstall in England, and the poet's corner of every newspaper of the land—from the mighty *Times* to the most insignificant parochial publication—carried odes to the Lady with the Lamp. Children, lifeboats, ships, waltzes, even race-horses were called after her; and to-day, visitors to London are duly impressed by the imposing monument erected to the memory of all Crimean heroes, fronting which are statues of Sidney Herbert and the Lady with the Lamp. In such a manner did the *vox populi* of a grateful country canonise its heroine.

By the year 1837 Florence Nightingale startled her ultra-conservative parents by trampling underfoot the conventions of the age as regards careers for women. She decided to adopt nursing as *her* career. This, she pointed out, was her mission in life, her call from God. So tenaciously did she foster this ideal that she succeeded not only in making her name synonymous with ' nurse ', but in winning positive recognition as the pioneer of modern nursing. She succeeded because she had three definite methods of approach.

As a preliminary step she enlisted in her cause the help of several important public personalities. To mention but a few, there were Sidney Herbert who served her unto death; Archdeacon Manning, who for a while encouraged her; Richard Monckton Milnes, who loved her; and countless London doctors of note who collaborated with her in the years after the Crimean War. She boasted of the power she wielded over these men, and claimed to know some of them " off by heart."[3] Certainly, she bent them to her will. With women, on the other hand, she was singularly unsuccessful, finding them in general devoid of sympathy; and she summarily dismissed them all as ' *females* '. The fact is that she does not appear to have had the capacity for winning womanly confidences or for arousing female sympathy, which possibly explains her inability to make any hand of the Scutari nurses.

In the second place none realised better than did Florence Nightingale the inherent possibilities of a fiery and vitriolic temperament. Self-willed to the point of fanaticism, she followed her own bent with a vigour which brooked of no interference. As a child her stubborn tantrums had proved unfailingly effective in breaking down parental opposition: she found them no less effective in the wider sphere of public administration. She simply had to have her own way, no matter what the inconvenience thereby entailed for others. A woman of strong passions, she was a hard-headed logician and a severe critic, not lightly turned from her course, impatient of delay, and not very tolerant of opposition.[4] Indeed, when opposition came, her violent outbursts, while generally producing the desired effect, antagonised many persons who under other circumstances would have been likely to champion her cause. This was especially so in the Crimea, where she provoked the doctors, terrified the ladies and brought out the worst in the nurses.[5] Captious rather than captivating, she could be cynical, even vindictive, and she failed to tincture her administration with that kindliness which can win over even the most intractable. Her dangerous temper intimidated all with but very few exceptions. Mother Mary Francis Bridgeman belonged to this resolute minority.

Thirdly, Florence Nightingale was a highly efficient business woman who knew well how best to utilise money. Not that she valued money as such; nor did she ever consider it as a means for buying support. She regarded money as a powerful lever for circumventing bureaucratic inertia, and for instituting and maintaining what she considered necessary reforms over the heads of lethargic and unco-operative officials. This was her method of procedure in the militry hospitals where, with *The Times* Fund at her disposal, supplemented by her own private income, she was financially equipped for the task entrusted to her. She spent lavishly; but it is worth noting that every single penny of her own money was refunded to her after the war.

Endowed, it would seem, with an almost super-human capacity for hard work, Florence Nightingale was utterly regardless of personal fatigue. She was equally inconsiderate towards others. Witness in this respect her ruthless treatment of Sidney Herbert, whom as a dying man she forced to continue with the scheme she had in mind for the re-organisation of the War Office. Sidney Herbert was one of those men whom she knew " off by heart "; and in her own strange way she had an abiding affection for him; yet she literally worked him to death, and in his last days when he was suffering the agonies of renal disease, she could only find words to upbraid him for having failed her. Such was the gratitude accorded to Sidney Herbert for the exertions of his public career in favour of Miss Nightingale. For others she was ever a dangerous enemy; in his case she was a formidable friend.

While she was yet in her early thirties, Florence Nightingale claimed to have visited " all the hospitals in London, Dublin, Edinburgh; many county hospitals and some of the naval and military hospitals in England."[6] Her experience included as well certain Paris hospitals, a period with the French Sisters of Charity and two prolonged visits to the Fliedner Institute at Kaiserwerth on the Rhine, which she declared was far from having trained her, "for the nursing there was nil."[7] Lastly, since the Nightingales usually had their winter quarters on the continent, she had opportunity to visit hospitals in Berlin, Lyons, Rome, Alexandria, Constantinople and Brussels. In each of these institutions she took copious notes, mainly on administration, sanitation and ward construction, and appears to have interested herself more in hospital management rather than in the details of practical nursing.

The natural outcome of such inspection was that Florence Nightingale probably knew more about hospitals than anyone else in the England of her day. Few, if any, could surpass her in her views on sanitation, good drainage, fresh air and pure water. For one who was neither medically nor scientifically trained, she possessed a vast fund of information on things medical and scientific; but this information made her too dogmatic, too insistent on maintaining her own views, too authoritarian in inflicting them on others. Anything which did not coincide with her opinion must be wrong. Under this impression, she held that the theory of contagion was utterly ridiculous! She adhered to this unbending attitude all through life—not hesitating to dictate even to the leading doctors of her day—and consequently she was " quick to censure, slow to praise, and unreasonably impatient of criticism."[8]

The record of hospitals visited in the course of her continental travels, however, does not argue conclusively that Florence Nightingale was a trained nurse. Even in those days when State registration and certification were unknown, and when experience alone was the main criterion of the nurse, Miss Nightingale had little actual experience. A visit to a hospital does not transform the visitor into a nurse; neither does it give any claim to practical experience as such—and Florence Nightingale did not continue long enough in any hospital to qualify for recognition as a nurse even according to the limited requirements of her day. Kaiserwerth was the one exception. She remained there for three months working with the Lutheran Deaconesses. Yet Kaiserwerth when she knew it was only in its infancy and gave then but little indication of its future efficiency. It cannot therefore be accounted as having equipped Florence Nightingale with the qualifications of a trained and experienced nurse. Taken all in all, the main outcome of Miss Nightingale's travels was to give her a peculiar aptitude for the work of hospital administration. It is as a reformer and an administrator rather than as a nurse that she deserves recognition. And it was principally in this capacity that she went to the Crimea.

From the terms of her War Office appointment Florence Nightingale was recognised as 'Superintendent of the Female Nursing Establishment of the English General Hospitals in *Turkey.*' Her commission, however, despite the official precision of its wording, contained a serious and fatal flaw. It designated Turkey as her sphere of operations. Miss Nightingale took it for granted that her superintendence extended to all the military hospitals: the base hospitals on the Bosphorus, as well as the British hospitals of the Crimea. Her opponents on the other hand would restrict her sphere of activity. According to them, she was to confine herself to the hospitals on the Bosphorus. Her writ did not run in the Crimea, which was Russian, not Turkish territory. Friction resulted at a later date with the members of the medical profession who resented her interference in the Crimea and who used the ambiguity of her letter of appointment as their standing-ground.

The deadlock created by Florence Nightingale's arrival in Scutari led to an extremely delicate situation: a situation which could have been possibly obviated had the doctors been a little less touchy and she a little more tactful. Did they but realise it, she was the person best equipped towards rectifying matters for them. She had influence at her back and she had money in her hand. Her experienced eye could detect at a glance the administrative evils most requiring attention, and she had the ability plus the courage to tackle what was certainly a herculean task of reform. The Barracks Hospital lacked a sanitary expert: sanitation was her forte. Orderlies required regimentation: she would attempt that too. She could, in fact, make herself useful in practically every branch of the administration; and on arrival she seems to have had some such intention—subject nominally to the medical officers, but actually according to her own fads and fancies. Herein lay the snag. Her urge to dominate and legislate was too strong, and the initial antagonism of the doctors to her appointment led to the most lamentable consequences.

Miss Nightingale decided at once to abandon the idea of co-operation and to inaugurate her reforms in spite of the doctors, and in direct contravention of the provisions of her charter which stated that she was to " carry out the duty of her appointment " under the orders and direction " of the Chief Medical Officer at Scutari."[9] Notwithstanding this direction, her behaviour in Scutari was, on occasion, a deliberate defiance of army regulations, while at the same time her vaunted devotion to duty led to difficult and paradoxical situations. " What I have done," she wrote to Sidney Herbert, " could not have been done had I not worked with the medical authorities and not in rivalry of them."[10] Here was a supreme example of what Sir Edward Cook described as the " contradictions in Miss Nightingale's aim, thoughts and character."

Generally speaking, Florence Nightingale got little support from the medical staff in the Crimea. Some few staff-surgeons championed her, notably one Doctor McGrigor, whom she duly rewarded by intervening with the War Office in favour of his promotion. She had other sympathisers appointed to Medical and Sanitary Commissions, the better to protect her interests, to ensure as it were, reliable evidence; but as time wore on and Miss Nightingale became more dictatorial, her supporters began to thin out. Even her favourite Dr. McGrigor became less enthusiastic; so did Doctor Cumming, medical officer at Scutari; and so numerous were those who eventually ranged themselves against her that she complained bitterly to Sidney Herbert that " there is not an official who would not burn me like Joan of Arc if he could; but they know the War Office cannot turn me out as the country is with me."[11]

Dr. Andrew Smith and Doctor (later Sir) John Hall were at that time the two most outstanding personalities of the Army Medical Department. Dr. Hall was Inspector-General and Chief Medical Officer of the Army. Dr. Andrew Smith was Director-General of the Army Medical Service. Neither of the two approved of Miss Nightingale, but considered that she and her nurses were an insufferable nuisance foisted on them by Sidney Herbert, and Dr. Hall made no secret of the fact that " the romantic enthusiasm with which their labours were viewed in England was not shared by the medical men, either civil or military " in the Crimea. But while they ever remained hostile to Miss Nightingale, the opposition of these two medical officers to female nurses as such, shortly underwent a radical change. They became the staunchest supporters of Mother Bridgeman and the Irish Sisters of Mercy, whose " quiet, efficient and unostentatious manner of performing the duties to which they had vowed their lives, was a model of nursing worthy of being imitated by all."[12]

Florence Nightingale gained entrance into the Barracks Hospital at Scutari because she was invested with powers which it was difficult, even impossible to resist. Once inside, she insinuated herself into every section of the administration until by the time of Mother Bridgeman's arrival she was, in fact, purveying the hospital with " an almost aggressive energy "; she was Almoner of the Free Gift Stores, and dispenser of *The Times* Fund. Her purveying activities which set up a rivalry between herself and the Purveyor, drew a rebuke even from Sidney Herbert, who considered that she was carrying them on too long and too far. His advice, " founded on what he had heard from impartial sources," was that she " should altogether give up purveying."[13] His admonition fell on deaf ears.

Florence Nightingale's position in Scutari was that of an unusually active public functionary attending to a multiplicity of duties which cannot have entailed much actual nursing. To use her own expression, she was the Barracks Mistress. " I always expected to end up my days as a Hospital Matron," she wrote in November to Dr. William Bowman; " but I never expected to be a Barracks Mistress."[14] In the latter capacity she administered the Barracks Hospital, and though there were times of emergency when she was long hours at a stretch " in attendance " in the wards, most of her time was spent at her desk in a wing section of the hospital called the " Tower of Babel " from the confusion which constantly reigned there.

That the amount of actual nursing done by Florence Nightingale is slight is borne out by her own *Statement to the Select Committee of the House of Commons,* in which she states that she " sometimes " dressed wounds in Scutari Hospital.[15] There is also a statement from a patient admitted to the same hospital in December 1854. He speaks of Miss Nightingale as a very kind lady: " Sometimes we get a visit from her in the wards, and if a nurse is required for a patient she sends one . . ."[16] The repetition of the " sometimes " is too significant to be overlooked.

Actually, there cannot have been very much surgical nursing done in any of the hospitals on the Bosphorus where, except for occasional emergency operations, the majority of admissions were cases of cholera, dysentery and scurvy, which required medical rather than surgical treatment. Most of the operations were performed hurriedly and under unbelievably primitive conditions at the front, sometimes in the Balaclava hospitals, more often than not in some convenient field or back-yard. The survivors were afterwards sent down to the base hospitals. Taking into account the dead-march tempo of the hospital transports and the fact that antibiotics as we know them to-day were unknown in the period of the Crimean War, it is only natural to conclude that the majority of those who survived the surgeon's knife at Balaclava were either dead or convalescent on arrival at base. Consequently, the Scutari hospitals specialised in medical nursing; and as this was Miss Nightingale's locale during the greater part of her superintendency, the obvious inference is that she was hardly involved in any surgical work. In Balaclava, on the other hand, the emphasis was mainly on surgery, but here Miss Nightingale took little or no part in the work of the hospitals.

As for such operations as were performed in Scutari, Miss Nightingale's participation can hardly be termed active. She was an impassive spectator, communicating her own contempt of pain to men whom pain was already rendering delirious. In Kinglake's history of the Crimean War one reads that " the magic of her power over the men was felt in the room—the dreaded, blood-stained room—where operations took place. There perhaps the maimed soldier if not yet resigned to his fate, might be craving death rather than meet the knife of the surgeon, but when such a one looked and saw that the honoured Lady in Chief was standing beside him—and with lips closely set and hands folded decreeing herself to go through the pain of witnessing pain, he used to fall into the mood of obeying her silent command and—finding strange support in her presence—bring himself to submit and endure."[17] One wonders if the foregoing was one of those passages in which Florence Nightingale complained that Kinglake was making her into a ' Tragedy Queen.'

Miss Nightingale's usual hour for visiting special cases was in the dead of night when, lamp in hand, and accom-panied by a lady or a nurse, she made her way through the gloomy wards and corridors of the makeshift Barracks Hospital. Fanny Taylor, her frequent companion on these rounds, remem-bered that it " seemed an endless walk and one not easily forgotten. As we slowly passed along, the silence was profound; very seldom did a moan or a cry from these multitudes of deeply-suffering ones fall on our ears. A dim light burnt here and there. Miss Nightingale carried her lantern, which she would set down before she bent over any of the patients. I much admired her manner to the men—it was so tender and kind."[18] . . . Thus did the Lady with the Lamp become a legendary figure, a popular heroine, and the darling of a nation.

Biographers have so dramatised Miss Nightingale in this role of ministering angel at Scutari that at a superficial glance it becomes easy for the unwary to form the impression that she was the epitome of the perfect nurse. Others, fortunately, not content with such ready-made conclusions, probe deeper when they find the Lady Superintendent herself writing to Sidney Herbert that " nursing was the least of the functions into which she had been forced," and stating on another occasion that she was " actually clothing the British Army." That nursing was the least of her functions is not surprising in view of the prolific correspondence which issued from her pen; the hours she spent doling out goods from the government stores; the statistical pamphlets she compiled for Sidney Herbert's benefit. Superadded to all these were the constant reports she sent in against the doctors; her written complaints about those with whom she worked; her habitual tendency to detail those matters redounding to her own personal credit.[19] And all this at a time when Scutari hospital was understaffed and over-crowded. In December 1854 the number of patients reached a peak of two thousand four hundred and thirty-four.

Against such a background the hostility of the medical staff becomes more comprehensible. But their unbending attitude did not deter Florence Nightingale. Her urge to power would not be denied, and despite accumulated opposition she was by December 14, beginning to " queen it with absolute power" when she discovered that forty-six nurses with Mary Stanley in charge were even then approaching Scutari.[20]

The impending crisis was simple enough and easy of adjustment, but Florence Nightingale's handling of the situation was unfortunate. She remonstrated with Sidney Herbert; she threatened to resign; then she refused to regard Mary Stanley as anything but a rival and so brought the Crimean nursing project into disrepute by engendering a bitter feud which undid much of the real good done by the nurses, both religious and secular, in the military hospitals. She also deprived the Barracks Hospital of the services of Mother Bridgeman and her Irish Sisters who in time came to be recognised as the most efficient nurses of all.

Neither Sir Edward Cook nor Mrs. Woodham-Smith has successfully explained in a manner favourable to their heroine her unexpected reaction to the portended arrival of Mary Stanley's party. Even her friends in London found it inexplicable. Among others, Doctor Bence Jones wrote asking her, " What has led you to write so strongly against more nurses coming out? How is it that your opinion of the nurses is so much worse than that of others? How is it that you seem to think the evil much outweighs the good, whilst others think the good outweighs the evil?"[21]

It is true that Florence Nightingale knew of the latent and sometimes active hostility manifested towards the nurses, and it is therefore possible that she hesitated from provoking further prejudice. But there is also a positive argument in favour of judging her reaction to be largely a question of pique. She felt that her authority had been publicly flouted and her position under-

THE LADY WITH THE LAMP 89

mined by the assignment of the new party to Dr. Cumming. She denied that etiquette demanded such a procedure in deference to the principal medical officer at Scutari. She had been so assigned herself; but, of course, her case was a special one, and she refused to be mollified.

A more generous and less ambitious character would have endeavoured to make the best of the situation by quietly assimilating the new arrivals. Even granted that Sidney Herbert had failed her, it was unjust of Florence Nightingale to make Mary Stanley's party suffer for a misunderstanding of which they were totally unaware. And Sidney Herbert did not deserve the caustic letter, written in haste and at white heat, on December 15, *just two days before the* Egyptus *berthed*.[22] So great was her haste to give expression to her anger that she did not wait to hear what were the War Office arrangements made for the new party in so far as they referred to herself. Her letter was one at which many men might have taken offence, and which none but Sidney Herbert would have overlooked. She told him in scathing tones that he had sacrificed the cause so dear to her heart; that he had sacrificed her—" a matter of small importance "—; that he had sacrificed his own written word to a popular cry, and had made it impossible for her to continue any longer as Lady Superintendent. The quartering of the new arrivals she declared, was a " physical impossibility "; their employment, " a moral impossibility," and she prophesied that " of course these unemployed women would go to the devil."[23]

The letter carried a cogent postscript. " The proportion of Roman Catholics," wrote Miss Nightingale, " which is already making an outcry, you have raised to twenty-five in eighty-four." Such a consideration was intolerable, all the more so as Florence Nightingale was obsessed with the notion that the Sisters of the second party were bent on a spiritual rather than a medical mission; that they were in fact, coming to the military hospitals as " assistant or female ecclesiastics."* Because of this hastily formed impression, she took a settled dislike to the Irish Sisters and condemned them all out of hand. It was an unfortunate development. Sectarian controversy was then rife in Scutari, and Miss Nightingale's attitude of undisguised hostility served to inject further bitterness into an already aggravated situation.

There was also a footnote to Miss Nightingale's letter: " Written 15 December. Posted 18 December." This she did in order that Sidney Herbert should not think she had written on

---

*This phrase occurs frequently in the Nightingale Papers.

the spur of the moment. It nevertheless remains that the letter was written *and* posted before Florence Nightingale met any of the party of nurses who arrived on the *Egyptus* on December 17.

At this juncture, it will make for greater clarity to deal first with Miss Nightingale's disposal of the secular personnel of the party, before re-introducing Mother Bridgeman, the allocation of whose Sisters presented a greater problem than was at first expected.

With Mary Stanley, whom she met on December 21, Florence Nightingale adopted an attitude of freezing officiousness. Mary Stanley was more than ordinarily upset at this interview. Symptoms of unrest, fomented by delay, were making it increasingly difficult for her to maintain any semblance of cohesion between the ladies and nurses billeted in Therapia. Her suggestion to Miss Nightingale, as she informed Mother Bridgeman on the following day, was " whether though the number of nurses be limited, any of my ladies can be admitted as visitors under the direction of the chaplain, and that the same plan should be adopted by you and your Sisters, supposing that Father Ronan on his arrival should approve and wish it." Miss Stanley also suggested that they " should all be placed in a detached house, there being no accommodation in either hospital," and she " offered to remain and start the whole under these conditions " in either the Barracks or General Hospital at Scutari.[24]

The uncompromising reply was that Miss Nightingale did not want " female ecclesiastics " scampering about the place and that she was totally against the scheme for religious visiting. Writing to Sidney Herbert after this interview Florence Nightingale quoted Mary Stanley as having stipulated that " ten of the Protestants be appropriated as assistants by the chaplains and ten of the nuns by the priests, not as nurses but as female ecclesiastics."[25] But there was nothing in Miss Stanley's proposal to justify such language; the phrase " female ecclesiastics " was entirely of Miss Nightingale's own coining. Further argument was futile. The only positive outcome of the interview was that Florence Nightingale lent Mary Stanley £90 to defray the present expenses of her party. Their allowance had only catered for the cost of travel; consequently they were in sore financial straits, marooned as they were like " so many Robinson Crusoes " on the unfamiliar shores of the Bosphorus.[26] A little later Miss Nightingale advanced another loan of £300, *all of which was refunded to her by the Treasury.*

Stunned and hurt, Mary Stanley wrote to Mrs. Herbert that " it needed all her love for Flo " not to feel injured at being treated

" so officially."[27] But there was nothing for it. On December 24 she was again summoned to Scutari, this time with Dr. Meyer and Mr. Percy, Doctor Cumming and Mr. Bracebridge in attendance. Miss Nightingale, now in a somewhat calmer mood, suggested a compromise. As yet, she would not even consider employing any of the newly-arrived nurses, but because it would be unwise to send the entire party back to England, she offered to accept five of the Irish Sisters to replace the five from Norwood whom she intended to send home. This compromise was actually forced on Florence Nightingale. Lord Napier, secretary to the Embassy, pointed out to her that there were issues other than religious ones involved. Considerations of political and national pride had to be taken into account, he said. Recalling Mother Bridgeman's kinship with Daniel O'Connell, he inferred that there would be— metaphorically speaking—a ' rebellion ' in Ireland if she and her Sisters were sent away. Florence Nightingale therefore yielded, but in such a manner as not to increase the number of Catholics already staffed in the Barracks Hospitals. The dismissal of the Norwood Sisters was her solution. Her stated reason for the dismissal was that child welfare in which the Sisters specialised made them hopelessly unsuited to the requirements of military nursing; but it appears too that their white habits got somehow on her nerves.[28]

For one who owed so much to Catholic Nursing Sisterhoods, Florence Nightingale's opinion, as given about this time in one of her reports from Scutari, is revealing. She was desirous all the time to include Catholic Sisters in her staff, and she actually did so to the end. But her reasons for so doing were practical, not sectarian. In the first place, many of the soldiers were Catholics; and secondly, her apprenticeship in nursing had shown her the excellent qualities, as nurses, of the Catholic Sisters, whose presence on her staff would ensure a certain permanency as against the matrimonial deluge which was sweeping away so many of the secular nurses. In December 1854, Florence Nightingale had ten Sisters under her jurisdiction—five from Bermondsey and five from Norwood.

> " Excellent, gentle, self-devoted women," she wrote of them; " more fit for heaven than a hospital. They flit about the wards like angels without hands among the patients, and soothe their souls, while they leave their bodies dirty and neglected. They never complain; they are eager for self-mortification. But I came not to mortify the nurses, but to nurse the wounded."[29]

As Lady Superintendent at Scutari, Florence Nightingale, as time went by, had less and less use for Sisters, and would possibly have dispensed with them were it not that in her more judicious moments she realised that to do so would bring odium on the cause she had at heart.

Mary Stanley's feelings after her second interview with Miss Nightingale are expressed in a leter to Dr. Manning, dated December 24: " I confess that I have got to be convinced that more nurses are not needed. If the experiment is a failure I concede the point; but if—as I am told here and we heard at home—it is successful, I do not understand why the comfort is to be so limited. . . . Florence requested me formally in presence of Dr. Cumming and Mr. Bracebridge to *succeed her at once.* I refused this most decidedly for every reason."[30]

One of Miss Nightingale's main objections to Mary Stanley's party was that it consisted of too many ladies; she was totally against the " lady plan " which she declared, " ended up in nothing but spiritual flirtations between the nurses and the patients."[31] It was an article of faith with her that a lady could not be a good nurse. Ladies, she said, were unlikely to be well-trained; it was the trained ' hospital nurse ' that she preferred. But Mary Stanley remained long enough in the military hospitals to show that ladies could safely and with good effect be used as nurses, and that efficient ladies were actually better than ordinary nurses on account of their better education and greater self-command. She also conclusively established that a greater number of nurses than that contemplated by Miss Nightingale might be usefully employed in the hospitals, and that furthermore, they were urgently needed there.

By January 1855 the situation in Therapia was becoming untenable. The strain of the past weeks was beginning to tell on Mary Stanley. She was dispirited at the futility of her negotiations with Miss Nightingale. Doubts as to the success of her undertaking were taking definite shape in her mind when help came unexpectedly and simultaneously from Lord Raglan, the Commander-in-Chief, who required nurses for Balaclava, and from Lord Stratford de Redcliffe, who decided to open an extra hospital on the Bosphorus.

The General Hospital at Balaclava, opened in September 1854, presented the same pattern of administrative chaos as did the hospitals at Scutari. It operated on a rotating staff of orderlies drawn from the Ambulance Corps, it was not even moderately equipped and it was hopelessly overcrowded. Miss Nightingale had a strong objection to sending her own nurses to the Crimea.

A " dread of their escape from systematic control " appears to have dictated this objection, but when Lord Raglan asked, in January 1855, for eight nurses to assist the army surgeons, he could not well be refused.[32] Lord Raglan was one of the few upon whom Florence Nightingale showered her constant benevolence. It was accordingly decided that volunteers for the Crimea should be selected from Mary Stanley's party and that they should be placed under the superintendence of a Sellonite Sister, one Miss Langston, who was herself under the jurisdiction of Miss Nightingale. In this way, seven from Therapia—two ladies and five nurses—got employment in Balaclava where they gave general satisfaction to Dr. John Hall and his colleagues. One of the seven, Miss Weare, became superintendent of the Monastery Hospital at Balaclava at a later date; another, Mrs. Elizabeth Davis, became head cook at the General Hospital.

Three other members of Mary Stanley's party were sent home, one because of ill-health, two because of intoxication. Two others were sent on private cases to Pera, a suburb of Constantinople. Miss Nightingale agreed to take thirteen of the remainder. These were to replace several of her own nurses whose continued irregularities were a further cause of prejudice with the Scutari medical officers. The following extract from an entry book of Scutari Barracks Hospital, and preserved in the Convent of Mercy, Kinsale, is worth noting as indicative of the general character of these first Nightingale nurses.

|  | *Appointed* | *Discharged* | *Cause* |
|---|---|---|---|
| Mrs. Besant | 21 October | On arrival | Old age |
| Mrs. Wilson | ,,    ,, | ,,    ,, | Intoxication |
| Mrs. Falkner | ,,    ,, | December 21 | Impropriety of conduct |
| Mrs. Coyle | ,,    ,, | ,,    ,, | Incompetency |
| Mrs. Jones | ,,    ,, | ,,    ,, | Intoxication and theft[33] |

Fanny Taylor was among the thirteen selected by Miss Nightingale for duty in Scutari. She remained there but a few weeks, choosing rather to work under the more gentle rule of Mary Stanley whom she regarded as in every way more suitable for the position of Superintendent of the nurses.

By the end of January an old Turkish Cavalry Barracks which had been obtained by Lord Stratford from Abdul Medged, the reigning Sultan, was converted into a hospital and made ready for the reception of the over-flow from Balaclava. This hospital, the Barracks Hospital, Koulali, was situated like Scutari on the Asiatic shore of the Bosphorus, but about five miles further north and nearer to the seat of war. It was opened on January 27, 1855.

Miss Nightingale had at first a nominal superintendence over this hospital, but as she never even once visited Koulali, she was presently relieved of the responsibility. The hospital was placed under the authority of Lady Stratford de Redcliffe; and she, with the approval of her husband, of Lord William Paulet, Military Commandant at Scutari, and with the sanction of the medical officers, appointed Mary Stanley as Superintendent. This was the final solution to Miss Stanley's dilemma: her party of ladies and nurses was at last assimilated* in the military hospitals of Balaclava, Scutari and Koulali.

Meanwhile, in England, those concerned with the despatch of the nurses were shocked to hear of Miss Nightingale's untoward reaction. Sidney Herbert was hurt and dismayed at the angry vehemence of her letter, though he replied in terms of courtesy and kindness and without any trace of the bitterness which Miss Nightingale's invective might have evoked in a less noble-minded man. Mary Stanley's letters also made painful reading for Mrs. Herbert and Dr. Manning. Mrs. Herbert wrote at once to Mrs. Bracebridge—she dared not address Miss Nightingale—saying, " I am heartbroken about the nurses, but I do assure you that if you send them home without trial you will lose some really valuable women."[34]

Manning's reply on New Year's Day was more lengthy. He was grieved to learn that Florence Nightingale had not desired a second set of nurses. Nevertheless he was slow to accept her ruling on the matter, convinced as he was of the urgent need there was for implementing the nursing personnel.

> " I cannot conceive that with 4,000 or 5,000 wounded, sick and convalescent there can be lack of service required, far beyond the number hitherto sent," he wrote to Mary Stanley. " It always seems to me that one head can set two hundred hands to work; and even though there should be no accommodation, no present employment and many incapables, I cannot believe that they will not all be wanted in a short time, when the distribution of work is as thoroughly carried out as our hospitals demand and as the French actually

---

*Not *dissolved* as stated by Nightingale biographers.

accomplish. I say this in bar of any wishes that they had not been sent, or any thought of sending them home again."[35]

Dr. Manning was similarly disturbed on the Sisters' behalf, all the more so as " certain Catholics in England from the first have criticised the mission." Such considerations notwithstanding, Manning was still confident of success. His letter ends with a caution to avoid all precipitation: " Whatever is done, let nothing be done in haste. An undertaking so public, so conspicuous, so gainsaid and so good, must not fail or even show weakness."

Florence Nightingale's harsh treatment of Mary Stanley and the Sisters offended Dr. Manning, caused a rift in their friendship and lost her the benefit of his counsel. Intimacy was never again re-established between her and the future Cardinal, and though they corresponded on matters of mutual interest for many years after the Crimean War, their letters are uneasy, casual, impersonal. Thus did high-handedness cost Florence Nightingale yet another admirer and sever a long-standing association between two eminent Victorians.

## CHAPTER 8

## MOTHER SUPERIOR AND LADY SUPERINTENDENT

FOR five days after her transfer to Galata Mother Bridgeman was ignored by Florence Nightingale. On the fifth day, December 22, a courier despatched by the Lady Superintendent, presented to her the following but discouraging letter:

" Dear Madam,

Allow me to welcome your arrival and to thank you for your kindness in coming out to aid us in our necessity; at the same time to explain to you the difficulty and painful position in which I am placed by this act of the War Office in sending forty-six more females, making our numbers eighty-four, whereas by our utmost exertions we can only admit fifty into these hospitals, with the consent, that is, of the Medical Officers.

In this most perplexing position, I am compelled to exercise my judgment in making a selection and to send back some of the party I already have, both Catholic and Protestant, in order to make room for an equal number of the new party.

My question to you is, can you divide? Five of your nuns who would not probably object to being under the Reverend Mother here as Superior, are all that I can receive—and to their arrival I was looking forward with anxiety and joy. I must have a conversation with you about the disposal of the remainder.

Believe me,

Yours gratefully and truly,

Florence Nighingale."[1]

Miss Nightingale's protestation of anticipated " anxiety and joy " scarcely synchronises with the five-day freeze which followed the Sisters' arrival. Mother Bridgeman decided to answer the letter in person. Taking as her companion Sister M. Bernard of Chelsea, who was professed under Mother M. Clare Moore in Bermondsey, she crossed in a caique to Scutari. Viewed from across the Bosphorus the Barracks Hospital had an appearance of grandeur, but at close quarters the illusion vanished. It was a dirty, yellow, square, stone building, surmounted by towers at

each angle, the whole structure with its cracked masonry presenting such a picture of dilapidation and neglect that Florence
Nightingale on first beholding it was minded of the inscription
at the entrance of Dante's *Inferno*: " Abandon hope, all ye who
enter here."

The Sisters, as they climbed the slope from the rickety landing-
stage, were confronted by a panorama of rubbish-strewn mud.
Tin cans, pewter plates, miscellaneous breakages from the hospital littered the quadrangle, in the centre of which an enormous
pile of offal told its own story of waste and mismanagement.
Groups of convalescents, some lacking an arm, others a leg,
hobbled around the courtyard. Their listless, emaciated
appearance, coupled with the agonising shrieks of new arrivals
being jolted mercilessly over the rough uneven ground, added
to the macabre scene; while the sight of an araba-load of
coffinless shroudless corpses being carted off for burial recalled
for Mother Bridgeman the horror and hideousness of famine
conditions at home. Over and above all this was the fetid
stench from within the hospital which assailed the approaching
Sisters while they were yet some twenty yards from the entrance.

The interior of this great shell with its damp streaming walls,
its oozing floors and its reeking corridors was exactly in keeping
with its tumble-down exterior. There was no " Welcome " on the
mat; nor were the visitors received with any sign of friendship
by Mother M. Clare Moore. Just a cold hand-shake after which
she showed them into " the one room occupied by her five
Sisters and the five from Norwood." Mother Bridgeman noted
in her diary her astonishment at seeing the Sisters " so soiled
and neglected-looking " crowded together in this miserable room
which, she said, " opened into a thoroughfare of dirt and
confusion."[2]

How explain the unfriendliness of Mother M. Clare to the
newcomers? After all, they were members of her own Congregation, and two of Mother Bridgeman's fifteen had come from
St. Maries of the Isle, Cork, the convent over which Mother
M. Clare would have been superioress had she not been sent
on an extended " loan " to Bermondsey. Was Rutland Street
and what should have been its happy memories forgotten?
Apparently so; for by December 1854 the superioress of
Bermondsey had attached herself so unreservedly to Florence
Nightingale and was so well established in that lady's good
graces that she seemed to have resented sharing the " privilege "
with any other. This icy formality was unfortunately the relationship which was to prevail between the two superioresses while

the Crimean War lasted. Nightingale biographers have tended rather unhappily to labour this point, with Mother Bridgeman always the villain of the piece, whereas a glance at the conventual archives of the period leads to the inference that any hostility there was stemmed from the English superioress who chose whenever possible to exclude Mother Bridgeman's community from all contact with her own.

Manning was not unduly worried over this "coldness" between the two superioresses. "Paul and Barnabas had a sharp contention," he remarked. "Why not Mother Francis and Mother Clare?"[3]

After what seemed an interminable delay Mother Bridgeman and Sister M. Bernard were eventually received by Miss Nightingale. She invited them to lunch. It consisted of "a small remnant of musty cheese, a scrap of dirty butter in a bowl, some sour bread and some cold potatoes." Mother Bridgeman thinking that such spartan fare was Miss Nightingale's daily ration pitied her—until she heard that Mr. and Mrs. Bracebridge saw to it that she was usually served with more palatable delicacies. Later, her domestic staff included Alexis Soyer, the celebrated French chef. Others were less fortunate: "A delicate Puseyite Sister, the daughter of Lady Erskine, could not get as much as an egg for her breakfast, and often went to her ward fasting when she could not eat the food set before her."[4]

This first interview between Mother Bridgeman and Florence Nightingale ended in a deadlock. Each was all the while measuring the other; the impression in each case was unfavourable. Mother Bridgeman began by assuring Miss Nightingale that as it had not been in her power to make herself superioress of the Sisters, neither was she at liberty to divest herself of her duties, nor to transfer the Sisters without their own consent and that of their superiors in Ireland. Miss Nightingale was not impressed and refused to appreciate the difficulties of the situation.

Mother Bridgeman next urged that if the Sisters could not be accommodated in the hospital, Miss Nightingale might secure a house for them in Scutari whence they might come daily to work in either the Barracks or the General Hospital. But when this and "every other proposal" was rejected, Mother Bridgeman realised that contrary to her own expectations and to the predictions of Manning, she had before her "an ambitious woman to deal with; a woman on whom she could not possibly rely."[5] As for Miss Nightingale, *she* brought away from this interview a new nickname to add to her already lengthy collection. Henceforth she refers to Mother Bridgeman as "the Reverend Brickbat."[6] The

interview over, Mother Bridgeman was resolved that future trans-
actions between herself and the Lady Superintendent should be
expressed, if possible, in writing.

While in Scutari Mother Bridgeman called on Father Michael
Cuffe, senior chaplain to the Catholic forces (and incorrectly
cited in some works as a member of the Society of Jesus). Contacts between Reverend Mother and Father Cuffe though not
always serene were sufficiently cordial to disprove the suggestion
of friction implied in the Nightingale papers and by some of the
Nightingale biographers. Father Cuffe was Mother Bridgeman's
mainstay in difficulty and her principal adviser in her present
dilemma. Far from refusing his ministrations, as claimed in the
Woodham-Smith biography—she actually sought him out in her
difficulties. Father Cuffe, who disliked Florence Nightingale and
who objected to her arbitrary dismissal of the Norwood Sisters,
was forthright in his instructions. His advice, as reported in due
time to Archbishop Cullen, was

> "Let Mother Bridgeman and her nuns by no means take up
> quarters in these hospitals until our Ecclesiastics at home are
> made aware of how the Norwood Nuns are being treated,
> and hear their verdict."[7]

But while Mother Bridgeman set a high premium on Father
Cuffe's advice she could not always follow his instructions. For
instance, the reply from 'Ecclesiastics at home' was so long
delayed that she had to act in this matter according to her own
judgment and to take a step which she prayed would be ultimately
to the satisfaction of all.

On her return to Galata she told the Sisters that anyone who
wished to go to Scutari on the proposed terms, namely, a temporary transfer of obedience to Mother M. Clare, might write to
her superiors for permission. Four Sisters wrote: Sisters M.
Elizabeth and Winifred from Liverpool, who were refused; Sister
M. Aloysius from Carlow, who afterwards changed her mind ;
and Sister M. Bernard from Chelsea. Sister M. Bernard got the
required permission, but by the time it arrived, all fifteen Sisters
had found employment.

The Norwood Sisters were got rid of in humiliating fashion on
December 23. They were given a few hours' notice to prepare
for departure.

> "Then," wrote Father Cuffe, "in their white habits they
> were marched between two files of soldiers through the main
> gate of the hospital, together with some nurses who were

being discharged for misconduct. At the outer gate Miss
Nightingale called a list of names and formally dismissed
them. They had to trudge through the public streets of
Scutari, wait a considerable time at the boat-station without
any shelter on a December day, and then embark to spend
Christmas on the seas, placed under no other protection than
that of the captain of the vessel in which they were to travel."[8]

Also dismissed were a number of Sellonites for whom Florence
Nightingale entertained a certain antipathy. One of them, Sister
Elizabeth Wheeler, who disapproved of her methods, had written
to England describing the dreadful state of the wards in Scutari
Hospital. Her letter, published in *The Times* on December 8, 1854,
led to a searching investigation before the Hospitals Commission:
an investigation from which, however, Miss Nightingale emerged
with unimpaired prestige. She had seen to it that a number of her
own supporters were elected to the Board of Enquiry.

The dismissal of December 23 was not without its aftermath of
bitterness. Father Cuffe said it out-Heroded Herod who " sent the
Blessed Virgin across the desert." *The Tablet* carried an article
protesting against Miss Nightingale " fulminating her spiritual
edict against the admission of, and in fact, banishing nuns from
the hospitals in Scutari." Another contributor objected to invest-
ing " a pretended nun " with such absolute power of condemning
and dismissing.[9]

Strangely enough, there was no objection from Southwark. Dr.
Thomas Grant, who was so elated and complimented when the
Government accepted the services of Sisters, had now no protest
to utter when the Sisters of his choice were rejected by a representative of the same Government. As matters stood, he could
expect little sympathy from his fellow ecclesiastics who had
openly disapproved of his arrangements. Silence was therefore
his refuge; but he had learned his lesson the hard way, and for
the future, he took good care to look before he leaped. His lordship's reticence on the Norwood episode was indeed so guarded
that his biographer Grace Ramsay seemingly knew nothing of the
dismissal or of the subsequent discomfiture of her subject. The
incident is altogether omitted from her writings.

On the Protestant side, offence was taken because the Sellonites
were returned to England labelled as inefficient. Epithets such as
" Socinian "; charges of " Popish plots " and " Jesuit conspiracies "
were hurled at the Scutari nurses. *The Cork Constitution*, a non-
Catholic publication, condemned the entire nursing project as a
cover for promoting " Papal, Conventual and High Church views;

that it was perfectly dishonest in professing to do one thing while really doing another."[10] Miss Nightingale herself, whose suspected High Church views gave offence to Low Church followers, was denounced as an " Anglican Papist " and accused of partiality to Mother M. Clare. Mother M. Clare in turn, was denounced by Father Cuffe as a " plotting woman " by whom he had been himself misled.[11]

Charges and counter-charges continued to fly to and fro between England and Scutari, and ultimately led to the publication of an explanatory article in *The Times* of January 9, 1855.

" While the good which the nurses have done is incalculable and admitted by everyone," stated the article, " the success of the experiment as a feature of the Medical Department of the Army on war service cannot be considered as decisively established until certain religious difficulties which have arisen are put to rest ; for . . . in an effort to organise a good band of nurses from the material supplied by an outburst of zeal and devotion at home, there is some danger of the whole undertaking coming to an abrupt conclusion."

Controversy raged so long and so furiously that Florence Nightingale, to use her own expression, had to endure both the " Protestant howl " and the " Roman Catholic storm." It could hardly have been otherwise. Her habit of interference in matters ecclesiastical—Catholic, Protestant and Presbyterian—was bound to evoke criticism. People could even speak of her in the Crimea as " Priestess, Miss Nightingale." The pity was that she did not understand the philosophy of toleration.

On December 24 Mother Bridgeman wrote to her bishop, Dr. William Delany, asking his permission to fall in with Miss Nightingale's suggestions. She wrote also to Miss Nightingale asking if she was resolved to have but one superior at Scutari, and if the five Sisters she intended to admit were to make an unqualified transfer of obedience to Mother M. Clare Moore; how the remaining ten were to be disposed of ; if and when they were to return home; and that if all were to be kept and subdivided, how the services of a chaplain would be secured to them. She requested that she might be allowed " to see, sustain and direct the Sisters as the novelty and difficulty of their position might require "; and her final appeal was, " Will you co-operate with me in changing the Sisters from one locality to another if I should find it necessary and expedient for them?"[12]

" Believe me, my dear Miss Nightingale," she continued, " you will find us most anxious to co-operate cordially with you . . . and it is not a difficult spirit which urges me to ask replies on these points, but a pressing wish to see what can be done to extricate us from the painful position in which we are mutually placed, as well as to deliver my own conscience from all future responsibility about the Sisters I have brought out from different communities under express conditions which I cannot infringe without the full consent of all those concerned."

The letter concluded with an offer: Mother Bridgeman would go to Scutari as a Sister with four others, " and with them labour under Reverend Mother of Bermondsey's direction" provided that the remaining ten might be safely lodged where she might conveniently visit them. Their continuance in Galata she declared would be " a serious inconvenience and a positive injury " to the Sisters of Charity who could not re-open their boarding school while their visitors were in possession of the dormitories. If only on that account, Mother Bridgeman felt obliged to ask Miss Nightingale for alternative accommodation for the Sisters.

But Florence Nightingale would not be won over by Mother Bridgeman's overtures ; not even when Mother Bridgeman so obviously desired to meet her half-way. In fact, she chose deliberately to misinterpret Reverend Mother's letter, for on December 28, she complained to Sidney Herbert that the Reverend Brickbat was leading her " the devil of a life, determined to force an entry into the Barracks Hospital with all her fifteen nuns *vi et armis*."[13]

Equally unreliable was the letter Mrs. Bracebridge sent to Liz Herbert on the same day:

" I grieve to say that Miss Stanley's *false position* is already working fearful mischief ; she is acting a very double part and is in league with the Reverend Mother Bridgeman of Kinsale to *force* Flo, if she can, to give way and appoint them together to the General Hospital where they can work their proselytising unmolested."[14]

Mother Bridgeman had her own reasons for wishing to be among the five accepted in Scutari. Being an excellent nurse, she was eager to get to work. She was concerned to share with her Sisters the difficulties she anticipated would be their lot. She felt that they would need her support and advice in the novel and trying surroundings of a military hospital, and she feared that without her own direction there would be few others to trouble about their welfare. Subsequent events proved that she was correct. Mother M. Clare Moore had little or no thought for the Irish Sisters.

Indeed, Father Cuffe believed that her "influence over Miss Nightingale was so injurious" to their interests that he wrote asking Bishop Grant to recall her.[15]

Before sending off her letter (December 24), Mother Bridgeman received a second communication from Florence Nightingale. Not at all intimidated by the recent 'Roman Catholic storm' Miss Nightingale began again to interfere in matters ecclesiastical, this time to the tune of transferring the obedience of five Sisters from Mother Bridgeman's jurisdiction to that of Mother M. Clare Moore, without the least regard for Mother Bridgeman's doubts and scruples. Claiming the right of selection among the Irish Sisters, Miss Nightingale's first choice fell on Mother M. Clare's former novice, Sister M. Bernard of Chelsea, and she asked Mother Bridgeman for four others

> "whose qualifications you will have the goodness to discuss with me at your earliest convenience, to act under me in all matters relating to hospital service, and under the Reverend Mother in all matters relating to religious discipline."

She expressed her willingness to confer on any difficulties which Mother Bridgeman might anticipate, and mentioned that there was accommodation in Therapia for the ten remaining Sisters.

> " I know from Miss Stanley, as well as many other sources," she concluded, " the immense value of the services of your nuns, and am duly grateful to you for coming out . . ."[16]

Mother Bridgeman who had not yet despatched her own letter, merely added a postscript by way of reply to the above, to the effect that its contents expressed all she could do without further authority. While awaiting Miss Nightingale's replies to her queries, she intimated her readiness to remove to Therapia.

The transfer was effected on December 28, the feast of Holy Innocents. Mary Stanley, accompanied by the ever-faithful Angelo, came to escort the Sisters to their temporary home on the Bosphorus where they found Fanny Taylor and Miss Kate Anderson putting the final touches to Lord Napier's house for them. Once installed, they christened it the Convent of the Nativity. Here they lived apart and never left the Embassy grounds except to go to daily Mass at the French Naval Hospital, some two miles distant. A priest from Scutari came every week to minister to them. Apart from these visits they had " no Ecclesiastical Director, no head of the Mission, no earthly guide,"[17] and to crown all, Mother Bridgeman's letter of December 24 was still unanswered. The reply, dated Christmas Day and delivered on January 1, 1855, augured ill for the new year then beginning.

Florence Nightingale repeated in this letter what she had intimated on December 24—that five Sisters not including a superioress would be admitted to Scutari Barracks Hospital to act under herself and Mother M. Clare in matters of hospital routine and religious administration respectively. As for the other ten: they would have to remain in Therapia. She had "no power to dispose of them; they had not been consigned to her."[18] This question of non-consignment to herself was a matter of constant vexation to Miss Nightingale. Nor was she mollified at Sidney Herbert's assurance that she attached too much importance to the second party being consigned to Dr. Cumming.[19] Sidney Herbert, she felt, did not realise the loophole thus afforded Mother Bridgeman of evading her authority. Nothing would disabuse her of this notion even though Mother Bridgeman did not for an instant consider the consignment to Dr. Cumming released either herself or her Sisters from the duty of obedience to Miss Nightingale in matters of hospital routine.

To the question of securing the services of a chaplain for the non-admitted Sisters, Florence Nightingale informed Mother Bridgeman that there were "five Roman Catholic priests" for that purpose. It was to her a matter of little consequence that these five were dispersed over the length and breadth of the Crimea. In January 1855 there was one priest on duty in Scutari; there was another in Pera, and there were three with the regiments on different outposts in the Crimea.

The only concession allowed to Mother Bridgeman in respect of the five Sisters in Scutari was that of transferring them should occasion arise. Miss Nightingale's words were: "If you should advise a Sister to withdraw at any time, she can do so." There could be no denying the import of this pronouncement. Nevertheless when Mother Bridgeman at a later date took Miss Nightingale at her word, the anger of the Lady Superintendent was unleashed with a fury which even the War Office could not resist . . .

> The letter continues: "I can only know Sisters as nurses when they come here . . . and it is not in my province to enter upon any rules or order which affect you as coming from your Superiors."

Urging that the vacancies in Scutari be filled within three days, she concluded with special emphasis :

> " I must reluctantly decline accepting you as a second

Superior. In using my power of selection I am most unwillingly obliged to say this."[20]

Mother Bridgeman in reply referred Miss Nightingale to her communication of December 24 in which she had offered to go *as an ordinary Sister* to Scutari and to work under Mother M. Clare while awaiting directions from her bishop. She repeated that she and her companions would form but one community with the Bermondsey Sisters, and that she would not expect to be recognised as a second superior. She protested, however, against Miss Nightingale's right of selection on the very common-sense ground that Miss Nightingale was not in any position to judge of the suitability or unsuitability of the Sisters.

> " It is impossible, my dear Miss Nightingale," wrote Mother Bridgeman, " that you could have any just ground on which to make a selection amongst our Sisters as you know nothing of them. If you will kindly allow me to select, you may rely on my doing so to the best of my ability."[21]

Florence Nightingale would have none of this. She persisted in making matters difficult for Mother Bridgeman—and at the same time sent an exaggerated and mendacious complaint to Sidney Herbert that the " R.C. question " remained unsettled; that Brickbat, the Reverend Mother of Kinsale, was refusing to let five of her nuns go to Scutari without her, thereby showing that she had some second motive in view besides nursing. " Of course," she continued, there would be " a R.C. storm," but that she refused to let her " little society " become a hot-bed of " R.C. Intriguettes," and that the Reverend Mother of Bermondsey, who was " heart and hand " with her was doing her best to stop it.[22]

Mother Bridgeman made one last effort to save the situation. Feeling there was yet one appeal which Florence Nightingale could hardly afford to ignore, she recalled the recommendation of Dr. Manning

> " who assured us that we would surely find in Miss Nightingale a *kind and considerate friend,* who would never exercise her authority in any manner inconsistent with religious discipline or wounding to our feelings . . . and that we might come to you without fear."[23]

The arrow found its mark. On January 5, 1855, Florence Nightingale agreed that Mother Bridgeman should be one of the five Sisters to be employed in Scutari. Mother M. Clare was the bearer of the good news. She travelled by caique across the

Bosphorus and arrived in a blinding snowstorm at Therapia on the feast of the Epiphany.

The visit temporarily restored peace between Florence Nightingale and Mary Stanley. The Sisters were less fortunate. With an attitude in keeping with the weather Mother M. Clare gave them to understand " that it was not to nurse the sick they were needed, for as there had been no general engagement lately, the wounded were either dead or convalescent; that most of those then in hospital were only suffering from scurvy, dysentery and enteric fever, *and therefore needed no nursing!*" No engagement was expected until spring, and until then no more nurses would be required. The Sisters would have to be satisfied with employment in either the stores or kitchen.

> " Now at that time," wrote Mother Bridgeman, " there were about four thousand patients in the Scutari hospitals, and from fifty to ninety were buried daily."[24]

Miss Nightingale's whole attitude to medical nursing is summarised in the ultimatum delivered in her name by Mother M. Clare to Mother Bridgeman. Florence Nightingale was under the impression that surgical cases were the only ones requiring nursing care. For medical cases, such as dysentery, cholera, typhus etc., she considered that special diet was the main treatment and the principal concern of the nurse. It was the patient's own business to get better himself. She also stressed hygiene, but she had a supreme contempt for and a disbelief in the possibility of contagion. The better to prove her point, she would place operation cases in fever wards—even in beds from which fever patients had recently been carried off dead. Her attitude towards medical nursing possibly explains, as nothing else could, her keeping her nurses more often in the diet-kitchen than in the wards.

On instructions from Miss Nightingale Mother M. Clare appointed Mother Bridgeman as the first of the five,

> " as she would not only be the most important person of her community, but also the most agreeable to herself as a fellow-worker!"

Mother Bridgeman set but little store on the compliment, but she nevertheless went to Scutari on January 8, 1855, promising, in writing, to act while there

> " in such a manner as to give no one reason to complain or to cause the least inconvenience or division ".[25]

Her anxiety to be of use in the hospitals made her ready to go to any length to conciliate Florence Nightingale, even though she realised she could not further commit herself without permission from her bishop.

The Sisters chosen to accompany Mother Bridgeman to Scutari were Sisters M. Elizabeth and M. Agnes of Baggot Street, Sister M. Aloysius of Carlow and Sister Winifred of Liverpool. Sister M. Bernard of Chelsea was appointed presiding Sister in Therapia during the interim.

On arrival in Scutari Sisters M. Agnes and Winifred were sent to the hospital kitchen to work under Mother M. Clare who gave them little or nothing to do. Sisters M. Aloysius and M. Elizabeth were put sorting bales of linen in a rat-infested clothing store. Mother Bridgeman was ignored. Miss Nightingale refused to give her any occupation, giving as her excuse that " as she could not trust the paid nurses to go beyond their fixed duties, she should equally restrict " her in order to avoid their jealousy.[26]

Thus ignored and unemployed Mother Bridgeman had ample opportunity for observing " the utter disorder and irregularity which reigned throughout, and which no one seemed willing or able to control." Doctors and nurses appeared to be at sixes and sevens. Mother M. Clare was a perfect drudge. Orderlies had the law in their own hands, and came and went as they pleased. Preparation of food was disgraceful. Fanny Taylor records that she often saw " orderlies cutting up the carcases of sheep in the corridor close by the beds in which were men suffering from every form of disease."[27] There being no daily calculation of requirements, extraordinary shortages occurred. It was evidently nobody's business to see whether the patients got sufficient food, Miss Nightingale's whole pre-occupation being confined to giving out the contents of her store.

> " I am a kind of General Dealer," she wrote to Sidney Herbert on January 4, 1855, " in socks, shirts, knives and forks, wooden spoons, tin baths, tables and forms, cabbages and carrots, operating tables, towels and soap, small tooth combs, precipitate for destroying lice, scissors, bed pans and stump pillows."[28]

The two Sisters in the clothing store found the place so over-run with rats that they begged the sergeant in charge to leave the door open that they might escape the more easily if attacked.

> " Our home rats would run if you ' hushed ' them," wrote Sister M. Aloysius, the more nervous of the two ; " but you

might ' hush ' away and the Scutari rats would not take the least notice."

Another trial was Mrs. Bracebridge, whose fussy habits were a constant source of exasperation.

Interruptions and inconveniences notwithstanding, the Sisters managed occasional words of instruction with the Catholic soldiers and orderlies who came to the store. The ingenious answers which from time to time they received from these good fellows must have helped to bring some ray of sunshine into the otherwise drab austerity of their lives. For instance, Sister M. Elizabeth on one occasion asked an orderly if he had been lately at his duty. " Sure, Ma'am, ' *herself* ' goes regularly," he replied, " and won't that do for me too . . . ?"[29]

After some days Mother Bridgeman was permitted to serve out a few gallons of soup (from five to ten) daily. As the serving took little more than an hour and as she was forbidden to enter the wards, she was compelled to spend the greater part of her time in the cheerless garret which served as community room, refectory and dormitory for the combined Irish and English communities. Her feelings during these unhappy hours are best described by herself:

> " Oh! the misery of that time! To sit in that one room without occupation, without a place to which we might withdraw even for a few moments to seek reflection or to ask the aid and light we needed so much. To realise that we were surrounded by thousands of sufferers whom we had come so far to serve. To know that from fifty to ninety were dying daily. To be sitting idle in the midst of them and to be told by one against whose whim we had no appeal that ' these needed no nursing as they were not wounded.' To pass daily through the corridors filled with sick and dying fellow-creatures, to hear their moans and see their crying necessities, and to be debarred by Miss Nightingale from rendering them any of the services for which we had left our convents. All this, and *much more better untold*, combined to try us in a way one should have felt to appreciate."[30]

Fanny Taylor's account corroborates Mother Bridgeman's.

> " It seems impossible to describe Scutari Hospital at this time . . . for what an eye-witness saw was beyond description. . . . As we passed the corridors we asked ourselves if it were not a terrible dream. When we awoke in the morning, our hearts sank down at the thought of the woe we must wit-

ness during the day. At night, we lay down, wearied beyond expression, but not so much from physical fatigue . . . as from the sickness of heart occasioned by living amidst such a mass of hopeless suffering."[31]

At this time the death-rate in Scutari was alarmingly high. The insanitary condition of the hospital made it a breeding-ground for every species of virulent bacteria; and though Florence Nightingale is credited with restoring a measure of cleanliness in the wards, her anti-contagion complex virtually nullified all that was otherwise commonsense in her particular gospel of sanitation. Outbreaks of erysipelas and gangrene became common. Men stretched on filthy straw beds or low uncomfortable trestles developed suppurating bed-sores, the pus from which congealed on their coarse canvas coverings. They had seldom a change of bedclothes. Very few had pillows. Pillows were not an issue from the Government Stores. They could only be had on requisition from Miss Nightingale's Free Gift Stores; but where this requisition, duly signed and counter-signed, was lacking, no plea would induce the Lady Superintendent to deviate from the rules.

Such cast-iron adherence to out-dated regulations was the main source of weakness in Florence Nightingale's whole idea of hospital administration. These regulations, framed principally for home service, were hopelessly impracticable, and indeed positively injurious, when applied to the unforeseen contingencies of foreign service. The system, which precluded any action except through recognised channels, lacked the elasticity called for by a war emergency. The crisis in Scutari called insistently for flexibility, the necessity for which Miss Nightingale somehow did not realise, for we read that " when the practice of issuing on requisitions " was pronounced " vicious ", she continued as before, and ignored the orders of the Medical Board with the result that the Barracks Hospital at Scutari presented the most extreme picture of misery offered by any other war hospital of the east.[32]

Though Mother Bridgeman chafed at the helplessness of her position, there appeared to be no immediate remedy to hand. Father Ronan, S.J., had not yet arrived. She was being cold-shouldered by Mother M. Clare and ignored by Miss Nightingale. To crown all, she found she had inadvertently displeased Father Cuffe when against his advice she placed herself at the disposal of Miss Nightingale. Father Cuffe made no secret of his disapproval. " Nuns are like priests," he wrote to Archbishop Cullen; " and priests have their faults; so too have nuns." [33]

But while Father Cuffe disapproved of Mother Bridgeman's

acquiescence and pronounced "such a step not a prudent one," he continued to stand by her. The same is true of his colleague, Father Thomas Moloney; though the latter's interest in the affairs of Mother Bridgeman and her community soon took on the form of unwelcome interference which greatly aggravated their already grievous difficulties. Father Moloney was the priest whose ministrations Mother Bridgeman had declined shortly after her arrival: she did so because Father Moloney was endeavouring to establish himself as Superior and Spiritual Director of the community in place of Father Ronan who had been appointed to that office by the competent authorities at home.

Florence Nightingale's hands were ultimately forced by the outbreak of a cholera epidemic in mid-January which carried off four surgeons and three nurses, and which made imperative the employment of extra nursing personnel in the wards. In this way Mother Bridgeman and her Sisters were finally introduced to the squalor, the misery and the despair of Scutari Barracks Hospital.

> "Where shall I begin, or how shall I ever describe my first day in the hospital at Scutari?" wrote Sister M. Aloysius. "Vessels were arriving daily, but there was not an available bed. The sick were laid on the floor one after another till the beds were emptied of those already occupying them. Many died immediately after being brought in. . . . The look of agony on their poor dying faces will never leave my heart. . . . If stretchers were bringing in some new patients from the vessels, others were going out with the dead. . . ."[34]

The majority of admissions died in a matter of hours. If death be awful everywhere, it was truly so in that stricken military hospital.

The prevailing terror of officialdom was a God-sent opportunity for Mother Bridgeman. Late and early she and her Sisters were busy in the wards, promoting the ease, comfort and cleanliness of their patients; administering hot wine and brandy, rubbing in solutions of mustard and turpentine, all in an effort to relieve the vice-like grip of a disease which claimed nine victims out of every ten. Mother Bridgeman used her own stuping remedy, to the evident satisfaction of the doctors who delegated her to administer the chloroform treatment they were then introducing. For obvious reasons neither nurses nor orderlies could be so trusted.

Into the wards where the fever was at its worst went the Sisters, caring little for the remonstrations of some faint-hearted medical officers for whom fear of contagion was a greater consideration than was adherence to the path of duty. These men never ventured beyond the doors of the wards; they contented themselves with an

"All right, Sir," from an orderly within, and then passed on.[35]
Week in, week out the fever continued to rage, spreading panic
among the nurses and claiming so many victims that one could
say that death seemed to be almost tired out. There was a crying
need now, not alone for the nurses in Scutari, but for those others
who were willing to help, but who were still living in idleness at
the government's expense in Therapia. Yet Florence Nightingale
seems not to have realised this need.

Extermination of vermin went hand-in-hand with the duties of
nursing. The beds in Scutari were literally alive, and it was long
before the Sisters could make their patients even tolerably comfortable. Cleanliness was eventually one of their prime achievements, though more often than not their own clothing took the
surplus of what was eliminated from the beds! Even so, there was
still opportunity for the higher functions of religious nursing:
during the epidemic the Sisters applied themselves whenever
possible to the religious welfare of the many Irish Catholic patients
in the hospital. The sight of the nuns acted as a balm on these
poor fellows who kept on repeating to each other, " Sure, and it's
our own Sisters, glory be to God!" Mother Bridgeman was asked
one day, "All I want to know, Ma'am, is, are you one of our own
Sisters of Mercy from Ireland?" On hearing her reply, he said,
" God be praised for that; I lived near the convent in Mary-
borough before coming out here." It goes without saying that these
Irish patients idolised the Sisters. The Englishmen were equally
grateful for even the smallest service: " I care not for creed or
difference of opinion," said one. " To me you are all angels of
mercy, and on the part of my comrades and on my own behalf I
express our grateful acknowledgements." [36]

Before long the religious influence of the Sisters was widely felt
in those gloomy wards of Scutari Barracks Hospital, where,
kneeling by the bedside of the dying, they spoke words of faith
which brought back the recollection of saving truths perhaps long
since forgotten; words of hope which lit up the pathway to the
grave; words of charity which afforded a foretaste of that kingdom
where charity alone of all the virtues shall continue forever. They
saw to it that no Catholic was allowed pass through the valley of
the shadow without receiving the consolation of the Last Sacraments and the benefit of every comfort provided by Mother
Church for the journey to eternity. Deaths were still numerous,
but the sting of death was gone, and in its place was
a holy and calm resignation quite at variance with the vaguely-
hopeful longings of the less-fortunate non-Catholic patients. The
latter, accustomed to a more attenuated form of Christianity, and

neglected in great measure by their own ministers, were deeply impressed by the energy and devotedness of Father Cuffe, Father Moloney and the Sisters of Mercy. Unfortunately, their desire for instruction provoked an outburst against the Sisters on the part of Miss Nightingale and the Reverend John Edward Sabin, senior Protestant chaplain at Scutari.

Miss Nightingale wrote in white hot fury to Lady Canning that " the second party of nuns who came out now wander over the whole hospital out of nursing hours, not confining themselves to their own wards but ' instructing ' (it is their own word) groups of orderlies and convalescents on the corridors, doing the work of ten chaplains and bringing ridicule on the whole thing while they quote the words of the War Office." [37]

Florence Nightingale, in lodging her complaint, made light of two significant issues: she deliberately ignored the utility of the Irish Sisters as nurses, and that the imparting of instruction to Catholics was a peculiar feature of their vocation as Sisters of Mercy.

Mother M. Clare also joined in the complaint. She felt the Irish Sisters ought to be more discreet and told Mother Bridgeman to confine herself to instructing the Catholics ' in secret ', because, she said, the Sisters were accepted principally as nurses. Mother Bridgeman's reply to this observation is not on record, but on February 22, a letter from Bishop Grant led Mother M. Clare Moore to alter her opinion on the matter. His lordship wrote:

> " We are anxious that you should always be *Nuns* as well as *Nurses;* and our fear in England is that Miss Nightingale may have given you so many duties in the latter capacity that you are unable to attend to anything else. I believe you are allowed full liberty of speaking to Catholics about religion, and I do not know what else we can expect; but if you are reduced to mere *Nurses,* she has more authority over you than we ever intended to give." [38]

As against Mother M. Clare's opinion, Mother Bridgeman was insistent that the Irish Sisters came out to the military hospitals not merely as nurses, but as nursing Sisters of Mercy; that they would continue to minister to the spiritual as well as to the temporal necessities of the Catholics; that she would " ever openly maintain this freedom and right to instruct Catholics, and would not continue in the British hospitals if prevented from so doing." [39]

The contrast between the two superioresses was never more clearly etched than on the present occasion. Mother M. Clare Moore remained to the end the tool of Florence Nightingale.

Mother Bridgeman stood on her own two feet and did so with her accustomed dignity and calmness. Her portrait at this time, as depicted by one of Miss Nightingale's biographers, represents her as an " Irish nun of ardent and rebellious temperament . . . loud-voiced, assertive, voluble. . . ." [40] The biographer has clearly made her own of Dr. Manning's pronouncement; but while adding to the original, has omitted Manning's modification that Mother Bridgeman was also " truly good, devoted and trustworthy." Thus amid good report and bad, the work continued until the third week in January when two important letters reached Scutari from Sidney Herbert. One was for Miss Nightingale; the other for Mother Bridgeman.

In addressing Florence Nightingale, Mr. Herbert made no attempt to urge in his own defence the reasons which prompted and justified his action. He admitted that in sending extra nurses to Scutari without previous consultation with her he had— technically at any rate—failed to keep his agreement with her. He refused to hear of her resignation and authorised her to send Miss Stanley's party back to England at his expense, if on full consideration she thought such a course feasible. Lord Stanmore in his memoir of Sidney Herbert remarks that it is possible that Mr. Herbert may have foreseen that when Miss Nightingale found herself armed with such authority, " she would hesitate to incur the responsibility of using it." If so, he was right; for when a few days' reflection had cooled down her first impetuosity, she pronounced it to be a " moral impossibility " to send away all the new arrivals.[41] She made the best of what she considered a bad job—to the ultimate advantage of the wounded soldiers both Catholic and Protestant, in the military hospitals of the east.

Equally apologetic was Sidney Herbert's letter to Mother Bridgeman and inconsistent when measured against that received by Florence Nightingale. Mr. Herbert began by assuring Mother Bridgeman that he had " acted under a misconception of Miss Nightingale's wants and wishes " in sending out the second party of Sisters and nurses to Scutari. " Under these circumstances," he continued, " Miss Nightingale has been advised by me to select such of the Sisters and nurses as she considered the most efficient for the work in which she was engaged, and to send back the remainder." [42]

Both Sir Edward Cook and Mrs. Woodham-Smith credit Miss Nightingale with having received authorisation to send the entire second party back to England. No copy of Sidney Herbert's letter to Miss Nightingale is known to be extant, and as to its precise contents we have only Miss Nightingale's own account; but the discrepancy between it and the letter to Mother Bridgeman is too remarkable to be overlooked. The question naturally arises as to whether Sidney Herbert really gave Florence Nightingale the authority she claimed, or whether she framed that particular clause on her own, in hopes of enhancing her prestige by the assumption of such absolute power of non-appellate dismissal. It is possible too, that if Sidney Herbert *did* issue such contradictory directions, he did so in an effort to conciliate as best he could these two formidable personalities. In the event, he failed hopelessly.

Considerations of " advantage to the public service " prompted Mr. Herbert to add to his second letter a significant postscript, the implications of which give an entirely new interpretation to Mother Bridgeman's so-called subsequent " rebellion " against Florence Nightingale.

> " I am informed here," he wrote, " that your kind services may very possibly be required in Galata, which, if it relieve you from your present difficulties, I should be glad to hear had been the case."

Whatever Florence Nightingale might allege to the contrary, Sidney Herbert did not wish the Sisters of Mercy to return to England. Such was Mother Bridgeman's interpretation of the postscript, which was to her a *carte blanche* authorising her to secure employment for her Sisters elsewhere than at Scutari. She decided therefore to withdraw from the Barracks Hospital as soon as opportunity offered. But to her dismay, she discovered that it was no easy matter to escape from Florence Nightingale. It proved as difficult to secure an exit from the hospital as it had been virtually impossible to effect an entry.

At this juncture it is necessary to bear in mind that Mother Bridgeman set out for the Crimea with the express intention of working under Florence Nightingale's superintendence in the military hospitals. That part of her agreement was identical with the arrangements made by Bishop Grant for the Bermondsey Sisters. No idea of breaking her contract entered her head. Even when Florence Nightingale proved most difficult, Mother Bridgeman still showed a readiness to serve her. It was only on receipt of the letter from Sidney Herbert that she decided to embark on an entirely different course of action.

She came out to serve the army; then serve the army she would —if not in Scutari, at least in one or other of the base or field hospitals. And she determined to secure work not alone for the five Sisters she had with her in the Barracks Hospital, but also for the remaining ten abandoned in Therapia. Sidney Herbert's letter was a partial solution to her difficulty; the opening of Koulali hospital was the final answer to her prayer. It was a constant theme of Florence Nightingale's references to the Sisters that " they claim the order of the War Office which don't exist."[43] She did not know of Sidney Herbert's letter to Mother Bridgeman. Sidney Herbert did not then or at any later date, enlighten her as to his correspondence with Mother Bridgeman, even though that correspondence was Mother Bridgeman's *vade-mecum* to emancipation and to ultimate success. But in January, 1855, the struggle was only beginning. Florence Nightingale, though she had at first rejected the Sisters, endeavoured for the rest of her time in the military hospitals to reassert her authority over them. Matters were never quite the same again for her; and though she might fume and fret, it was all to no avail. Mother Bridgeman's careful handling of the ensuing conflict was verifiable evidence of her relationship with the man whose greatest boast was that he could drive a coach and four through any act of Parliament.

The arrival of Father Ronan, S.J., on January 21, 1855 brought matters to a head. Father Cuffe, in representing to him the difficulties in which the Sisters were placed, gave him full particulars of the past and present state of affairs, of " the character and temper of Miss Nightingale," and while impressing upon him the " necessity of firmness in his demands of her concerning the Sisters," he advised him to state his requirements in the form of propositions to which a clear " Yes " or " No " might be the answer.[44]

Father Ronan accordingly drew up the following conditions which he submitted to Florence Nightingale a few days after his arrival, and after consultation with the Bishop of Constantinople.

" That the fifteen Sisters of Mercy last arrived be placed under Mother Bridgeman, for she is their duly appointed Superior and cannot transfer her authority to any other.

" That ten of these fifteen be sent to Koulali, and the remaining five be employed in either the General or Barracks Hospital at Scutari. If in the latter, they are to form a separate community under Mother Bridgeman.

" That all the Sisters, those from Bermondsey as well as those recently arrived, should have, besides proper accommodation as nurses, an oratory to which they can retire for religious exercises.

" That as the Order of Mercy requires its members to attend to the spiritual instruction of the Roman Catholics as

well as to the relief of the sick, the Sisters shall have full
liberty throughout their respective hospitals to instruct Roman
Catholics, especially when requested by the patients themselves, or by the Roman Catholic Chaplains in attendance.

" The Sisters of Mercy on their part, pledge themselves not
to interfere with the religious concerns of the Protestants.
They also engage, to the best of their ability, to give undis-
tinguishing relief to the corporal sufferings of all, and to
promote   amongst   them   all   respect   for   the   hospital
authorities."

Mary Stanley who was present at most of the meetings between
Father Ronan and Miss Nightingale, was impressed by his " quiet,
firm, respectful and gentlemanly way of treating with her."[45]
When Florence Nightingale tried to evade the issue, however,
Father Ronan became adamant and intimated his intention of conducting the Sisters home if the proposed terms were not complied
with in due time. Whereupon Miss Nightingale promised to
comply in as far as was in her power. She received a copy of the
above agreement from Father Ronan; Mary Stanley got another;
Mother Bridgeman, a third.

On the assumption that his chaplaincy and guardianship
extended to the Bermondsey as well as to the Irish Sisters, Father
Ronan duly called upon Mother M. Clare Moore. Mother M.
Clare objected to his " interference "; henceforth he limited his
care to Mother Bridgeman's fifteen.[46] Mother M. Clare's action
had the unhappy effect of widening the breach between the two
communities.

Five of the Irish Sisters were subsequently assigned to the
General Hospital at Scutari, which till then had been administered
by some of the Bermondsey Sisters. Previous to their transfer
Mother Bridgeman who had decided to go to Koulali, selected
Sister M. Elizabeth of Baggot Street as presiding Sister, and
appointed Sister M. Paula from St. Maries of the Isle and Sister
M. Clare of Kinsale to replace herself and Sister M. Aloysius.

Miss Nightingale approved of the change; she acknowledged
Mother Bridgeman's right to visit the Sisters in the General
Hospital whenever she pleased and bade her quite a friendly
farewell on January 25. That evening Mother Bridgeman and
Sister M. Aloysius returned to Therapia to rejoin their companions,
then commonly known as the " Kinsale Nuns." All ten looked
forward to the opening of Koulali Hospital where they hoped to
have greater facilities for their work than had been hitherto
accorded to them.

## CHAPTER 9

## LIFE IN THE GENERAL HOSPITAL

THE winter months of 1854-1855 saw the sufferings of the troops on the Chersonese Heights above Sebastapol move steadily towards a climax. The climatic variability of Crim-Tartary, the absence of even the most essential supplies, the archaic methods of the British military establishment and the prolonged misconduct of the war produced an enormous crop of definitely avertible evils. Soldiers conducting a siege under conditions which developed in them the germs of incipient disease, passed into the sick list with such increasing rapidity that the virtual extinction of the army was threatened.

The inherently anarchical nature of warfare becomes more increasingly apparent when its arrangements are left to the discretion of War Office officials who make their preparations on the assumption that the almost infinite complexity of active service logistics can be fitted into a system of regulations which at best might be made to work in the co-operative effort of a small provincial town. This procedure of " muddling through " inevitably collapses; then by trial and error something relatively efficient emerges. But it emerges only when money has been spent like water and soldiers in their thousands have paid for it with their lives. Such was the situation in the Crimea. What was planned and undertaken without sufficient information, was conducted without sufficient care or foresight. It is not our task here to deal with the campaign as such; nevertheless, certain points must be made.

The British Army was virtually out of action from December 1854 until March 1855, a period during which the utmost confusion reigned at the base of operations. In the beginning of 1855 there were 16,000 out of a total of 35,000 British soldiers on the sick list, 3,500 of whom were in the camp before Sebastopol.[1] The corresponding French figures were 8,000 casualties out of 65,000. At the end of January no less than 23,076 ineffectives filled the British hospitals, the majority of them suffering from zymotic diseases which ordinary prudence and foresight could have easily averted.[2]

In the bitter cold of that first Crimean winter, the soldiers on duty were sometimes so petrified as to be unable to pull their triggers. Officers writing reports found their ink-wells frozen. Tents were blown away and the unfortunate troops, surrounded by thousands of miles of desolate steppe, and lashed by tornado-sleet and snow, pelting drizzle and rain were reduced to an indigence worse than beggary. Nicholas I had made no empty boast in saying that " Generals January and February " would be his best allies.

The eight-mile Woronzoff Road, the only line of communication between Sebastapol and Balaclava, became a squelching mud track. This necessitated the abandonment of wheeled vehicles in favour of pack animals, an expedient which reduced to one-third the transport capacity of each beast. Not infrequently the cavalry were set to work as pack drivers to carry up supplies of biscuits and pork to the infantry and artillery on the heights. The inevitable results of such avertible complications were unusual shortages of food and fuel and fodder, all proceeding from one common source, namely, official ineptitude and administrative miscarriage.

" Calamity unparalleled in the history of calamity " was Florence Nightingale's verdict on the catastrophe. Those who died could count themselves fortunate; it was God help those who were sick. To our modern ideas the preparations for their reception were rough in the extreme. So it appeared too to William Howard Russell who in his indignation determined " to let the nation know with what majesty the British soldier fights." Russell's disclosures appeared in *The Times* on January 23, 1855. He was then in Balaclava watching the arrival of casualties from Sebastopol. The sick and fevered men, strapped on French mule litters,

"formed one of the most ghastly processions that ever poet imagined. Many of these men were all but dead. With closed eyes, open mouths and ghastly attenuated faces, they were borne along two by two, the thin stream of breath visible in the frosty air, alone showing they were alive. One figure was a horror—a corpse, stone dead, strapped upright in its seat . . . the head and body nodding with frightful mockery of life at each stride of the mule over the broken road. No doubt the man had died on his way down to the harbour. As the apparition passed, the only remarks the soldiers made were such as this, ' There's one poor fellow out of pain anyway.' Another man I saw with the raw flesh hanging from his fingers, the naked bones of which protruded into the cold air, undressed and uncovered. This was a case of frostbite I think . . . All the sick on the mule litters seemed alike on the verge of the grave."[3]

In England Russell's disclosures gave rise to a storm of public indignation levelled against those government officials whose archaic methods had involved the army in such calamities. And when it was recalled that the victims of this neglect were the men who had stormed the Alma's heights, who had "run the gauntlet" with the Light Brigade at Balaclava, and who had fought their way to victory amid the fogs and mists of Inkermann, national grief gave fuel to the general indignation. The crisis called for drastic measures, for sweeping changes. Lord Aberdeen's Cabinet, though popularly called the ' Second Administration of all the Talents ' began to totter.

When Parliament assembled on January 23, 1855, Mr. Roebuck, the Radical M.P. for Sheffield, introduced a motion for an enquiry into "the condition of the army before Sebastopol and the conduct of those departments of the government whose duty it has been to minister to the wants of that army." [4] After much discussion Mr. Roebuck's vote of censure was carried on January 26, by a majority of 157 votes, and a governmental landslide followed. Lord Aberdeen's ministry was swept from office, and after three successive and unsuccessful appeals to Lord Derby, Lord Lansdowne and Lord John Russell, a new Government under Lord Palmerston took over.

In the ensuing reshuffle, the offices of Secretary *for* War and Secretary *at* War were amalgamated, Lord Panmure replacing the Duke of Newcastle as Secretary of State. Sidney Herbert became for a short time Secretary of State for the colonies and then resigned. His retirement from public office did not appreciably diminish Florence Nightingale's prestige in either court or parliamentary circles. Lord Palmerston knew her personally ; she was on dining terms with several members of the Cabinet ; and Lord Panmure, while not as compliant as Sidney Herbert, showed a distinctly qualified deference to her wishes. He had the reputation, however, of being thick-skinned, and he proved impervious to the customary barrage of letters which had served Miss Nightingale so well with Sidney Herbert. It took well over a year before she succeeded in wringing from him a precise definition of the extent of her authority as Lady Superintendent of the military hospitals.

On the whole, the election of a new Government brought about no decided change for the better in the management of the army. The Cabinet continued to be the preserve of the same chosen

families ; its offices were openly recruited by favouritism ; and
in fact, except for a few top-level switches, the new administration
was identical with the one just cashiered. Lord Palmerston then
could ill afford to jeopardise his position by unmasking the incompetence of his colleagues. He contented himself with calling certain
officials at the front " a knot of incapables," but he did little to
unravel the knot. Not a single official was recalled, and Lord
Raglan continued " with aristocratic hauteur to repose in ease and
tranquillity among the relics of his army."[5]

Situated less than a mile from Florence Nightingale's headquarters, the General Hospital at Scutari stood on a cliff edge overlooking the Sea of Marmora. It was the first of the Levantine base
hospitals, the first example of a newly-centralised system of military medical administration which was to replace the old and out-
dated regimental machinery. Opened by Lord Raglan early in
1854, it could accommodate about one thousand patients ; having
besides, good quarters for doctors and chaplains. Everything in
the establishment worked smoothly at first under Lord Raglan's
personal supervision ; but when he moved up to the Crimea leaving Major Sillery in charge, and when fever struck the army, the
slender resources of the General Hospital became gravely overcharged. Major Sillery had neither money nor authority in any way
equal to the task ahead. Dr. Menzies, the senior medical officer,
was similarly handicapped ; and in less time than it takes to tell
the hospital laboured under the same deficiencies for which the
recently-opened Barracks Hospital was a byword.

The doctors were nothing if not conservative. They performed
their duties within the narrow groove prescribed by " regulations."
Beyond that they were apathetic, even stubborn. " Ill-salaried, ill-
treated by the State, schooled down into habits of resignation,
and bending under a load of professional work . . . they acted as
though there should be no discontent . . . They even went to the
length of refusing to acknowledge a want."[6] They were jealous
of Florence Nightingale. They resented the intrusion of females
into their department. Of nuns they knew little and cared less;
but Fanny Taylor records that by degrees " their initial hostility
evaporated before the skill and charm " of the five Sisters of Mercy
who came to their aid in January 1855. At that time the nursing
staff of the hospital consisted of Miss Smythe, the Lady Superintendent, two ladies, three Sellonites, five Sisters of Mercy and
about ten nurses.

The quarters allotted to the Sisters in the Barracks Hospital
were palatial in comparison with what awaited them in the
General Hospital. Sister Winifred describes for us a dimly-lit

Convent of Mercy, St. Ethelburga's, Liverpool.

General Hospital
Kulalee Nov. 6/55.

Dear Madam—

I never gave up the right to withdraw my Sisters from Scutari or elsewhere. So long as we are engaged in a Hospital under your authority we acknowledge your obedience in nursing details. — Were I about to place any of my Sisters in a Hospital under your control I should of course have referred the matter to you but it is not so. In Dr Hall's official communi-

Letter of Mother Bridgeman to Miss Nightingale. *vide* p. 199.

-cation he mentions that you
have quite given up the General
Hospital in Balaclava, and
to it he invites us.

I trust this will fully explain
all. Believe me to be
&c &c

Sr W. F. Bridgeman

To Miss Nightingale

[*Facsimile of a handwritten letter*]

be far as my officers have

recognise the right — of any sister of
interfere in the way only of I ... &
Advice of any one placed here & ...
should advise a sister to withdraw as any
from, the ... do so.

Yours faithfully & truly

Florence Nightingale

Extract from Miss Nightingale's letter of 24 December, 1854, giving Mother Bridgeman the right of withdrawing Sisters from the hospital at Scutari.

*vide* p. 104.

and badly-ventilated garret, immediately under which was an apartment called " Scutari Hall," the stench from which could not be eliminated by even the strongest deodorants, even were such amenities then available. The room was unfit for human occupation; its atmosphere was enough to induce attacks of nausea on all but the healthiest constitutions. Miss Nightingale was nonplussed on perceiving the Sisters' dismay. She promised to provide a second room for them : a promise forgotten until Sister M. Clare caught fever. The doctors then intervened.

The sole equipment of the room was a bed, knife, spoon, bowl and tin plate for each Sister. There was neither table nor chair; meals had to be taken picnic-fashion on the floor. The unvarying menu was " goat's flesh, and something they called mutton—black, blue and green in colour; coarse sour bread, rancid butter, milk-less tea " and for the ladies a glass of wine or brandy.[7]

" It was an effort even for those in health to sit down to those meals," wrote Fanny Taylor. " We forced the food down as a duty, but some of the ladies became so ill that they really could not touch it. . . . Quantities of milk and eggs were taken to Miss Nightingale's and the Bracebridges' rooms, but could not be furnished for the rest of the party."

Miss Smythe proved to be a kind and gentle Superintendent. As already noted her staff, excluding the Sisters, consisted of two ladies, three Sellonites and about ten nurses. The nurses were rather more ornamental than useful, but the remainder of the party, once they found themselves working on their own accord under Miss Smythe, applied their best energies to the task.

Generally speaking, the routine of the General Hospital was similar to that followed in the Barracks Hospital, with the administration at an even lower ebb. Florence Nightingale took her superintendence of this hospital rather lightly, at least, until the Irish Sisters took up duty there. Its management for some time had been in the hands of orderlies, who seem to have been the very worst of a very bad lot. Fanny Taylor did not hesitate to call them brutes. They performed their duties with utter neglect and carelessness, with reckless indifference to the wants of the patients, and considered their own convenience always and above all things.

Take, for instance, their system of serving meals. They placed the food on the head-board over each bed, and left it there to be taken or rejected by the patients as their strength and appetite prompted. In the distribution of stimulants, a day's allowance was given to the orderly each morning, with instructions to distribute it in small doses at regular intervals during the day. What really happened was this: whatever the orderly did not himself appropriate, he administered at one draught to his patients, who were not unnaturally more often than not *found drunk in bed!* The doctors, as a precaution against this irregularity, were obliged to reduce the amount of stimulants below what some cases, properly nursed, would have required.[8]

Chronic mismanagement of supplies was the main cause of disorder in Scutari General Hospital. The hospital was dependent on Miss Nightingale's stores for the many extras not supplied by the Quartermaster. Here again the demand for requisitions halted the supply, and while valuable time was lost in quibbling over regulations, an abundance of private gifts—preserves, cordials, sweetmeats, biscuits etc.—mouldered for want of distribution. Thus it happened that a large portion of the amenities sent out by private charity was wasted, and few of the supplies ever reached the sufferers for whom they were destined. This condition of want in the midst of plenty was one of the unnecessary ingredients of the sufferings endured by England's fighting men during the Crimean War. It was proved again and again that unlimited supplies of food were available all during the war but were withheld because they had not been applied for through the proper channels!

Another cause of confusion in the base hospitals was Florence Nightingale's refusal to commit the distribution of supplies to anyone but herself. She was the sieve through which everything must flow. This, she said, was her inalienable right as Lady Superintendent; but she carried the practice too long and too far. She put an absolute veto on the use of private funds, and by commandeering the bulk of supplies sent from England to Scutari, made it increasingly difficult for others to take any initiative in the hospitals. Only once did anyone attempt to side-track Miss Nightingale in the stores. Mrs. Bracebridge gave away some articles—towels, shirts and handkerchiefs—to those who helped unpack them. The angry scene that followed when Miss Nightingale got wind of the matter, discouraged all such acts of bounty for the future.

In fairness to Miss Nightingale, however, it must be admitted that by keeping steadfastly to the regulations by which the Commissariat was administered, she believed she was discharging the duties of her appointment in the manner expected of her. The pity was that she did not realise that circumstances alter cases; and though she worked herself to the bone by her efforts in Scutari, it still remains true that much of the good she could have done was undone by her reluctance to deviate from rules which were proved to be inapplicable to the current emergency.

In vain did Fanny Taylor make repeated appeals for extra relief for the General Hospital. The answer was always the same: Florence Nightingale could not countenance any departure from regulations. Undismayed, Miss Taylor went straight to *The Times* Commissioner, and though she had been warned that he was a very dangerous person, "her heart was too sick to enter into controversy."[9] She laid her list of requirements before the Commissioner and had the satisfaction of seeing them delivered at the hospital next morning.

By boiling water on make-shift stoves, the ladies made beef-tea for those who were too sick to swallow the regulation diet, and lemonade for their thirst-crazed fever patients. In their own room the Sisters re-cooked and served the best of the food they had salvaged from the head-boards. The assistant surgeons helped whenever possible by issuing extra-diet rolls, but fearing a reprimand from the staff surgeons, their co-operation was necessarily limited. It was not that the staff surgeons were indifferent to the well-being of their patients; they simply disliked signing requisitions which put them under a compliment to Miss Nightingale. In any case, it was a matter of impossibility for these surgeons to write requisitions enough for their patients' wants, considering that extreme cases in Scutari were counted by hundreds. Moreover, most of the staff surgeons were men of routine; they were slaves to a system which, denying a man when young the privilege of exercising his judgment, left him with little initiative when he attained the higher grades of his department. The situation is aptly summed up by Lytton Strachey in his remark that Victorian officials in general were "tied fast, hand and foot, with red tape."

News of the attempted reforms in the General Hospital infuriated Florence Nightingale. At her instigation, Dr. Cumming visited the hospital, forbade cooking in the wards and brought the beeftea and lemonade interval to an end. Beyond that he did not interfere. The Sisters who had taken over the administration of the wards, the preparation of meals in the diet kitchen, and the cleansing of the patients, were giving such general satisfaction that Dr. Cumming decided to leave well alone. His visit, on the whole, was unfortunate. Referring to it at a later date Fanny Taylor wrote in her memoirs that

"it was very hard work, after Dr. Cumming's order had been issued, to pace the corridor and hear perhaps, the low voice of a fever patient, ' Give me a drink for the love of God ',

and have none to give. . . . or to see the look of disappointment on the faces of those to whom we had been accustomed
to give the beef-tea. The assistant surgeons were very sorry
they said for the alteration, but they had no power to help it
—their duty was only to obey. On one occasion an assistant
surgeon told us that Dr. Cumming had threatened to arrest
him for having allowed a man too many extras on the diet
roll. Amid all the confusion and distress of Scutari hospital,
military discipline was never lost sight of, and an infringement
of one of the smallest observances was worse than letting
twenty men die from neglect!"[10]

And indeed, for those engaged in the General Hospital, death
became more familiar than the ordinary events of life. It was
heartrending, wrote one of the Sisters, to see patients wasting away
under every form of disease, surrounded by every accumulation
of misery, and to be helpless in the face of that want. For the
fevered lips there was no cooling drink: Miss Nightingale's orders
forbade it. For the sinking frame there was no nutritious food ;
for the sore limb no soft pillow; for many no hands to help. Sad
it was to see these men die one after another; to know that after
death they would lie in shallow unmarked graves, and that save
in the loving hearts of home they would be soon forgotten.

The columns of figures for the Scutari hospitals from November,
1854, to February, 1855, show a steadily mounting mortality rate.
" From eight per cent upon the cases treated in the four weeks
which ended on November 11, it rose in the next four weeks to
fifteen ; in the next, to seventeen ; in the next, to thirty-two ; and
in the next (the four weeks of February, 1855) to the enormous
proportion of forty-two per cent."[11] These statistics are glaringly
out of tune with the already growing importance adhering to Miss
Nightingale's reforms in the hospitals. In February a Sanitary
Commission was appointed to investigate the sanitary conditions
of the military hospitals. The commission consisted of Dr. John
Sutherland, an official from the Board of Health; Mr., later Sir,
Robert Rawlinson, a civil engineer; and Dr. Hector Gavin who
was accidentally killed and replaced by Dr. Milroy. This commission said Florence Nightingale, " saved the British Army." The
commissioners reported unfavourably of the hospital conditions
at Scutari and in the Crimea, and their investigations and dis-
coveries led to the introduction of reforms which by March 17
had succeeded in partly remedying the evils. Among other things
they decontaminated the water supply ; they cleared the toilets of
enormous accumulations of filth ; they removed the decaying car-

cass of a dead horse from the main sewer pipe of the hospital and ordered all rubbish to be removed. Down went the death rate —and up went the fame of Florence Nightingale. She got the credit for the work of the commissioners who pushed on to the Crimea to carry out further investigations there.

" I have an unbounded admiration of Miss Nightingale's qualifications," wrote a certain deputy medical officer in a report to the Roebuck Committee; " but I see dozens of things placed to her credit which I know she had nothing to do with."[12]

Restricted and limited as they were, the five Sisters at the General Hospital soon won esteem and admiration from the entire medical staff, both Catholic and Protestant. All with whom they had dealings " appreciated the purity of their character, the disinterested piety of their lives, and their universally acknowledged usefulness in the sacred vocation of ministering to the sick and wounded soldier."[13] The doctors had only one complaint: the Sisters were too few in number.

Miss Nightingale was soon a frequent and unwelcome visitor at the General Hospital. Previous to the Sisters' appointment there, she had scarcely ever bothered with it. She now found fault with the Sisters' work and tried in every possible way to disparage them in the eyes of the doctors ; but without success. The doctors might indeed be harassed, but Doctor O'Flaherty, the principal medical officer, became the Sisters' staunchest advocate and refused to listen to any complaints against them. A letter written about this time (March 1855) by Dr. Gavin, a young Dublin physician staffed in Scutari, is at once indicative of the general attitude of the medical staff towards the Sisters and of the under-current of hostility and intrigue against which they worked:

" We have several of the Sisters of Mercy out here and they are adored by the soldiers. Still, they have many difficulties to overcome, for here, even here, where all Christians ought to make common cause, there is bigotry and jealousy, not indeed on *their* parts, but on the part of those about whom so much is said in praise at home. And I can assure you that our Catholic Sisters are the only nurses here who do not intermeddle with the surgeons and presume upon their positions . . . The people at home expend much misplaced praise upon those who do not deserve it."[14]

Sister Mary Clare went down with fever soon after her arrival at the General Hospital. Dr. O'Flaherty provided her with a comfortable, airy and nicely-situated room, and attended her personally during her illness. Matters were otherwise at the Barracks Hospital where two of the Bermondsey Sisters had also contracted fever, and were left, on Miss Nightingale's instructions, in the one room with the other three who were not ill. Mother Bridgeman, on a visit to the invalids, was disturbed at finding all five Sisters cooped together in the dark, and could not help thinking that Florence Nightingale's way of " showing her pro- fessed appreciation for Mother M. Clare was, to say the least of it, extremely odd."[15]

Dr. O'Flaherty's kindness to the Sisters in the General Hospital was not confined merely to his solicitude for Sister M. Clare. On the recommendation of Father Ronan, S.J., he secured a larger room for them which, when renovated and cleaned up, served also as a hospital chapel. Crowds of patients and con- valescents congregated there on Sundays for Mass and Benediction. Space was necessarily limited; the Sisters were obliged to devote the early hours of successive Sabbath days to piling away their mattresses and all other movables in an effort to accommodate the worshippers. Writing on Easter Sunday one Sister recorded:

> " We had a hundred men at Holy Communion this morning. One, whose mother had assured him that he had never been baptised, makes his First Communion to-morrow. Father Ronan baptised him in our little oratory. We get benediction to-night in real missionary style, without monstrance, cope or thurible. Several new companies have come in. Some men asked Father Ronan ' where was the convent ' which amused him greatly. . . ."[16]

Florence Nightingale was so infuriated at Dr. O'Flaherty's arrangements for the Sisters that she ordered them out of their old quarters before repairs in their new room were complete. Then with a characteristic gesture she assumed proprietorship of this second room as though she were, in effect, the landlady. She walked in on the Sisters whenever she pleased with never a " by your leave," and never tired of telling them they were only there on sufferance. What was even more serious, she intercepted their letters and gave them little satisfaction when they protested against such unwarranted censorship. It required a letter from Mother Bridgeman to settle matters.

> " I assure you, dear Miss Nightingale," wrote Mother Bridgeman, " I feel more than I can express at having my Sisters placed under the control of anyone. . . . who could

be guilty of so much negligence in so delicate a matter as that of opening letters addressed to others."[17]

No further letters to the Sisters were opened, though Miss Nightingale continued to censor other arrivals and despatches, and the nurses were powerless against her.

Miss Smythe was the next to come under Miss Nightingale's wrath. She was relieved of her duties in the General Hospital. She was, however, only too glad to shake the dust of Scutari off her feet, and went at once to Koulali where she was shortly joined by Fanny Taylor. But Miss Smythe did not long enjoy the comparative peace of Koulali. She contracted typhus and died before the end of March.

The new superintendent, a Miss Tebbutt, was one of Mary Stanley's ladies who had become attached to Florence Nightingale. A bitterly anti-Catholic Unitarian, Miss Tebbutt made life so extremely difficult for the Sisters that two considerations alone deterred Mother Bridgeman from removing them from the General Hospital. The first was the thought of the numerous Catholic patients who would be neglected if the Sisters were withdrawn. The second was the letter she received from Most Reverend Dr. William Delany in reply to her own letter of December 24, 1854. The Bishop approved of her arrangements to date.

" You have done great service, I hope, by placing yourself temporarily in connexion (sic) with the Bermondsey Nuns. It is thereby rendered manifest to all parties that you are not influenced by any kind of selfish feeling whatever. Should any new emergency arise . . . you have my full consent to act according to your own prudence, on which I fully rely. " I consider your mission, in addition to the blessings it contains, . . . to be of the utmost importance in the interests of religion; and should its failure be ascribable . . . to any precipitancy or imprudence on our part, I would consider it nothing short of a calamity. . . .
" You will, accordingly, retain your post until it is manifest to all men that you abandon it only through necessity ; and I recommend therefore that you continue to give the services of such Sisters as may be required . . . always provided that the Religious form a community under their own Superior."[18]

After the above, there was no immediate release for the five Sisters in Scutari, around whose heads there raged a constant turmoil of bickerings, angers, intrigues and jealousies. That the annoyances they had to endure were legion is clear from the following extract written by Sister M. Paula to St. Maries of the Isle:

> " You have no idea of all we have to contend with here—such bickering and prejudice. Our recollections of the East will certainly not be sunny ones. Of course, we did not expect them so. Do please, dear Reverend Mother, get prayers at St. Maries and everywhere you can for us. They were never more needed."

Sister M. Paula wrote her letter at Easter, 1855. It was a time when Florence Nightingale was more than usually upset and angry. Koulali hospitals were in operation since the end of January, and the system there introduced threatened to overshadow her own administration in Scutari. She had been dead against the Koulali plan from the beginning. She had urged Mary Stanley not to take more than 'five of the remaining Irish Sisters there. The Reverend Brickbat, she said, showed such an appalling " want of brains " that the scheme could not but fall through.[19] But after two months Koulali was already on the way to success ; and Florence Nightingale, having repeatedly refused offers of collaboration from Mother Bridgeman, knew that she had only herself to blame for this unexpected turn of events.

Lord Panmure became her refuge. She wrote to him demanding that her authority over the military hospitals and their nursing personnel be put on a firmer footing. His reply, when it came, was not exactly to her liking. In April, 1855, Lord Panmure appointed her Almoner of the Free Gifts in all the British Hospitals in the Crimea. As it turned out, Miss Nightingale had to wait another ten months before she was officially invested with full control over the entire nursing staff. Meanwhile, she continued to campaign against the Sisters. " I think they will have to go," she wrote to Sidney Herbert. " They say they are inefficient, sombre, disliked—very unlike the Bermondsey Nuns."[20]

Doctor Peter Pincoffs, a civilian doctor then employed in Scutari, gives a contrary opinion. Like Florence Nightingale, Dr. Pincoffs was a non-Catholic. Unlike her, he was unprejudiced. His recommendation, therefore, carries the greater weight.

> " Greatly to be admired," he says, " is that company of educated women who voluntarily exchanged the comforts and refinements of home for the dangers they were sure to encounter in a military hospital. Here, as everywhere, the Catholic Sisters of Mercy did their duty bravely and well,

under the superintending direction of their worthy Reverend Mother.

I must confess to a leaning towards Catholic Sisters as nurses *par excellence* . . . All with whom I have ever come in contact have shown themselves intelligent and docile as assistants to the physician ; patient and uncomplaining under any accumulation of work ; invariably gentle in manner towards the patients ; and so thoroughly conversant with the practical part of their business, that all the help they gave was done handily and expeditiously.

It has occurred to me that to pass a lifetime in the cheerful performance of duties ofttimes revolting in the last degree, it must require the all-powerful incentive which actuates these women, who literally ' work out their salvation ' and purchase Heaven at the price of complete renunciation of all earthly joys."[21]

In one other sentence, Dr. Pincoffs singles out the factor which in his eyes gave the Sisters their superiority over the other war nurses, the Sellonites not excluded. This was their ' implicit obedience,' which he calls the " strength of all Catholic communities."

To the foregoing, the Honourable and Reverend Sidney Godolphin Osborne adds his own voice in praise of the Sisters. Referring to their living quarters he remarks :

" Whatever of neglect may attach elsewhere, none can be imputed here. From this room flowed a well-directed stream of untiring benevolence and charitable exertions. Here there has been no idleness, no standing still, no quibbling with any requisition made upon those who so cheerfully administered the stores at their disposal."[22]

Such recommendations to the contrary, the following letter from Sister Winifred, dated March 15, 1855, reveals a definite campaign of prejudice and suspicion against the Sisters.

" The High and Low Church parties and other Biblicals of the East are all up about us, and there are numbers of them congregated here. They look on us with suspicious eyes ; and not only that, but they are constantly on the alert to substantiate, if possible, some charge of proselytism against us."

Sister Winifred was homesick: she ends her letter with a yearning wish for three special consolations—" the peace and security of convent life, her quiet cell, and Father Collins to talk to." She was never again to enjoy them.

Charges of neglect of duty were being constantly imputed to the Sisters by Florence Nightingale, but without foundation. Father Moloney's investigation of the matter on April 13, 1855, led to the following vindication of the Sisters by Doctor R. J. O'Flaherty, the senior medical officer of the General Hospital, who despite his Celtic surname was a non-Catholic in so far as he subscribed to any religious belief.

" It affords me great pleasure to be able to send my opinion as to the manner in which the Catholic Sisters have performed the duties allotted to them in this hospital. I feel I cannot too highly extol their assiduous attention and benevolent exertions in the performance of these duties, and to contribute all in their power to the comfort and recovery of the sick under their charge."[23]

Florence Nightingale now came forward with the more insidious charge of proselytism which became her theme song for the remainder of the war. She insisted that the Sisters were bent on a spiritual rather than a medical mission, and the better to substantiate some accusation against them she had them placed under strict supervision. But for all that, she could discover but a single incident which suggested even remotely that the Sisters were proselytising. Sister M. Elizabeth was said to have taken advantage of the delirious condition of a patient in order to " convert and rebaptise " him before death, and to have neglected her hospital duties while making converts among the non-Catholic patients. The charge, as such, was false. The idea of " rebaptism " is an anachronism in Catholic terminology. Florence Nightingale, of course, could not know this ; but as her accusation has been repeatedly adduced as proof positive that the Sisters of Mercy were secretly proselytising in Scutari, it calls here for careful enquiry.

It happened that among the casualties admitted from Sebastopol in February, 1855, was a young Irishman, a victim of frostbite and delirious with pain. He lingered on in semi-coma for a few days, during which Sister M. Elizabeth was in constant attendance at his bedside. He died clasping her crucifix. A man of fifty a few beds away, being touched by the Sister's kindness to the young soldier was prompted to tell her his own sad story. He, too, was Irish, the son of a mixed marriage. As a child he had contracted some unknown ailment from which he had been cured by a priest on his mother's promise to do her duty and bring him up as a Catholic. After her death he lapsed. " But oh! " he said, " the sight of ye, Sister dear, has brought a dreadful feeling over me.

And then ye are so kind, God bless ye. I never saw anyone like ye out of the Church."

Very carefully Sister M. Elizabeth explained to him the regulations concerning religious matters obtaining in the hospital. "Your religion must be marked on your bed," she told him. " Will you have ' Catholic ' or ' Protestant '?" The man did not hesitate. " I'll be marked a Catholic," he said, " though it will stand against me in my regiment."[24] He kept his word ; whereupon Sister M. Elizabeth prepared him for Confession and had Father Moloney administer Extreme Unction to him. On the following day the man became delirious and died.

The charge, duly reported by Florence Nightingale to Sidney Herbert, elicited from him the instruction that

> " the Nun who has broken rules and attempts to proselytise ought to be sent home, for it is the only way to work upon the others. The real mistake we made in the selection of these ladies (between ourselves) is that they are *Irish*. You cannot make their lax minds understand the weight of an obligation."[25]

Sidney Herbert has been described as a man upon whom the good fairies seemed to have showered all their most enviable goods ; a man of whom it was difficult not to say that he was a perfect English gentleman ; and he was deeply religious. Attractive though he was, his sentiments on the Sisters of Mercy, as expressed in his private correspondence with Florence Nightingale, are certainly revealing of the prejudices of the Englishmen of his time, not merely against Catholics, but against the Irish as such. Miss Nightingale on receipt of his instructions, lectured Sister M. Elizabeth on the impropriety of speaking to the patients, but found her " quite incorrigible and just like the Reverend Brickbat."[26] It became necessary in the long run for the Reverend Brickbat herself to come to the rescue ; and though her interview with Florence Nightingale had only a negative result, the following dialogue indicates that the Mother Superior was as able in argument as she was efficient in nursing skill.

Florence Nightingale introduced the subject of religious instruction with, "Reverend Mother, it must be very unpleasant for the Sisters to be obliged to speak to the soldiers."

" It is part of our vocation, Miss Nightingale," replied Mother Bridgeman. " We are accustomed to speak to all classes of people on matters connected with our Holy Faith."

" But," pursued Miss Nightingale, " to speak to those rough sergeants and orderlies seems to me so hard."

" Sergeants or privates, old or young, Miss Nightingale, are alike to a Sister of Mercy. We can speak to them sick or well, with as much ease as to one of our school children."

" But do you think it suitable for a woman to take upon herself the duty of a priest?" asked Miss Nightingale.

" By no means ; but our Sisters are too well instructed to attempt such a thing," replied Mother Bridgeman. " Moreover, the least instructed Catholic soldier could easily distinguish between the duties of a priest and those of a Sister of Mercy. The priest's duties are to preach and instruct with authority, to hear confessions, to administer the Sacraments, to offer the Holy Sacrifice and to govern his flock with proper jurisdiction."

" Wherein then does the duty of a Sister of Mercy consist?" asked Miss Nightingale.

" The Sister of Mercy's duty, besides the corporal works of mercy," said Mother Bridgeman, " is to attend to and sympathise with the suffering, gently to instruct the ignorant, to advise and influence the erring, negligent and wayward; in short, to do for, or supply to those Catholics what a good mother might or should have been to them."[27]

Florence Nightingale was, for once, at a loss for a reply ; matters were getting beyond her. Mother Bridgeman, seeing her own advantage, pressed the point still further with the question, " Has anyone had reason to complain that the Sisters neglected the common duty of nursing for that of religious instruction?"

" No ; never," came the reply.

" Well then," continued Mother Bridgeman, rising, " when the very laborious duties of nursing intermit, if the Sisters—instead of lying down or otherwise resting or amusing themselves as others do—go to add to their labours by instructing the Catholics, who has reason to object?"

Florence Nightingale suddenly remembered a most important engagement. The interview was over, and Mother Bridgeman returned to Koulali well satisfied with the outcome of her visit.

It is regrettable that similarly precise records of other interviews between Mother Bridgeman and Florence Nightingale are no longer available. Such papers as are to hand suggest that not all their meetings were as calmly concluded as was this one. Letters from the Sisters referring to occasional *entre nous* exchanges between Reverend Mother and Lady Superintendent confirm this opinion ; while the constantly recurring references to " certain other incidents better left untold " which abound in the Bridgeman diary suggest that on occasion Mother Bridgeman and Florence Nightingale had some tempestuous encounters.

But if Florence Nightingale found it difficult to subdue Mother Bridgeman, she had a certain satisfaction in having control over the five Irish Sisters at the General Hospital. For the time being, they became her more immediate target. She endeavoured in every way to make their position impossible—restricting their sphere of activity to a minimum, interfering with them at every hand's turn, annoying them by her high-handedness—but failing withal to undermine the steady influence they wielded over the patients.

The strict attention which the Sisters paid to the duties of the sick ward ; their unceasing prayer and tender watchfulness ; their self-denial and gentleness to the wounded soldiers, all combined to make every hour of their time an hour of instruction to those among whom they moved. From the beginning converts were numerous, though the Sisters, scrupulously observant of their contract, used no means to promote conversions save that of silent prayer and the legitimate influence of example. On all sides they removed prejudices and gained friends, it being generally admitted by eye-witnesses that though religion was the motive of all their actions, they drew no distinction of race or creed, and never took advantage of their position to promote what was regarded in official circles as "their iniquitous scheme of proselytism."

## CHAPTER 10

## KOULALI

KOULALI Barracks Hospital was situated some five miles above Scutari on the Asiatic shore of the Bosphorus. Its special convenience was a deep-water jetty which facilitated the removal of patients from the hospital transports. It was a square red building, three storeys high, and though smaller than Scutari hospital, was nevertheless an imposing structure. Facing the hospital were a row of stables and a riding school which were later converted into a fever annexe and a convalescent home. Lady Stratford de Redcliffe was patroness of Koulali. Doctor Tice was senior medical officer there. Mary Stanley was superintendent. Miss Nightingale's nominal superintendence over Koulali hospital terminated in April, 1855, by special order of Lord Panmure ; notwithstanding which she continued to interest herself in its development.

At the time of its opening, January 27, 1855, the Barracks Hospital was in a deplorable state. Its wards were filthy ; its beds lice infested; its sanitation faulty; its medical arrangements inadequate. There was little food ; there was less clothing ; there was scarcely any fuel, and the stores were so grossly understocked that " an ounce of arrowroot or sugar was worth its weight in gold; while a saucepan to boil it in, or a spoon to stir it with was guarded by its possessors with a dragon-like vigilance."[1] The resultant mortality figures were so high that in February they exceeded those registered in Scutari. According to Kinglake, Koulali statistics averaged fifty-two per cent; Scutari, forty-two.

" In Koulali we realised what protracted war was," wrote Mary Stanley. " Some days and scenes are stamped upon one's memory. Who will forget the arrival of the first batch of invalids? There was the huge wood fire in the stove-less kitchen, the large cauldrons of water set on, the basins of arrowroot mixed, thrown in and stirred with a long wooden pole for want of better implements. Then came the melancholy procession . . . Worn out men dragging their weak and weary frames along, some supported on each side, some carried on stretchers. Besides the mournful sight of the processions of the sick, there was the still sadder sight of the dead, borne away from the dead-house to the cemetery on the hillside."[2]

The arrival on January 29 of another three hundred patients made imperative the opening of a second hospital. A disused infirmary attached to the Barracks was requisitioned for this purpose, its occupants, some two hundred prisoners of war, being temporarily evacuated elsewhere. Situated half a mile above the Barracks, the infirmary, which became known as Koulali General Hospital, was erected on a spot where according to tradition there once stood a church dedicated to St. Michael the Archangel, to whom was entrusted the guardianship of all buildings and fortresses along the Bosphorus.

The lay-out of the building followed the usual Turkish plan. It was a miniature of Scutari General Hospital: a two-storeyed quadrangle built on the slope of a hill with its main entrance opening on the second floor. Round the quadrangle ran an upper and a lower corridor out of which the wards opened, each ward holding about thirty beds. The rooms were square, with a stove in the centre of each. A row of rooms including the general kitchen, stores, guard-room and servants' quarters faced the main entrance in the courtyard. The hospital's capacity averaged about four hundred ; but its seams were often strained to bursting point in the early months of 1855 when the last of the winter victims came pouring in.

The hospital was formally opened on February 2, and was placed under the direction of Dr. Hamilton, who was subsequently transferred to the field hospitals, and was replaced in Koulali by Dr. Guy. The nursing in the General Hospital was confided to the Sisters of Mercy under Mother Bridgeman's supervision, " subject, of course, to the Lady Superintendent appointed by Lord William Paulet ; but Miss Stanley . . . being stationed at the Barracks Hospital, wished Reverend Mother to take full charge of the General".[3] Mary Stanley's arrangement is remarkable as affording the only instance in which members of a Religious Congregation were given official status as administrators in a British Military Hospital.*

The arrangement did not go unchallenged. Lord William Paulet was downright in expressing his disapproval. Mary Stanley's application to him for permission to bring the Sisters to Koulali was greeted by him with, " Yes, I don't mind; but just sprinkle some nurses through them and keep them out of my sight when I go there."[4] Of a like disposition was Lady Stratford, whose fears of Romanism and Jesuitry were considerably aggravated by the

---

*The situation was otherwise in France: *vide* p. 321.

knowledge that Father Ronan, S.J., was coming to Koulali as part of Mother Bridgeman's entourage!

It appears too that Father Cuffe was ruffled. He disapproved of the prominence given to Father Ronan, and considered it an indiscretion to have sent a Jesuit to the Crimea as an army chaplain. In his letters to Archbishop Cullen he comes out vociferously against

"the Jesuit and his nuns! How formidable they sound in the Protestant ear! What envy against religion both together create! The nuns may be mastered but a Jesuit cannot. Your Grace knows only too well Protestant opinion on these matters; and *that* Protestant opinion is still the opinion wherever the British Government has sway . . . The word 'Jesuit' may be a passport to Heaven, but I fear years are to come before it will be a passport to an English camp."[5]

In spite of his outburst, Father Cuffe's loyalty to the Sisters never wavered ; but his opposition to Father Ronan was noted with satisfaction by Florence Nightingale, revealing as it did a split among the ranks of the Catholic clergy. When the Crimean War was over and her mission about to end, she invoiced this information at the head of a long list of miscellaneous complaints to be presented by Sidney Herbert to the War Office. On April 4, 1856, she told him that

"those who say there is a 'Popish Plot' here are quite mistaken. It is not a Popish plot but a split of the R.C.s against themselves. The seculars are divided against the regulars, and the regulars against the seculars. This we have often seen before, but never so much as now. But as the old Whig families are said to have a Tory heir apparent in order to be 'in both ways,' so the R.C.s have one set of priests and nuns *with* the Government and one against it. Mrs. Bridgeman and the Jesuits are *against;* the secular priests and the Bermondsey Nuns *for.*"[6]

With the possible exception of Mother Bridgeman, the person most gratified by the opening of Koulali was Dr. Manning.

"Thank God: I trust the twenty* will continue all at work," he wrote to Mary Stanley on February 8. "The return of any of them would be a most mischievous and serious event. We cannot be too cautious, and I doubt if Florence Nightingale, certainly not the Herberts, knows how sensitive the Catholic

---

*15 Irish Sisters; 5 from Bermondsey.

Church is—from the Holy Father to the wounded Catholic soldier—as to the respect due, not to the person so much as to the character of a Religious."[7]

For the Sisters, living conditions in Koulali were not much better than in Scutari, " but the work we had come to do was there in abundance, and we were allowed do it freely and graciously. Miss Stanley and the medical officers seemed thankful for our services."[8] The Sisters had three rooms allotted to their use: a small community room, a dormitory, and a tiny closet which they fitted out as an oratory. The Blessed Sacrament was reserved in this oratory ; hence the duties of the sick call entailed none of the locomotive activity required of the chaplains in the other military hospitals. Five Sisters went daily to the nearby Barracks Hospital ; all ten resided in the General Hospital.

We get some idea of their initial difficulties when Mother Bridgeman in her *Diary* describes her first experiences. It took weeks of scrubbing and scouring to make the place even reasonably clean. There was no kitchen properly so called, no place where food could be prepared but an open-air Turkish cookhouse fitted with charcoal braziers. Here were installed some enormous boilers " to which one had to climb a ladder to get water by dipping receptacles over the top." Until the establishment of a diet-kitchen, this cookhouse was managed by Mother Bridgeman, assisted by a cosmopolitan group of Turks, Greeks, Maltese and Sardinians. " Bono Johnny " they called her—' Johnny ' was the name they applied to all foreigners—and though good-natured and willing, their bad French and worse English led at times to frustrating complications and to many trials of temper. Eventually an indigenous Esperanto of nods, smiles and gestures saved the situation. Crises cropped up like mushrooms. Several of the ladies collapsed from overwork ; many of the nurses had to be dismissed for misbehaviour—by Easter all but two had been sent home—and an ever-increasing number of patients entailed such extra labour in the hospital that " the whole burden fell upon the Sisters who admirably fulfilled their duties, giving great satisfaction to the Lady Superintendent and the medical officers."[9]

When, by degrees, the General Hospital began to take shape, its administration was essentially different to that followed in Scutari. From the very beginning it operated on the simple rule that the perception of want suggests the need of supply; that if a man has no shirt, he needs one ; that if he is obliged to lie naked in bed while that shirt is being washed, he needs a second one; that a drink asked for at midnight by a dying man, must be given at once, or not at all ; and that the wants of an individual patient cannot always be measured by a common yardstick or be accommodated by a general ruling made by a department hundreds of miles away from the theatre of action. Whatever Florence Nightingale might say, deviations from a general order were not necessarily breaches of discipline, especially when applied to a crisis of such magnitude as that existing in the Crimea. Furthermore, the *Manual of Regulations* for the management of military hospitals at home and abroad was prefaced by a sensible paragraph to the effect that " though framed principally with a view to home service, the regulations should be observed also on foreign service, *wherever it may be practicable.*" In Koulali, this final clause was taken as implying that the regulations, like the medical formulary attached to them did not preclude the adoption of emergency measures, and Dr. Tice of the Barracks Hospital and Dr. Hamilton of the General Hospital acted accordingly.

In the first place, the requisition system was whittled down to a minimum. Each division was administered by a Sister of Mercy and a Protestant lady or nurse who accompanied the doctor on his rounds, received his orders, made a note of them and presented them to the store-keeper who promptly issued the requirement. Florence Nightingale might quote Dr. Cumming as saying that the nurses in Scutari did little else but " walk about carrying note-books in their hands ",[10] but the beneficial result of the system was that a good deal of time was saved, the patients were never left long in want, and the medical officers were satisfied. The ladies from their own private resources supplemented the issues from the stores; Mary Stanley took care that a supply of free gifts was always sent to Mother Bridgeman ; and the good offices of Mr. Stowe of *The Times* helped to tide the General Hospital over its emergency period until the appointment of a new Purveyor made possible the introduction of several important reforms.

The Purveyor, Mr. Scott Robertson, successor to Mr. Ward who had died of cholera, was a Scotsman and a Protestant. He gave Mother Bridgeman full charge of the linen store. On his recommendation, issues from this store did not depend on a doubly-signed requisition slip as at Scutari. The establishment of a laundry ensured a constant supply of clean clothes for the hospital.

Mr. Robertson also fitted up for the Sisters an extra-diet kitchen and provision store in which were kept all the supplies necessary for special ' invalid cooking' together with the private gifts received for the hospital. As for 'invalid cooking', diets varied according to sickness. A man might be on full diet, half-diet, low-diet or spoon-diet. Those on spoon-diet were allowed special extras called ' invalid foods' which included milk, eggs, arrowroot, rice, sago, lemonade and port wine. At times, fowls, mutton chops and potatoes were listed among the ' extras '. Sister M. Joseph Croke took over the management of the provision store, which was kept so well stocked that it was necessary to make but one requisition on the Purveyor every day. Emergency requisitions could be made on the Sisters' store by obtaining Mother Bridgeman's signature. Mr. Robertson who made this ruling, stipulated also that the clerk of the general stores could accept in cases of extreme emergency requisitions endorsed by her in lieu of signatures from Dr. Hamilton or his colleagues.[11] At the end of each month the Sisters, at their own request, presented to the Purveyor an account of the expenditure of their stores.

> " Sister Mary Joseph was an excellent accountant," wrote Fanny Taylor. " It was a pleasure to look at her books, and they gained great commendation when they went to the Purveyor's office to be checked."

In a comparatively short time, everything in Koulali General Hospital was in working order, and was managed not only on principles of benevolence to the patients but of economy towards the Government. General Storks, who succeeded Lord William Paulet in command of the Bosphorus, reported that " the cheapest of the four hospitals is Koulali."[12] The four hospitals were Scutari, Koulali, Smyrna and Balaclava.

The extra-diet kitchen was run on typical conventual lines. Each meal was announced by a bell. Breakfast was at seven ; the regular dinner at twelve-thirty ; tea at four. At the sound of the dinner bell the orderlies would queue up in a passage before an open window or ' turn ' leading to the kitchen. " After the calling of the diet roll, chops, fowls, soups, vegetables, etc. were served and portioned according to the patients' needs, so that the Sister or lady on duty had only to hand to each his dinner in a hot covered plate."[13] Invalid foods—rice, sago, egg puddings and arrowroot—were similarly distributed. From such efficiency of service it followed that meals in Koulali were never insipid, each patient got an adequate share, and there was comparatively little waste. In the late afternoon drinks of lemonade or barley water were distributed, after which the requisitions for the following day were listed. By degrees, the death rate began to subside: by the first week of April it had dropped to one-twentieth of what it had been when the hospital was opened on February 2.[14]

The wards in Koulali were classified according to disease. The diseases were similar to those in Scutari ; the number much less ; the treatment different. Here we may anticipate somewhat. At this period Lister and Pasteur had just begun the work which was to revolutionise the medical world. As regards the theory of infection, they had a disciple in advance in Mother Bridgeman but not in Florence Nightingale, who to the end of her life persisted in ignoring its possibilities.

The dominant feature of the nursing done in Koulali was that of strict personal supervision. By careful attention to diets, medicines, and stimulants, the Sisters had the opportunity of seeing to the needs of each patient and of checking on necessary changes. Special attention was given to the bedside care of the critically ill. Night duty was undertaken, especially when opiates were ordered by the doctors and when the chloroform treatment for cholera was being used. Above all things, the Sisters in every detail of hospital duty acknowledged the jurisdiction of the medical officers, without whose permission and sanction they initiated nothing on their own.

Florence Nightingale's system on the other hand, left the distribution of diets, medicines and stimulants to the discretion of orderlies and ward masters, and a considerable part of the nurses' time was spent in non-nursing duties. Miss Nightingale did the rounds of the hospital at night time, but she objected to the introduction of night duty and insisted that she alone had the right to decide on the allocation of the nurses. Her attitude to the Koulali system was one of vigorous opposition; but the superiority of that system is attested to by the fact that she began to revise her own methods to such an extent that the scheme for military nursing which she submitted to the War Office after her Crimean experiences, was in many ways identical with that introduced by Mother Bridgeman.

Every detail of the daily routine in Koulali was carefully supervised, and though alterations were made from time to time, not a single innovation was attempted without the express approval of the senior medical officer.[15] If for no other reason than this, the Koulali doctors looked upon the Irish Sisters and Mary Stanley's ladies as their most valuable assistants. Harmony and co-operation marked their relationship from the beginning. Nor did differences of religion lead in any way to friction. Most of the doctors were non-Catholics, yet Mother Bridgeman speaks with gratitude of the constant kindness and courtesy of all without exception. Of Dr. Hamilton she says, " He was to us a kind brother. Indeed, *we* did not experience either opposition or distrust from the medical officers. They were, for the most part, Protestant Dissenters, yet all were exceedingly polite and kind."

The Sisters had their friends among the Protestant clergy also, some of whom accompanied their overtures of friendship with the request that they be permitted to send their collars to the new laundry. The well-starched coifs and guimps of the Sisters quite took their fancy. Mother Bridgeman agreed to take the ministerial collars—but the task of laundering them fell on Sister Winifred who worked under the most primitive conditions, her only facility being a tea-pot filled with boiling water, which was her nearest approximation to an iron!

Not least among Mother Bridgeman's achievements in Koulali must be counted her reformation of the orderlies. This she effected by training them in cleanliness and by relieving them of their control over the stimulants. For the future, the stimulants were to come direct from the stores to the Sisters, each of whom, attended by a ward sergeant and an orderly, administered the drinks as ordered by the doctors. " The orderlies lost their per-quisites," observed Mother Bridgeman in her diary, " but they were all the more sober for it and not the less devoted to the Sisters." Many of these orderlies were Irish—some of them con-valescents—whose wit and humour had evidently not suffered from their experiences in the trenches. Among others, there was Dick, who insisted on being called Richard on Sundays; Patrick, who was always " kilt with the drought," more especially when the stimulants were on the rounds; Thomas, whose lurid vocabu-lary earned him some severe rebukes from Mother Bridgeman, but who never failed to greet her with, " More power to ye, Ma'am—and would ye have e'er a lozenge in your pocket?"[16] The lozenge was always forthcoming . . .

It must not be assumed however that Mother Bridgeman tried to make teetotallers of the Koulali orderlies. None liked better than she to see them enjoying themselves, provided they kept within the limits of sobriety. On St. Patrick's Night she gave them permission to celebrate in traditional fashion: they began by forming a ring around herself and cheering her to the echo! The only delinquent that night was Patrick, who as he was returning to Ireland in a few weeks, went just a little too far in drinking Mother Bridgeman's health. Seeing her displeasure, he was most apologetic, and " begged her very humbly to forgive him this once, saying that he would not take a drop o' drink again till he got home."[17] On the whole, there was comparatively little drunkenness in Koulali, a circumstance which Fanny Taylor attributes to the influence of the Sisters.

The improvements introduced by Mother Bridgeman in the General Hospital were emulated and with reasonable success by Mary Stanley in the Barracks Hospital. Indeed, there is every possibility that without the " milder influence " of Mary Stanley, " the reaction against the ' monstrous regiment of women ' (a reaction not allayed by Miss Nightingale's sharp tongue and masterful interference) might have succeeded."[18] Though perhaps not as talented an administrator as Miss Nightingale, Mary Stanley had a quiet efficiency and amiability of disposition which enabled her to make a success of her venture in Koulali, even in spite of the want of discipline in most of her collaborators. But her delicate health began soon to suffer from strain and accumulation of work, and she was anxious to return home. Florence Nightingale's behaviour upset her as nothing else could have done, especially when an appeal she made for extra nurses was turned down by Miss Nightingale in a chilling letter which cancelled forever a friendship which meant much to Mary Stanley. " I have nothing further to say," wrote Miss Nightingale. " And for ' explanation ', I refer you to yourself. I have nothing to forgive. For I have never felt anger. I have never known you. There has been no ' difference ' between us—except a slight one of opinion as to the distribution of Articles and the manner of doing so to Patients. The pain you have given has not been by differing nor by anything for which forgiveness can be asked, but by not being yourself, or at least what I thought yourself. You say truly how I have loved you. No one will ever love you more.— Florence Nightingale."[19]

Mary Stanley's decision to leave Koulali was not due to squeamishness, nor did it imply any neglect of duty as a recent biographer of Miss Nightingale suggests: " After two months of hospital life Mary Stanley found herself utterly dis-illusioned . . . she had found fleas on her dress . . . and felt anxious to return home before the strain had quite worn her out."[20] Mary Stanley's work in Koulali was nobly done. Thanks to her endeavours, the Barracks and General Hospitals had become satisfactory establishments. She was quite justified therefore in quitting them. And it must be remembered that she had never intended to remain on in the east.

While in Koulali Mary Stanley had reason to remember Manning's conviction that she would like Father Ronan S.J. He it was who received her into the Church in March 1855. Manning had been her spiritual guide since the days when she first knew him as Archdeacon of Chichester. He had led her as he had previously led Florence Nightingale, to the door of the Church, and now she passed over the threshold to find at last that peace of soul which she sought and to add another illustrious Victorian name to the list of nineteenth-century converts from Anglicanism.

At her own request the ceremony of reception was conducted quietly; so quietly, that some of the Sisters were unaware of it until charges of proselytism and Jesuitry were once again in spate.

"I verily believe," wrote Mother Bridgeman in her *Diary*, "that the Sisters of Mercy caused more sensation and alarm than the Russians at the British Embassy in Turkey during the spring and summer of 1855, and gave more anxiety to the representatives of the English Church than his Satanic Majesty could have done, had he appeared in visible form in the British Military Hospitals of the East!"

Mr. Sabin, the senior chaplain, represented to Lord William Paulet that the Sisters had "with cruel interference" meddled with the religious beliefs of the Protestants and had influenced Mary Stanley's decision. Lady Stratford, whose horror of Jesuitry had lately begun to be tempered with feelings of pride in the hospital, was told that she had been grossly imposed upon by Mary Stanley. Mr. Sabin wrote to the War Office to have the Sisters removed. Lord William Paulet followed suit, deciding in the meantime to avoid "the Mother" as far as possible.[21] Ostracisation of the Sisters followed; but Mary Stanley, not content with allowing such misrepresentations go unchallenged, asked Dr. Hamilton if he could confirm or contradict the rumours then afloat. She considered it her duty to send a detailed report to the authorities in England, and most of all to Manning who on February 4 had requested her

"to send answers with all speed to the following questions: Have any of the Irish Sisters disobeyed hospital regulations? Have they refused to work with seculars? Have they interfered with the religion of Protestants? These things have been stated to me. Pray put me in possession of all needful information . . . for I am embarrassed for want of it, and am held responsible."[22]

Doctor Hamilton's reply was all that Mary Stanley and Dr. Manning could have desired.

"Dear Miss Stanley,
I am not aware that any of the Sisters of Mercy have interfered with the Protestant patients regarding their religion; but I have seen on several occasions the greatest kindness shown by them to the Protestant patients under my charge. I may also add that any change regarding the Sisters doing

duty here would be highly injurious to the present perfect state of this hospital.

Frederick Gustavus Hamilton."[23]

Similar assurance came from Doctor Beatson, another Protestant staff-surgeon, who later cleared the Sisters of proselytising charges in Balaclava.

Lord Napier, secretary at the Embassy, also bore eloquent testimony. Citing an occasion on which he was commanded by Lord Stratford de Redcliffe to see after about two hundred Jewish refugees from the Crimea, he told how he went to the Ambassador and said, " Your Excellency, these people are cold and I have no fuel or blankets; they are hungry and I have no food; they are very dirty and I have no soap; their hair is in an indescribable condition and I have no combs. What am I to do with them?" The Ambassador advised him to get a couple of Sisters of Mercy who would " put all things to right in no time." Lord Napier went to Mother Bridgeman, explained his predicament, and heard her appoint two Sisters to accompany him. " They were ladies of refinement and intellect. I was a stranger and a Protestant, and I invoked their assistance on behalf of the Jews. Yet these two women made up their bundles and followed me through the rain without a look, a whisper, a sign of hesitation. From that moment my fugitives were saved. For weeks nobody saw the labours of these Sisters but myself, *and they never endeavoured to make a single convert.*"[24]

After the war, when relating this incident to an audience in Edinburgh, Lord Napier concluded: " The Sisters made at least one convert. They converted me—if not to believe in the Catholic Faith, at least in the Sisters of Mercy."

On her return to England in April 1855, Mary Stanley resumed her several charitable activities, and " while devoting herself with singular fidelity to her mother and brother, she still continued to organise works of philanthropy similar to those which under her father's auspices she had conducted at Norwich." Few of the outside world knew of what she did in Koulali, but her work and the spirit in which it was performed were fully appreciated by the medical and military authorities on the spot. Though she became a Catholic, " she retained an unceasing interest in the Church of her father and her brother, as well as a wide sympathy with every act of justice in whatever communion." Her brother, the Dean of Westminster, never criticised her for her change of religion; she continued to be ever his " darling Mary." After her death he erected a memorial sanctuary to her at Righi in the

Swiss Alps, over which he inscribed the words, "*Levavi oculos meos in montes.*"[25]

Mary Stanley died on November 6, 1879. Three days later Requiem Mass was celebrated for her in the Chapel of the Sisters of Mercy, Chelsea; after which she was buried, at her own request, in the family grave at Alderley, "under the mingled shade of the old yew tree and its mass of embracing ivy." The funeral was solemnised by her brother, the Dean of Westminster, her brother-in-law, the Dean of LLandaff, and the Rector of the parish. The scriptural text on the white marble cross marking her grave tells the passers-by that she was "Never weary in doing well. Gal. VI.10."

That Arthur Stanley was aware of the unpleasantness connected with his sister's mission to Scutari is seen from the letter he addressed to Lord Stratford de Redcliffe shortly after her return to England.

"... I trust I may be excused for taking up a few minutes of your time to express our deep gratitude for the kindness you have shown my sister. It is not for me to say anything of the public service which your Excellency has rendered in saving from utter wreck and failure the useful and benevolent scheme which my sister was sent out to assist. But I cannot forbear to tender the respectful thanks which my father would have written had he been still alive, for the support and sympathy which she has received from your Lordship and Lady Stratford at a time when she most needed it.

Yours respectfully and gratefully,
Arthur Penrhyn Stanley."[26]

Today, the "Mary Stanley Bed" in the Hospital of St. John and St. Elizabeth, St. John's Wood, London, perpetuates Mary Stanley's connection with the Sisters of Mercy who own and administer the hospital.

For Mother Bridgeman, the departure of Mary Stanley was a personal grief. But for her, the Sisters of Mercy would never have gained any footing in the British military hospitals; Florence Nightingale would have seen to that. In giving over the administration of the General Hospital at Koulali to Mother Bridgeman, Mary Stanley had run counter to strong prevailing prejudices. This we gather from an entry in Mother Bridgeman's *Diary* to the effect that

"To be a *Catholic* was a decided disqualification for the post of Superintendent of a British hospital—at least, so thought Miss Nightingale, Lady Stratford de Redcliffe, and other authorities on the Bosphorus . . . In giving us charge of a hospital, Miss Stanley aroused against herself the distrust and bigotry of all these potentates. She never afterwards ceased to suffer suspicions and misrepresentations, and to her, in giving us the General Hospital, the Institute owes in great measure any credit it may acquire from our mission. Had we not an establishment where we might fully carry out our own views and arrangements, we should have been obliged to drag along in the systems or want of systems of the secular ladies, in place of having them follow our plans (as they did at Koulali) and of being enabled to acquire for the Sisters of Mercy the high character for obedience, system, order, and good nursing which we certainly have at head-quarters and with the medical officers in general. Therefore, to Mary Stanley the Institute owes a debt, if the credit and character thus acquired be of any merit."

Florence Nightingale expected that with the return of Mary Stanley to England the hospital at Koulali would *ipso facto* close down. " I consider that Miss Stanley gone, Koulali will break up in all probability," she wrote to Sidney Herbert. " Try and work a civil hospital with ladies and nuns, and you will see what I mean. The ladies all quarrel among themselves; the medical men all laugh at their helplessness, but like to have them about for the sake of a little female society; which is natural but not our object."27   But Koulali did not close down. It continued for another six months to be what Miss Nightingale termed " the bitterest portion of her mission." Too late she realised that her refusal to accept Mary Stanley as a colleague was reflecting unfavourably on her Crimean nursing project.

By April 1855 all that remained in Koulali of Mary Stanley's original staff were two nurses and one lady. Of the other ladies, Miss Smythe had died and the rest had been invalided home. The nurses had been dismissed for irregularities too numerous to relate. Two days after Mary Stanley's departure one of the two surviving nurses caught fever, and as she needed the assistance of her companion, the work of the two hospitals devolved upon Fanny Taylor and nine Sisters of Mercy. The tenth, Sister M. Bernard, was dangerously ill. The Sisters, wrote Fanny Taylor, " already taxed beyond their strength, willingly and cheerfully undertook the additional work . . . and so admirable was their method, so unremitting their skill, that no patient (it may be confidently said) suffered from diminution of numbers."28

As the only survivor of the band in Koulali, Fanny Taylor became in effect superintendent of the Barracks Hospital. Lady Stratford vetoed her appointment. She suspected Miss Taylor of Catholic tendencies and of being " too much in sympathy with the nuns." At the same time Lady Stratford admitted that she herself was " also very fond of the Reverend Mother of Kinsale " but could not help thinking her " a very dangerous person." Other and equally inconsistent remarks of Lady Stratford place her in the category of those who seldom know their own minds. " I like the nuns," she admitted. " I cannot help it—their quiet dignity must win our respect . . . I know they are the best nurses, and if I were sick I would rather be nursed by them than by anyone else. I am pained to be obliged to say all this : but I am so afraid of Romanism and I am told they have come out here to proselytise."[29]

Lady Stratford's scruples are to a certain extent understandable; we can perhaps sympathise with her, though Mother Bridgeman's verdict on her was somewhat severe. She called her " a weak-minded silly woman, who was at the mercy of every knave, believed every idle tale without question, and so kept herself and us in perpetual agitation."

An extract from Fanny Taylor's memoirs portrays for us the overcharged atmosphere of Koulali after Mary Stanley's departure . . .

" I was alone in Koulali Barracks Hospital at Easter 1855. There were ten Sisters of Mercy resident at the General Hospital, distant about half a mile. My lady companions had all gone home, and I was anxiously awaiting another party from England to help me . . . I was very High Church and devoted to the nuns. We all lived in terror of being ' reported to the Government ' as proselytisers. The Protestant Ministers were on the war-path and watched our every movement."

In the eyes of the Protestant chaplains Fanny Taylor was indeed " far more obnoxious for her Catholic tendencies than any of those who had brought discredit on the work by their folly or misconduct."[30] Their hostility counted for little with Miss Taylor —except in so far as it led her to take a keener interest in the Catholic religion, which in those days of trial was more and more claiming her attention. It was during this same period of stress that she recorded in her book, *Eastern Hospitals and English Nurses,* her appreciation of the Irish Sisters of Mercy; and to her we are indebted for a striking characterisation of Mother

Bridgeman. Miss Taylor's characterisation forms such a contrast to that presented by the Nightingale biographers as to merit quotation in its entirety.

" The superiority of the Catholic Sisters of Mercy showed itself over all other classes of nurses engaged in the East. To them, work among the sick and suffering was no new thing undertaken in the heat of enthusiasm. To live for the poor had been for many years the resolve of each heart; for this they had gone through a long probation and preparation. Hence, the perfect unity of their work, the facility of one taking up what another might be interrupted in.

" Now, most of the ladies had had no experience whatever of nursing the sick and poor; and those who had, had learned it their own way, and in that way only could they carry it on . . .

" With regard to the Superioress of the nuns: she was not one placed suddenly in a new and untried position, incapable of entering into the difficulties of those working under her. Before being selected to rule she had learned to obey. However great her natural talents for governing and organising work, without that complete control she had long since acquired, there never would have been seen to so much advantage the remarkable feature that the act of one was the act of all, which was so observable in the Sisters of Mercy. Trained to a life of hardships, the health and strength of the Sisters withstood the shocks under which the health of the ladies sank; and they could continue under the strain of work to which the latter were wholly unequal. Routine they were accustomed to, and to the absence of the comforts of life they had become inured. Obedience was with them a habit; therefore they were not likely to fail in the rigid obedience required by the medical officers . . .

" Their hospital from first to last was admirably managed. The Mother had long experience in hospital work, and possessed a skill and judgment in nursing attained by few. The medical officers, Doctor Hamilton and Doctor Guy, fully appreciated her value; so did the assistant surgeons, and there was hearty co-operation between them. When the means of improvement were placed in her hands, they were judiciously used; and the hospital so improved that it became the admiration of all who visited it, and the pride of the ladies and nurses who worked in it. We used to call it ' The Model Hospital of the East.' "

## CHAPTER 11

## THE MODEL HOSPITAL

THE winter of 1854-'55 was a study in competitive horror in which the Commissariat and Quartermaster services of the English and Russian armies fought out a grim battle in which each excelled the other in blundering and ineptitude. By February 1855 the English had made some recovery. The Quartermaster services never became really good, but after the establishment of the Crimean Army Fund, the more stark horrors began to disappear. From now on the worst privations of the war were to be progressively remedied, but the army in the Crimea had still to contend with the double curse of cold and cholera; and statistics prove that even the Great War of 1914-1918, with all its mud and blood, produced no picture of misery more depressing than that afforded by the cholera-haunted trenches and miserable tents on the heights above Sebastopol. As yet there was no sign of capitulation: the failure of the allies to take Sebastopol in September 1854, had furnished Todleben, the Russian engineer, with the opportunity of strengthening the fortifications which now ran in a continuous semi-circle round the city, from the Redan on the east to the Quarantine Bastion on the west.

Russia placed her traditional dependence on Generals " January and February "; but the generals had directed their weapons impartially; and if whole English brigades perished in the trenches before Sebastopol, the roads leading from central Russia to the Crimea were marked with the bones of Russian dead. The situation steadily worsened, until repeated failures sent Nicholas I, the " Don Quixote of autocracy " to an untimely grave. His death on March 2, was received with apathy by subjects who knew him only as Nicholas Palkin, Nicholas the Flogger, and who lived in the hope that his successor would not be another crowned drill sergeant. Alexander II ascended the throne amid the universal hope that the new reign might bring a new deal, and for a while all his subjects wished him well. His task was not an easy one: the winter calamities had dispelled any illusions entertained by the Russians since 1812, and it required a greater than Alexander II to deal with the situation.

Towards the end of March batches of invalids, debilitated by malnutrition and exposure in the trenches, came pouring down from the Crimea into the already over-crowded hospitals on the Bosphorus. The majority of those received at Koulali were advanced cases of frostbite. On admission, their clothes had to be cut off; in many instances flesh and clothes were frozen together. Boots had to be eased off bit by bit; not infrequently the toes came away with the leather.[1] Poultices were applied with some oil brushed over them: next morning, the sinews and bones were seen to be laid bare! One soldier told how when lying ill at Balaclava one night, he tried to move his feet but found them frozen to those of a comrade who was lying near him. Others would venture no comment whatever on conditions at the front beyond a general admission that they had " a very hard time up there."[2] Along with frostbite there was an epidemic of low fever, something akin to the Irish famine fever, which so prostrated the men that they had not even the will to live.

One of the Sisters describes the treatment given to each contingent on arrival. " We have to wash their faces and hands, and cut their hair, etc., and the dirt is such that the sheets look as if they had been used to scrub the floor." Within two days most of the patients would be so prostrate as to need spoon-feeding with wine, sago, or arrowroot, " for if these things were left beside them they would not take them. They feel a kind word and sympathy so much on arrival . . . that they often cry and seem more grateful for that than for anything else." Gratitude was expressed in a variety of ways. " Oh, I do like to have you come to see me that way," said one on being asked how he had spent the night. Another asked, " Sister, is it wrong for me to say, Ma'am, that the way you take care of me reminds me of my mother?" A third declared that " It's meself that's proud to see you this morning, Sister; and isn't it meself that knows who's the best doctors in the hospitals nowadays." Perhaps the most touching tribute of all came from the patient who asked the Sister in his ward if she had had enough to eat that day, " because, Sister, Ma'am, you gave me a piece of chicken for my dinner and I kept some of it for you."[3]

Skilful treatment, palatable food and constant nursing did much to arrest the progress of the fever. Deaths were numerous at first: some patients were beyond all human aid. But though denied the joy of recovery, their last hours were made comfortable and peaceful by those little acts of kindness and considerateness which are the special mark of every nursing Sister. In Koulali the Catholic soldiers had every consolation of their religion. Few, if any, left the hospital without making their peace with

God, and Mother Bridgeman has left on record the fact that "many apostates were reconciled." Fanny Taylor, in her memoirs, is even more explicit. "Those who had lived long years in sin," she said, "once more sought out their Saviour; and those whose last remembrance of prayers and sacraments had been in days gone by, in the shelter of their homes, now returned to the God of their youth."[4] Fanny Taylor herself was also to discover the God of her youth in Koulali.

Operations on the frost-bitten were performed by Doctors Humphrey, Guy and Beatson. Surgical facilities in Koulali at the time show a vast improvement on conditions obtaining in Scutari, where "operations were done upon boards put up on two trestles."[5] There were no screens in Scutari; the occupants of each ward had full view of the torture they themselves were in turn to undergo without the blessed oblivion of chloroform. Miss Nightingale got a screen from Constantinople shortly after her arrival in November 1854, but three months later—in February 1855—the members of the Sanitary Commission were horrified at the conditions prevailing in the Barracks Hospital and its alarming mortality figures. A month later again, on March 10, William Howard Russell could remark on "how strange it is we get up so few convalescents from Scutari. The hospitals there seem to swallow up the sick forever."[6]

The picture from Koulali was entirely different. Writing to Liverpool, Sister M. Elizabeth speaks of the "formidable preparations" for operations going on in her ward. At the end of the ward, we are told, is a "large table with a white sheet on it. Surgical instruments, splints, bandages, lint, etc., are in readiness on this table." During operations, "a Sister of Mercy, in a stiff white apron, with scissors and surgical instruments at her side," assists the doctor. Later, she may be seen "accompanying the doctor on his rounds, receiving his orders, or holding up a frost-bitten limb for his inspection, which she dresses, binds up and bandages."

The wards were arranged as follows. In the centre of each was a table, called the Sister's or lady's table, on which was a book of regulations for day and night nursing. A row of trestle beds lined each side of the ward; the heads of these beds had open bars, on top of which was a narrow ledge to hold medicines, cups and dishes. A printed card over each bed indicated the case history of the patient. The card was not originally intended to bear any record of the patient's faith, but "the regulation was early made on account of the mistakes and absurdities which the want of it sometimes caused."[7] At the end of the ward was a long dresser in which plates and tins, knives and forks were kept. Two locked compartments of this dresser were assigned to the ladies' and Sisters' use, and in them were kept linen and wine and other articles likely to be needed in a hurry. The simplification of the requisition system has been already explained.

The arrival of a new party of nurses on April 19 brought the nursing personnel at Koulali up to forty-two: thirty-two nurses and ten Sisters of Mercy. Accompanying the group was Father Woollett, S.J., a newly-appointed chaplain for the Crimea. His visit to Koulali was the final grace for Fanny Taylor. Within four days he had dispelled her remaining doubts, and she pronounced her act of Faith before him in the camp kitchen. To-day, Miss Taylor has a special niche in Church history, where as Mother Magdalen Taylor, foundress of the Poor Servants of the Mother of God, her name will be ever held in blessing. Before this, and after her return from the Crimea she founded *The Month*, which she edited for a year before handing it over to the Jesuits who run it with such distinction to this day. It was to Fanny Taylor that Cardinal Newman, searching in his waste-paper basket, and finding *The Dream of Gerontius*, sent the manuscript, which was subsequently published in *The Month*.

Among the recent group of ladies who had arrived from England was a Miss Emily Hutton, whom Lord William Paulet selected as Lady Superintendent in place of Mary Stanley. It was decreed that Miss Hutton would be responsible only to Lord William, except in details of hospital work, in which she was under obedience to the Principal Medical Officer. Florence Nightingale had been relieved of her nominal superintendence over Koulali by order of Lord Panmure, who appointed her instead ' Almoner of the Free Gifts in all the British Hospitals of the Crimea '. Lord Panmure wished " to separate the different hospitals as far as nursing was concerned, because the multiplication of hospitals at some miles distance would make any real supervision from Scutari impossible."[8] Sidney Herbert added his own impressions on this head, by assuring Miss Nightingale that such an arrangement would be by far the best for her. It appears that the War Office authorities were keen on trying out systems of military nursing other than that advocated by Florence Nightingale. This probably explains Lord Panmure's reluctance to clarify her position with regard to supreme control of the entire nursing personnel which she demanded. Sidney Herbert mentions three distinct systems then on trial: that run by Miss Nightingale at Scutari; the Smyrna division consisting of " ladies and paid nurses in equal proportions without the Roman Catholic Sisters "; and the Koulali system of mixed religions. It could be that acquiescence with Lord Panmure's wishes indicated on Mr. Herbert's part a reluctance to sponsor any further Miss Nightingale's cause with the Minister for War: as the Crimean War continued, his support of her became less and less enthusiastic.

Notwithstanding Lady Stratford's " most earnest injunctions that she should not permit herself to be fascinated by ' the Mother '," Miss Hutton and Mother Bridgeman became close friends.[9] At Miss Hutton's request, and with the approval of Lord William Paulet, Mother Bridgeman retained the superintendence of the General Hospital, Koulali, but five Sisters continued to give their services to the Barracks Hospital, where they discovered in Emily Hutton a second Mary Stanley.

" Miss Hutton I cannot praise too highly," wrote Mother Bridgeman. " I have never had dealings with a more honourable upright mind. We never had the slightest difficulty with her—or with the Medical Officers. Many of them, indeed, are worthy of honourable mention in connection with this mission of ours."

Lack of accommodation necessitated the renting of a house on the Bosphorus at £600 per annum for Miss Hutton's nurses. To say nothing of the expense entailed in the upkeep of this " Happy Home on the Bosphorus," the conduct of its inmates was such as to bring ridicule on the whole establishment. Mother Bridgeman reports that in a short time there were " three engagements, and many others who seemed most willing to be ' engaged ' if opportunity offered, but . . . the doctors had evidently no desire to become the heroes of an eastern romance." The paid nurses were guilty of " the grossest misconduct, even in the wards. One might suppose they were resolved to verify all that had been said against sending out secular ladies and nurses."[10] Matters were the same in Smyrna and Scutari, hospitals under Miss Nightingale's jurisdiction. In Smyrna they brought the English name into discredit with foreigners. In Scutari, a Miss Salisbury was put under arrest for stealing £100 from Miss Nightingale's stores. Immoral conduct and intoxication continued to be constant reasons for dismissal.

Mother Bridgeman's was not the only voice raised in criticism of the nurses. Miss Nightingale criticised them. At one time it was estimated that she had 125 hired nurses under her supervision ; only two of whom did she single out for praise. These were Mrs. Shaw Stewart, one of Mary Stanley's party who was accepted in Scutari, and Mrs. Roberts whom she afterwards staffed in St. Thomas's Hospital, London. The medical officers were constantly critical of the nurses, who were, in fact, criticised at one time or other by all persons interested in promoting the scheme for female military nursing.

The matter was still under discussion in 1862 as may be inferred from the following article published in a March issue of *The North British Review* of that year:

> "While in the Crimea our hired nurses disgraced themselves by incompetency and disobedience, and many of our volunteer ladies were obliged to return home ill or worn out, the Sisters of Mercy held on with unflagging spirit and energy —never surprised, never put out, ready in response, meeting all difficulties with a cheerful spirit, a superiority owing to their previous training and experience."

Spring brought about a lessening of disease and a corresponding drop in the number of patients being sent to the base hospitals. Koulali was never again to be overcrowded, but there was always a floating population sufficiently large to keep the Sisters constantly busy. To nursing duties were added those of letter-writing for the patients, the training of orderlies as ward masters, the supervision of the extra-diet kitchen, laundry and stores. In applying themselves to these multiple duties the Sisters won respect and admiration from the doctors, from many of the Anglican clergymen and from the patients without exception. Their influence over their patients was enormous, states Fanny Taylor. In deference to the Sisters bad language and barrack-room ribaldry were practically eliminated in Koulali. Not an angry word or curse did Mother Bridgeman ever hear save one ; and the apology of the culprit on this occasion was probably sincere if a bit unorthodox : "Ten thousand pardons, Ma'am. I'd much rather curse before the Minister than before you!"[11]

On April 18, Archbishop Cullen sent Mother Bridgeman a Papal Blessing from Pio Nono, with instructions to "hold your ground until you shall be sent away by force, but do not let your enemies frighten you away." It was timely advice. Mother Bridgeman has been described as "Irish enough to obey," and the ultimate success of the second party of Sisters was largely due to her.[12]

Conversions among lady volunteers and patients soon evoked wild charges of proselytism against the Sisters. Miss Hutton began to be assailed on all sides. Florence Nightingale fanned for a time the old embers of religious animosity in an effort to compromise the Sisters, until Mother Bridgeman determined once and for all to terminate such embarrassments by declaring herself "willing and able to investigate, and to insist on proof for every charge which could be traced to an author." All charges investigated resulted in complete vindication for the Sisters. " But this," said Mother Bridgeman, " was attributed not to our truthfulness or our innocence, but to our cleverness, our Jesuitry." Mr. Hewlitt, the most rabidly anti-Catholic clergyman then in Koulali, gave as his opinion that " that Reverend Mother is the cleverest woman I ever met." Mother Bridgeman adds that the " indignation of patients of every denomination was roused when any charge against the Sisters reached their ears ; and no one whom we had nursed could ever be found to aid in substantiating any of the reports set afloat. No one ever charged us with neglecting the duty of nursing. All admitted to the contrary."[13]

One accusation brought forward by a Miss Emily Anderson, at that time engaged to Mr. Hewlitt, was that to her " own certain knowledge " the Sisters had given religious instruction to Protestant patients. Mother Bridgeman, in an interview with Miss Anderson, asked in which ward the instruction was given.

" In my own," was the reply.

" By what Sister?"

" I do not know."

" What was the nature of the instruction? What was the patient's name?"

" I do not know ; but the man said, when complaining to the Minister, that he would know nothing of religion but for the Romish Sisters."

" And, Miss Anderson, how could you say that to your ' own certain knowledge ' the Sisters had violated their engagements, when you had no other grounds than the bare assertion of a man of whose name you are ignorant?"

" Well," said Miss Anderson, " the Sisters gave out Catholic books—I have some of them."

" That is not proof, Miss Anderson," concluded Mother Bridgeman. " You asked Father Ronan for some and got them for the Catholics. And again, when Sister M. Joseph was suddenly removed from your ward, you may remember she begged you would take up and keep for her the books she had lent the Catholics; none of which did you ever return. It is not hard, then, to account for your having our books."[14]

The interview ended with an outburst of tears from Miss Anderson who rushed off to Mr. Hewlitt with an exaggerated story, which eventually led to an exchange of letters between Father Ronan, S.J., and Mr. Hobson, senior chaplain at Koulali.*

*Vide pp. 307-308.

Miss Anderson withdrew the accusation; Mr. Hobson insisted that he wished " to be the last to do injustice to anyone, least of all to Mrs. Bridgeman and the ladies under her care,"[15] and for a while the Sisters were left unmolested. The engagement between Mr. Hewlitt and Miss Anderson ended as from this date.

Matters eventually came to a head when Sister M. Elizabeth of Liverpool gave *Maxims of Christian Perfection* to a Protestant patient without having first ascertained his religion, which for some reason had been omitted from his card. The Reverend Mr. Frieth found the book and subjected Sister M. Elizabeth to such a rigorous cross-examination that the Protestant doctor in charge asked him to leave the ward and later secured his removal from Koulali altogether.[16] Sister M. Elizabeth was exonerated on the recommendation of the patient who insisted that he himself had asked for the book, and that she had given it to him, believing him to be a Catholic. These two charges though unconfirmed were brought forward again and again, regardless of the fact that Mother Bridgeman repeatedly assured Florence Nightingale that she would " consider it a sin against God and a disgrace before man to violate the contract we had distinctly and deliberately made."

At Miss Nightingale's instigation, Lord William Paulet filed a detailed report of the Sisters' proselytising activities which he duly forwarded to the War Office. The complaint was reinforced by an urgent memorandum from Mr. Sabin, the senior chaplain at Scutari, asking Lord Panmure to " issue an order as to the interference of priests with Protestants while in hospital, and also as to proselytising, secretly or openly, that it might be clearly understood that the nurses or nuns are not to be used as teachers by direction of Romish or Protestant chaplains."[17] Pending a reply from Whitehall, it was proposed that sick wards in Koulali should be classed by creeds rather than by diseases—the idea being to remove the Protestant patients from all ' Romish influences.' The proposal was rejected by the doctors and by Miss Hutton. It was decided then to send Father Ronan to the camp, thereby depriving the Sisters of their greatest ally; but as Scutari was specifically mentioned in Father Ronan's letter of appointment, he was able to resist. And there the matter rested.

Sister M. Joseph Croke, who was on night duty at the time of these disturbances, mentions in her *Diary* that the Catholic patients alone of all those in military hospitals were the only ones to whom religious literature was denied. Bible-reading was encouraged, even to extremes, as the following incident illustrates. Sister M. Joseph usually visited her wards every half-hour to see that all was in order. On one such occasion she found a Protestant orderly " in the dead of night," reading the Bible to his sleeping charges, most of whom showed strong objections to his " loud, shrill tones." Sister requested the zealot to restrain his zeal until a more opportune moment, " to close his mouth, at least, if not his book." Somewhat nonplussed, be complied; and as Sister M. Joseph moved away she was beckoned to by an Irish soldier who whispered, " Sister, dear, I stuffed me ears with the sheet so as not to hear that fella's Bible!"[18]

Miss Nightingale's nocturnal visitations in Scutari Barracks Hospital formed a fitting background for the legend of the Lady with the Lamp. No such legend attaches to the work of the Sisters of Mercy; yet there is one arresting portrayal of their night activities in Koulali, and later in Balaclava. The writer, a doctor, declared the Sisters to be

" very attentive to their charge and eminently deserving the name they bear of Sisters of Mercy. They are attired from head to foot in deepest black; even their heads are carefully hooded; the only relief to this sombre attire being the double string of beads hanging from their girdle. I was quite startled on my first introduction to one of these ladies. Having a patient in a very critical state in one of the wards, I went down about midnight to pay him a visit. On opening the door, I beheld by the light of the wretched little lamp, just such a phantom as Bolivar has drawn in Lucretia—' darkness in every corner, and a tall figure, darker than the night, gliding from bed to bed '."[19]

There was evidently more than one lady and one lamp in the military hospitals of the Crimea.

Military and medical authorities were every day attaching more value to the Sisters. Even *The Times*, in an article on the advisability of increasing the nursing personnel in the military hospitals, admitted their superiority in the following manner:

" The hospital orderlies cannot as a body be put in any comparison with them, even on the score of regularity and strict obedience to orders—one need not say how much they fall short in the specific capacity for nursing. In speaking of such an extension, the Medical Officers evidently incline to rely on persons as have had previous hospital training, and have thus gained the power of working methodically. The Catholic Nuns, from their habit of simple obedience and submission, possess this power remarkably."[20]

The War Office reply to the complaints lodged against the Sisters was delivered to Lord William Paulet on April 27. In it, Mr. Benjamin Hawes declared it to be the wish of Lord Panmure that

> " clear and distinct orders should be promulgated throughout the hospitals . . . to the effect that no Protestant or Roman Catholic Chaplain should in any way, directly or indirectly, interfere with the religious opinions of any person whatever, belonging to, or professing to belong to a Church or creed different from that of which the Chaplain, Protestant or Catholic, is an appointed minister . . .
>
> And that with regard to Protestant ladies or nurses . . . it is to be a clear and well-understood rule that they are not to be used as Religious Instructors or Teachers by direction of any Protestant Chaplain, and that they are not to enter upon the discussion of religious subjects with any patients other than those of their own faith.
>
> With regard to the Roman Catholic Nuns, or Sisters of Mercy, they are strictly to confine themselves also within this rule, which is one laid down for their guidance by the proper authorities of their own Church, and to which they distinctly assented when nominated to the office, the duties of which they undertook."[21]

The document concludes with a threat of suspension on anyone infringing these regulations, for

> " unless they are strictly observed, it is clear that the hospitals may become the scene of religious dissensions and animosities, not more injurious to the peace and welfare of the sick, than calculated to mar the efficacy of those works of Mercy and Charity so pre-eminently inculcated upon us by the common religion we profess."

Mr. Sabin assured Lord William Paulet that for the Sisters this was a positive prohibition against speaking on religious subjects to *any* of the patients. Lord William gave a copy of the letter to Father Ronan, S.J., and one to Miss Hutton ; but seeing the latter's unwillingness to place such a restriction on any party, his Lordship became " quite confidential and complained of all the trouble he was having from the Protestant Chaplains."[22] Nevertheless, he requested Father Ronan to convey Lord Panmure's mandate to the Sisters ; which he did. Mother Bridgeman's handling of this new crisis affords once again definite evidence of her relationship with Daniel O'Connell. She wrote a letter to Father Ronan, requesting him to transmit it in her name to Lord William

Paulet, and expressed at the same time her hope that his Lordship's sense of justice would induce him to shield the Sisters from restraints and conditions subject to which they would not have undertaken the mission, and to which they still declared themselves unwilling to submit.

" So far as I understand the letter from the War Office," she wrote on May 13, " we have been observing its spirit hitherto. It says we are not to enter upon the discussion of religious subjects with any patients other than those of our own faith. We have never done so; and of this the number of convalescent Protestant patients who have been under our care are living witnesses.

It is also quite true that our Superiors at home consented to this, and gave us a written rule to this effect, which of course, we have inviolably observed.

In addition to all this, I signed an agreement with Government on behalf of the Sisters under my care, of which one of the articles was that we should not interfere in the religious concerns of the Protestant soldiers ; and I have regarded it as a point of honour and conscience that this agreement should be observed.

But it is equally true that we came out perfectly free to converse with Catholic soldiers on religious subjects ; that the Government did not intimate even the least desire to restrict our intercourse with them ; that if it did, we would not have come out under any such restriction, nor would we ever have become parties to any such penal law. Therefore, we must still feel ourselves free to converse with our Catholic soldiers on subjects connected with their eternal interests, when this does not interfere with the duty of attending and ministering to the temporal wants of both Protestants and Catholics.

As there seems much misconception with regard to our practice of religious instruction, would you, dear Reverend Father, kindly explain to Lord William Paulet the nature and extent of what we do in a religious way for our Catholic soldiers. That it simply consists in a few quiet and unostentatious words of advice, admonition or instruction, as occasion and leisure present themselves ; in a prayer for patience whispered into the ear of the sufferer; in some motives for conformity suggested ; but this *never* in such a tone or manner as to be unpleasant to the patient in the next bed, whatever his creed may be . . .

To witness the agony of pain and the lassitude of disease ;

to see the approaching death struggle; to think of the awful judgment soon to follow, and to be debarred from speaking a word of consolation or hope to the poor Catholic soldier, or from breathing a prayer for the grace then so much needed by him: this is a restriction to which we never can submit. It is one to which I feel sure neither England nor Ireland will ever expect us to submit.

How often have we not heard words like these from the prostrate sufferers: 'Oh Ma'am, when will you have time to say a little prayer for me? I know you have a deal to do, but oh, you would try to come if only you knew what a comfort it is to a poor fellow far from home when you come to him and kneel by his bed, and say a little prayer and talk a little bit to him.' The poor Catholics say that when we can spare them a few moments it affords them more comfort than all we can do to relieve their temporal wants.

And can we be expected to reply to them: 'I may not speak to you on religious subjects even though we both are Catholics. The Government in whose service you have sacrificed the vigour of your lives forbids it?' It seems to be too absurd to believe that under a Government such as England's is, such a restriction could ever have been thought of. That the Government intended it, I do not, for one moment, believe.

" We are willing," the letter concludes, " to labour our lives in the service of the sick and dying soldiers without distinction of creed. But as this duty is quite compatible with the sort of religious intercourse which we consider ourselves free to hold with Catholics, I feel quite assured that no upright or unprejudiced person would expect us to yield up our freedom on this point. *I*, at least, feel sure, that neither God, our Superiors, or our Country will expect it of us."[23]

Father Ronan waited on Lord William Paulet with this letter. The interview between them was absurd: every detail of Father Ronan's defence of the Sisters was parried by Lord William with, " They shall not instruct; they shall not instruct; on that I am resolved."[24] When about to leave, Father Ronan left for his Lordship's perusal Mother Bridgeman's letter, adding that he would return on the following day for a reply.

News of proceedings in the military hospitals evoked a strong protest from Bishop Grant of Southwark who, in a letter to Mother M. Clare Moore, expressed grave concern at

"Lord Paulet's threatened prohibition about speaking even to Catholics. If he puts this in writing," said the Bishop, " it will be contrary to the express agreement with Government ; and as it will reduce you to mere nurses and destroy your spiritual position, you will at once tell Miss Nightingale that it is your duty to return home."[25]

Dr. Manning was equally disturbed at the unwonted turn of events. He had " looked on in silence and amazement at many things, and not with approval at some," and his main fear was that " unless Providence avert it, we shall have a breakdown, not in Nursedom only, but in something more vital." To avert such a contingency, he visited the War Office where, having ascertained that " misrepresentation from Protestant sources " was the main cause of Lord Panmure's directive of April 27, he assured Mary Stanley that he did not anticipate any real harm, as he believed " Lord Panmure to be just in the matter." He added that he had " no fears for the Sisters . . . for with common prudence they will do well."[26] In the event, they did excellently.

It was a changed Lord William Paulet who awaited Father Ronan's return with the admission that " he never knew of one fair case being proved against the Sisters, and had never heard any but the most favourable accounts of their nursing." Having told Father Ronan that he had " snubbed Mr. Sabin that morning," Lord William admitted that he " never had any trouble or annoy-ance from the Roman Catholics," and he promised that in future he would receive no unproved statements against the Sisters, but that as long as they kept their contract, he would see to it that they should not be molested.[27] So much for Lord William Paulet ; yet he kept his word. He never again interfered in the admini-stration of Koulali, though from that time until he was relieved of his duties on the Bosphorus, he adhered to his original intention of " keeping out of sight of the nuns." He had but one interview ever with Mother Bridgeman, in the course of which she declined his belated offers of assistance, assuring him that the wants of the Sisters were being carefully attended to by their good friend and purveyor, Mr. Scott Robertson.

Restraints and restrictions to the contrary, the quiet and unostentatious efficacy of the Sisters could not for long be denied; for in Koulali it was a well-known fact that many a patient blessed the day that brought him under the watchful care of Mother Bridgeman and her community. Father Ronan has left on record that

" in the hospital near Scutari I suppose more than a thousand poor soldiers from the Crimea were prepared for death by me . . . I have never for one moment doubted that every one of these poor souls went straight to Heaven. In Koulali there were at least fifty added to the Church, and everyone received by me attributed his conversion, under God, to the Sisters of Mercy."[28]

Not by precept then, but rather by the example of their holy lives did these Irish Sisters of Mercy help to sow the seeds of the second spring of English Catholicism in the hearts of many of England's sons during the Crimean War. How this was effected we learn from the combined narratives of Mother Bridgeman and Sister M. Joseph Croke:

" If we knelt to whisper a prayer or instruction to a poor Catholic the almost breathless silence in the ward (where the majority were always Protestants) was quite thrilling. This was the more remarkable as the same respect was seldom shown to the officiating Protestant clergyman. Under such circumstances, the instruction on religious subjects given to the Catholics reached all in the vicinity of the one being spoken to, and on many occasions wrought miracles of grace."

Fine weather with its accompaniment of flies, fleas and mosquitoes gave rise to severe illness among the Sisters, several of whom were laid up with fevers brought on by unaccustomed climatic conditions. In Koulali, Sister M. Elizabeth of Liverpool was stricken with an infection of the liver, which necessitated cupping and leeching. Sister M. Bernard of Chelsea developed congestion and had to be anointed. In Scutari, Sister M. Clare Lalor of Charleville contracted fever ; and though it ultimately led to her being invalided home, her illness had the effect of focussing official attention on the miserable living conditions of the Sisters in the General Hospital. It will be remembered that at an earlier date Dr. O'Flaherty had provided them with an extra room, and that Florence Nightingale retaliated by depriving them of the one they already had. Acrimony of this nature was altogether alien to Koulali ; there, thanks to the good offices of Mr. Robertson, the Sisters had four rooms allotted to their use: a small community room, two dormitories, and a tiny oratory.[29] The oratory, decorated with loving care by the patients, was the Sisters' pride, the power-house whence they derived strength and courage to face each new day's vicissitudes. Here they could find refuge from turmoil ; here, security and peace. Here, above all, they had opportunity to follow the prescriptions of their saintly foundress, Catherine McAuley, whose exhortation to them on devotion to the Blessed Sacrament forms one of the most beautiful passages of their Holy Rule:

" Jesus Christ, really present in the Most Holy Sacrament, shall be the constant object of their love and devotion. They shall often reflect on the infinite charity He displays in that Ever Adorable Sacrament, and by frequent visits every day they shall pay assiduous court to their Heavenly Spouse on the throne of his love ; uniting their acts of adoration, praise, thanksgiving and homage to those of the Angels who continually attend Him in the Tabernacle. In all their sufferings and anxieties, in all their fears, afflictions and temptations, they shall seek comfort and consolation at the foot of the Altar where He lovingly invites them in these words: ' Come to Me, all ye that labour and are heavily burdened, and I will refresh you.' " (Ch. XII.)

Fanny Taylor tells that visitors to the General Hospital always called on the Sisters,

" for they were universally loved and respected, and they received all who called on them with the utmost courtesy and sweetness of manner . . . Their community room was a good-sized and pleasant one, furnished with the utmost simplicity . . . and the warm welcome we ever met there made it a pleasant resting-place after ascending the steep hill from the Barracks Hospital. Few of us had ever visited Nuns before, and we often remarked among ourselves the bright and joyous spirit which pervaded one and all. Their work evidently was their happiness, and we often marvelled at their untiring industry. They never seemed to pass an idle moment, for even in their leisure time they were always busy."[30]

On the score of work, there was only one complaint ever lodged against the Sisters ; that of overdoing things.

" Our few Irish Nuns here," wrote an army Chaplain (*The Tablet,* March 10, 1855), " are doing an immensity of good, and are every day more valued by the authorities, both medical and military. Early and late they carry on their work of charity without cessation. Sometimes I feel it my duty to remonstrate with them and require them to breathe a little fresh air and rest awhile ; but all that I can say seems useless, for Mrs. Bridgeman seems determined that she and her nuns shall be martyrs."

Silently and unobtrusively they worked, and it mattered not to them that Florence Nightingale was busy compiling lists for the War Office files and organising opposition against them. Theirs was a charity working quietly, silently, secretly, seeking to please and to merit the approval of Him alone who sustained and inspired it. Service was their motto: service of Christ in His, suffering members. This they had already pursued in the slums, the hospitals and the workhouse wards of many an Irish city. By coming to the Middle East to nurse the soldier instead of the pauper, they merely changed the scene, not the object of their charity ; its intensity, but not its motives. Little wonder then that the soldier patients reverenced these good Sisters who introduced into the squalid wards of the English military hospitals something of that sublime quality of Mercy, God's most tender attribute, which ' droppeth as the gentle rain from Heaven.'

Biographers of Florence Nightingale tend to overlook the fact that she was but a single individual among the tens of thousands involved in the Crimean War. The establishment of the Order of the Victoria Cross in 1856 was the Queen's recognition of those other countless heroes who in their country's cause had suffered and died on the bleak Crimean upland and in the mud and quagmires of Balaclava. The Grave of the Hundred Thousand outside Sebastopol contained as many English as Russian dead; but these, because they lacked a chronicler to transmit their names to posterity, must ever remain unsung. Florence Nightingale was more fortunate. A modern biographer of Henri Dunant accounts for her extraordinary popularity by enumerating among her advantages the fact that she spoke with the accents of aristocracy, was able to move freely among the top social strata of European society, was on familiar terms with Cabinet Ministers, and that intimate conversations over the afternoon tea-cups at her sister's residence at Claydon, Buckinghamshire, furnished valuable opportunities for impressing her ideas on persons equipped with the necessary authority for translating them from theory to practice.[31]

Having assured Sidney Herbert that the establishment at Scutari was in satisfactory condition, Miss Nightingale decided, in May, 1855, to visit the Crimea. The Crimean hospitals were four in number. The General Hospital, established in September, 1854 ; the Castle Hospital, opened in April, 1855 ; the Monastery Hospital for ophthalmic and convalescent cases, and the Hospital of the Land Transport Corps. A request formulated by Lord Raglan in the early spring accounted for the employment of female nurses in the General Hospital and the Castle Hospital. The nurses, a heterogeneous group recruited from the Sellonites, from Miss Nightingale's staff at Scutari, and from Mary Stanley's recently-arrived contingent, worked in the Crimea under their own superintendents, but all were ultimately responsible to Florence Nightingale—as *she* understood from her instructions from the War Office. From the time of her arrival at Scutari in November, 1854, her powers had been often called in question. Where the Crimea was concerned, her position was undoubtedly ambiguous. In the original instructions issued by Sidney Herbert she was named ' Superintendent of the Female Nursing Establishment in the English General Military Hospitals in *Turkey* '. Technically then, she had no jurisdiction in the Crimea. Nevertheless, she sailed from Scutari on board the *General Lowe* on May 2, and three days later arrived at Balaclava. On arrival, she decided to visit the Mortar Battery outside Sebastopol, where she mounted the centre mortar and was acclaimed by her entourage as " the heroic daughter of England sitting fearlessly upon this terrible instrument of war."[32] It was but a momentary triumph, for in every other aspect this, her first visit to the Crimea, was a depressing failure.

The medical authorities would not admit her claims. They were satisfied with matters as they stood in Balaclava. Dr. John Hall was adamant in declaring that Miss Nightingale should confine herself to within the limits of her commission from the War Office. That commission specified *Turkey;* the Crimea, being Russian territory, was outside the pale of her jurisdiction.

Plead as she might, Miss Nightingale could not break through this iron opposition on the part of the Crimean authorities. Nevertheless, she decided to remain in Balaclava, hoping at once to quell opposition and to institute some essential administrative reforms similar to those she had effected in Scutari. But the strain of events in the Barracks Hospital at Scutari had begun to take its toll: Miss Nightingale was not long in Balaclava when she collapsed. She had caught Crimean fever and was confined to bed until she was sufficiently recovered to undertake the return journey to Scutari.

## CHAPTER 12

## SEBASTOPOL

IN the six months between the accession of Alexander II and the fall of Sebastopol there could never have been any doubt that the Crimean War was virtually over. It was already clear that Russia's military power was only a sham, and that neither the blunders of the allies on the one hand, nor the stoicism of the Russian soldiers on the other, could save Russian arms from catastrophe. The genius of one man alone kept the besiegers at bay from September 1854 to September 1855. Todleben, the Russian engineer of German extraction, was the only soldier on either side in this conflict who proved his greatness. None of the allied commanders showed either originality or initiative ; and difficulties of command were frequently aggravated by divergence of aim between the English and the French.

In April Lord Raglan's effectives were increased by the arrival at Balaclava of fifteen thousand Sardinian troops. Italy had no interests in the issues between Russia and the Allies, but the Crimean War provided Count Cavour with the opportunity for a skilful diplomatic stroke. The Allies could do with help ; and Cavour, who was relentlessly pursuing the unification of Italy, foresaw that Sardinia, if she came in, would appear as one of the important powers of Europe, and as such could claim a seat and ventilate the grievances of Italy at the Congress which settled the terms of peace. Cavour's diplomacy was successful, for though there was little prospect of fighting when the Sardinians entered the war, they eventually fought their way with distinction to the conference table in Paris.

The improvement in the weather brought a corresponding improvement in the spirits of the troops. Those certified for hospitalisation were still numerous, but those remaining on duty became more efficient and began to regard life with brighter eyes. A company sergeant counted himself fortunate in being able to report to his staff-officer that "things were beginning to look rather better at last," because "the men were beginning to swear again!"[1] The army was now supplied not only with necessaries, but even with luxuries. Among the necessaries William Howard Russell mentions bread which is "brown but not sour, and which when eaten before it becomes stale is palatable enough." Luxuries included cheese, ham, sausages, vegetables, wine, Daffy's Elixir, game pies and tobacco, notwithstanding which, he adds, that disease still clung to the army.[2]

Nothing of moment occurred in the military situation while Miss Nightingale lay ill at Balaclava. The progress of the war was becoming increasingly sluggish—and this because the authority of the Commander-in-Chief to make the necessary day-to-day decisions for his army was reduced, as it were, to a nullity. The new electric telegraph had by this time pushed its way through most of the European capitals as far as Constantinople. Henceforth army generals were to be subjected to frustrating supervision by political authorities, and warfare was to become the chess-game of politicians. It was Lord Raglan's misfortune to be the victim for the new experiment. Day and night he sat at his desk writing answers to " nervous, tedious and unneccessary enquiries," weighted down by an unparalleled imposition of clerical labour, but unable to solve the problems of generalship which were becoming too much for him.[3]

Matters were less stagnant on the Bosphorus. Sardinia's entry into the war had repercussions which seriously affected Mother Bridgeman and her community. Rumours as to the possible occupation of Koulali by Sardinian troops were early in circulation. Such an eventuality would render further services on the part of the Sisters unnecessary; there could be no place for them in a military depot. Mother Bridgeman was therefore at a loss as to the absorption of her Sisters in the other military hospitals; but on one point she was adamant. She would not return to Scutari, nor would she ever work in a hospital under Miss Nightingale's superintendency.

Continued sickness among the Sisters was another source of worry. Early in June she informed Archbishop Cullen that

> " one of our Sisters is recovering from a second attack of fever, and must go home. Another Sister must accompany her. This, with a house-Sister who never goes to the wards, leaves but seven Sisters for the two Koulali hospitals. If more get ill, we should become, I fear, insignificant and inefficient. The Purveyor and Superintendent urge upon me to get two at least in place of those who return, to keep up my staff."[4]

The remainder of the letter gives Archbishop Cullen an account of the activities of the Sisters to date, and concludes as follows:

> " It is not at all improbable that we shall be asked to go to the Crimea where the most cases are being kept. In that

case we should, I suppose, require eight or ten more. A word of advice from Your Grace would be most acceptable."

The advice was not forthcoming. The question of getting more Sisters from Ireland was not easy of solution. Mother Bridgeman, realising the extent to which the California foundation (1854) had reduced numbers in Kinsale, decided against applying to her own community for extra volunteers. She hesitated also to apply to other Irish convents, remembering the " many embarrassments " which she and her Sisters " had had to undergo since coming to the East."[5] In any case, the Irish Hierarchy in general, and the Archbishop of Tuam in particular, frowned upon the venture. There appeared to be but one alternative: the Sisters must return to Ireland.

" And oh! " wrote Mother Bridgeman, " how nature cried out for Home Sweet Home! " Her decision was made. If not required in the Crimea, the Sisters would most certainly sail for home.

It was during Miss Nightingale's absence in Balaclava that Sister M. Clare's illness directed official attention to the conditions under which the Sisters in Scutari General Hospital laboured. They had still but a single room at their disposal, and despite Miss Nightingale's promise to Father Ronan, they had as yet " no oratory to which they might retire for religious purposes when not engaged in the wards." Nine Protestant nurses in the same hospital had five rooms allotted to their use. Mr. Robertson, who deemed it " unjust and unreasonable that Catholic ladies should be brought so far to serve the Government and be unprovided with the accommodation so necessary for their comfort," was not long in possession of these facts when he set about remedying them. We learn from the Bridgeman Diary that

" he set in good earnest to remove prejudices which others had been long striving to create and foster. He gave a store of his own, at great inconvenience, to Dr. Lawson, the Principal Medical Officer, and induced him to exchange it for a fine room adjoining that occupied by the Sisters. Through this room he had a partition drawn to make one half a dormitory and the other half an oratory. Then for the first time the Sisters had the Blessed Sacrament."[6]

It had taken eight months to secure even this minimum of comfort for the Sisters in Scutari. One consideration alone deterred Mother Bridgeman from withdrawing them. She mentions in her Diary that " only the imperative voice of conscience " could induce her to leave her Sisters in Scutari General Hospital:

she could not consider herself free to remove them as long as free communication with the Catholic patients was accorded them.

" Until God should manifest His will otherwise," she wrote, " I felt we must be content to do the best we could under existing conditions, and await patiently and submissively the course of His providence."

On June 2, Florence Nightingale left Balaclava for Scutari. Had Dr. Hall had his way, England would have been her destination, but his plans miscarried. At Scutari she was lodged in the house previously occupied by Mr. Sabin who went home on sick leave and who was superseded by Mr. Hobson as senior chaplain at Scutari. From Mr. Sabin's house Miss Nightingale began to administer as from her former headquarters in the Barracks Hospital. To the hospital personnel in general it was soon apparent that her illness had not impaired her capacity for work. For the five Sisters in the General Hospital her return portended a revival of misrepresentations attendant upon the erroneous assumption that the Sisters had " acted over her head " during her absense in the Crimea.[7]

Handicapped as she was by her slow convalescence, there was little she could do but write. Fortunately for the historian, these letters, too important to be lost to history, are preserved in the Archives in Kinsale. Miss Nightingale's first letter addressed to Sister M. Elizabeth Hersey, presiding Sister at the General Hospital, reads as follows:

" Dear Sister Elizabeth,

I could not but be a little surprised when I came home to hear that you had been carrying on negotiations with Dr. Lawson about another room, without reference either to Mrs. Bracebridge or Miss Tebbutt. I was the more surprised because you, so well-skilled and experienced in all the duties of a Community Life, must be the more aware of the danger of such a precedent and of the impossibility of any party hanging together at this rate. That you should have another room is an object for which I would have instantly exerted myself. And had you found me backward in consulting the comforts of my party, I could better have understood the tacit reproach which you conveyed against me by your independent action."

Mother Bridgeman cited three instances with which to disprove Miss Nightingale's protestations of exerting herself to provide extra accommodation for the Sisters " had she known " they required it. Provision of such accommodation was one of the written conditions proposed by Father Ronan, S.J. At a later date, when Miss Nightingale remonstrated on the unsuitability of the soldiers attending " service " in the Sisters' room, she was again reminded of the necessity. Sister M. Clare's illness brought the matter once more under discussion, but " Florence Nightingale would still not yield."[8]

The letter to Sister M. Elizabeth continues:

" Forgive me for saying what I am now going to say. It was only with my assent, as you know, that our Government and the authorities of this place admitted the Catholic Nuns; and only on condition that they should belong to my party . . . I owe it therefore to the Government to see that their views are carried out. And I am certain that you, who carry so much farther than we do, alas! the duties of obedience and unity, will see instantly the necessity of what I say.

" One more thing I am compelled to mention. Feeling that they were in the ascendancy here, I permitted that the Catholic Sisters should go to patients *not* in their own wards for purposes of religious instruction. I am now obliged to request that every Sister, whether Catholic or Protestant, will restrict herself to the wards to which she is appointed.

" I will ask you to show this letter to Reverend Mother Bridgeman, as I am still too weak to write much. And I will ask you to forgive me for any pain which it may cause you. I assure you it has not caused me less . . . Florence Nightingale."

At this point a recapitulation of events is advisable. In that section of the above letter referring to the War Office, Miss Nighingale apparently overlooked the fact that five Sisters of Mercy from Bermondsey had embarked for the Crimea two days before she herself received any commission to take a band of nurses to the military hospitals. Florence Nightingale had therefore nothing to do with securing governmental assent for the admission of Catholic Sisters into the army. The application of Bishop Grant of Southwark was the necessary " Open Sesame " for them. In the negotiations for the Irish Sisters, it was Manning who formed the necessary link between Convent and War Office. Finally, in claiming full control over the Sisters as part of her staff, Miss Nightingale (seemingly) ignored the fact that she herself had disclaimed all authority over the Irish Sisters on their arrival in Scutari in the previous December.

Mother Bridgeman's reply to the opening paragraph of Miss Nightingale's letter was concise. She referred the Lady Superintendent to the Purveyor, who took upon himself the duty of explaining the events which resulted in procuring what he considered "necessary and essential" accommodation for the Sisters. In an interview with Miss Nightingale, Mr. Robertson made the situation perfectly clear: the Sisters had had no share in the negotiations. But argument was futile. Miss Nightingale refused to be convinced, and there the matter rested.

In dealing with the remaining statements of Florence Nightingale, Mother Bridgeman required no intermediary. She pointed out to Miss Nightingale that

"with regard to that section of your letter which refers to the Sisters giving religious instruction to the Catholics, I have reason to know that where this does not interfere with the duty of nursing, the War Office acknowledges us free. I trust, dear Miss Nightingale, you have no reason to complain of any want of obedience as regards the duties of nursing on the part of the Sisters. At least, you have never intimated any such complaint to me."[9]

Meanwhile, Sister M. Bernard was considered to be sufficiently recovered to undertake the journey home. She was accompanied by Sister M. Clare Lalor. Both were seen on board ship by Mr. Robertson, who placed his own caique at their disposal and made all arrangements for their passage to England. Their departure reduced the number of Sisters in Koulali to nine, and in Scutari to four.

Miss Nightingale's latest regulation for the Scutari Sisters (as intimated in her letter to Sister M. Elizabeth) was that they should confine themselves solely to their own wards and not enter other wards without previous consultation either with herself or with her superintendent at the General Hospital. Hitherto, the Sisters while confining their nursing activities to their own wards, felt themselves free to visit Catholic patients in other divisions of the hospital. Referring to the new measure, Mother Bridgeman remarks that

"had the Sisters been thus restricted to their own wards for religious instruction, it would have deprived half the hospital of any, and sometimes indeed would have left one Sister or another sitting idle when her nursing wards had not as much as a single patient—which frequently happened for weeks successively."[10]

The Sisters did not concede the point to Florence Nightingale. Their interpretation of Lord Panmure's memorandum of April 27 was that they were free to introduce religious subjects with Catholic patients in the hospitals. And until the War Office should ordain otherwise, Mother Bridgeman decided " to let the Sisters go on as usual—gently—until the squib should fly off."

The squib did not fly off. Matters of more pressing urgency demanded Florence Nightingale's attention to such a degree that for a time she forgot all about the " insubordination " of the Sisters in the General Hospital.

The Bracebridges wished to go home. Their decision was a shock to Miss Nightingale; for though they had long since ceased to be anything but a source of annoyance to her, they were among her most loyal supporters. To lose them at a time when her position was more than ever in jeopardy was something she could ill afford. They sailed for England on July 28.

That same day Miss Nightingale returned to her old quarters in the Barracks Hospital where further shocks awaited her. The doctors wanted neither herself nor her hired assistants. The situation was a repetition of that obtaining in November, 1854. If anything, it was more pronounced; for the Scutari doctors had had enough of what Dr. Hall described as " a system of detraction against our establishments kept up by interested parties under the garb of philanthropy."[11] This they hoped to end by excluding Miss Nightingale from their hospital. Several of her erstwhile supporters were by now gone over to the opposition. Dr. Cumming was " nervous "; Dr. McGrigor had begun to side with Dr. Lawson, with whom the Lady Superintendent never saw eye to eye. Lord William Paulet has been described as a " broken reed." For the second time Florence Nightingale found herself confronted with an iron curtain of resistance in the Barracks Hospital. Still, she was not going to admit defeat. She determined to carry on as before, and with the help of influential friends at the War Office, to revisit the Crimea with plenary powers which none of her opponents would be able to gainsay.

In this matter she reckoned without the Bracebridges. Shortly after their return to England, Mr. Bracebridge (notwithstanding all admonitions as to the necessity of discretion) delivered an address in the Town Hall, Coventry, which amounted to an unrestrained attack on the British Army medical and military authorities. It was obvious that Mr. Bracebridge was but repeating a lesson learned in Scutari; but however much Florence Nightingale may have privately applauded these sentiments, she had no desire for so public a proclamation. But the harm was done. The Bracebridges, muddle-headed to the last, retired from the scene, leaving Miss Nightingale to deal with a new crisis which burst upon her at a time when it was more than ever essential for her to establish herself in the good opinion of the army authorities.

Meanwhile the allied armies were pursuing the siege of Sebastopol, where heavy losses in the early summer months were grim reminders of Russian tenacity. Henry Clifford, V.C., wrote at this time that " the English Government and people cannot eat their bread and butter and keep it too; and if they want Sebastopol, they must make up their minds to a slashing butcher's bill."[12] The butcher's bill was soon a grim reality.

In June the attack on the fortress was renewed when on the 6th the Mamelon hillock was taken by the French. Casualties were high: five thousand five hundred for the French; about seven hundred for the English. The after-battle scene, as depicted by General Sir Evelyn Wood, reveals

" dead men left lying about in every attitude imaginable, some half-buried in craters formed by shells. The bodies of others were literally cut in two parts. Some corpses were lying crushed under over-turned cannon, while others hung limply over fractured guns which were still on their carriages."[13]

The whole position of the allied armies was by this time one large burial ground. Still, the capture of the Mamelon was a signal victory; it gave the allies a vantage point overlooking the city and brought them much nearer their goal.

A joint attack on the Redan on June 18 was a costly failure. Misunderstanding between Lord Raglan and the French commander resulted in a holocaust of five thousand allied soldiers. Prominently placed in the vanguard of the attack were the 18th Royal Irish Regiment and the 88th, the Connaught Rangers. General Eyre expressed to the former the wish that " this morning you will do something that will ring in every cabin in Ireland." The response was a triple cheer for the General which drew upon the regiment a shower of grape from the Russian sharpshooters![14]

Of the Connaught Rangers the story goes that their leader, General Shirley, became temporarily disabled through having a shower of stones, earth and dust cast into his eyes. Some of the 88th, hurrying past him to the attack, and assuming him to be weeping, tried to cheer him up with a " Don't cry, General dear, but stop there, for *we're* going to take the place for ye."[15] Irish names were so numerous on the casualty list after this attack of June 18 that it was compared to the census return of a parish in Munster.

The failure of the English troops and the heavy losses sustained in the attack on the Redan were gravely detrimental to the health of Lord Raglan. Within ten days he was dead: struck down by cholera, care and overwhelming anxiety, the victim of England's unreadiness for war. Though he has been described as somewhat inept as a commander, Lord Raglan could inspire undiluted affection and respect, and though he lost a lot of battles, he won a lot of hearts. Florence Nightingale greatly admired Lord Raglan. His death marked a further secession among her supporters. His successor, General Simpson, seems to have regarded her in much the same light as did the medical officers.

The heat and drought of the Crimean summer played the same havoc with the health of the troops as did the rigours of the previous winter. By July there was slaughter in the Crimea, cholera in the camp, and the hospitals were again becoming full. They were soon overflowing; and despite the dirge chanted by William Howard Russell, the publicity campaign conducted by *The Times,* and the revelations of enquiry commissioners, red tapeism was as much in evidence as ever. Once again there was talk of Boards, Regulations and Requisitions, none of which could be departed from even to save a man's life. One woman alone, Mrs. Elizabeth Davis of Mary Stanley's party, and chief cook at the General Hospital, Balaclava, had the necessary initiative to cope with the situation. With a generosity bordering on extravagance, and which eventually went far beyond bounds, she distributed the contents of the Free Gift Stores, on the assumption that since these were the contributions of private individuals in England, they should not be subject to the deliberations of any Board.

In her *Autobiography* Mrs. Davis tells that information derived from eye-witnesses showed that the enforcement of the rule of requisitions produced in the ladies and nurses " a conflict between their feelings of natural duty and of formal restriction, and ended in general and conscientious disobedience." She admits that in the sight of " urgent need on one side, and open bales of undistributed free gifts on the other ", she did, at times, infringe on the Almoner's privilege. She supplied the naked with clothing and the dying with the refreshment they desired. The doctors do not seem to have objected to this breach of service regulations. Florence Nightingale was the only one to complain; but recalling that " it was a well-known fact that the Superintendent of the Nurses set not always an example of obedience to the medical authority," Mrs. Davis evidently considered that she had a precedent for her actions.[16]

Mrs. Davis never worked with the Sisters of Mercy in the Crimean military hospitals. She only knew of them by repute. " The nuns have been praised as the most useful labourers in the war hospitals," she wrote. " Their superiority appears to have consisted simply in their combination and subjection to established control among themselves." Her testimony is yet another indication of the valued services of the Sisters of Mercy in the military hospitals.

In the eight months of their administration in Koulali the Sisters had become so much part of the place that a visit to the ' Convent ' was the established rule for all callers at the General Hospital. Within the hospital, familiar scenes were once again re-enacted; outside, the garden was in full bloom. Men " just able to crawl out of their wards might be seen there basking in the sun, or trying their returning strength on the grass." The general atmosphere was one of happiness and contentment, each patient feeling that he had a home and was cared for. In the extreme heat, a canopy was erected over the garden. In fact, nothing which might redound to the comfort of the convalescents was omitted.[17]

The attachment of the patients to the Sisters was constant, even embarrassing. " Thanks be to God—a Sister of Mercy!" was the usual exclamation of new arrivals. Others, knowing the difficulties under which the Sisters were working, were quite vehement in their protestations that " Bedad, they'd blow the soul out of anyone who would dare lay a finger on them." And they meant it. One of them, a certain Colonel Connolly, travelling in County Carlow after the war and hearing a fellow-traveller speak disparagingly of nuns, handed the offender his card saying, " If you utter another word against these saintly gentlewomen, I shall call you out directly. Choose your weapons." [18]

The respect and attention accorded to the Sisters in Koulali is a constant theme in Mother Bridgeman's memoirs. " People are amazed," she wrote, " at the difference in respect the Protestant patients show to us and to the secular ladies; and how much they prefer being under our care. Poor fellows! I shall ever feel grateful for the courtesy and reverence they show us." Even the Turks had a salaam for the Sisters and flocked to Koulali with their ailments. The Sultan too, was appreciative and practical in his expression of gratitude. His claim to special mention in the annals of the Sisters of Mercy rests in the fact that he was the only ruler to make a public acknowledgement of his indebtedness to the Sisters by offering them remuneration for their services.

Earthquake shocks, an outbreak of fire, and rumours of an impending Russian attack introduced, from time to time, an element of excitement into Koulali. The earthquake, to quote Mother Bridgeman, was " just awful; but like everything awful here, it was soon blended with the ludicrous." From her vantage point at the oratory door, she saw a stream of frightened humanity trying to escape from the hospital, " the poor creatures in their various degrees of toilette, some tottering, some hobbling, all looking so eager to reach the door, more terrified than if they had seen a whole army of Russians coming." In spite of the imminent danger, Mother Bridgeman could not suppress a smile at the unusual spectacle before her. Years later she could still chuckle at the memory, even though she admitted to " a strange sensation " herself also, " a something which passed up one's spine as though one were on the conductor of an electric machine." [19]

By August it was clear that Sebastopol was becoming untenable. On the 16th was fought the battle of the Tchernaya, which gave the Italians their chance and brought the allies still nearer their objective. The end came on September 8, when the English under General Codrington attacked the Redan, and the French, led by MacMahon, bombarded the Malakoff. That night the Russians exploded all the mines which they had placed under their magazines and forts; they destroyed their few remaining warships, set fire to the town and called in their troops from the forts. By daybreak on the 9th, the entire garrison, carrying with them most of the wounded, had crossed the harbour by a hastily-constructed pontoon bridge. Once across, they burned the bridge and found safety on the heights to the north and east. After a siege of 349 days, Sebastopol was at last in allied hands, and the end of the war could be now only a matter of time.

By order of General Codrington, the casualties from Sebastopol were to be kept in Balaclava; none were to be sent to the base hospitals. Florence Nightingale disapproved. Her position in the Crimea being still in dispute, General Codrington's decision would bring her superintendency virtually to an end. It looked as if Dr. Hall was going to win after all. Dr. Hall expressed himself satisfied with Miss Weare's superintendency at the Monastery Hospital (Miss Weare was one of Miss Nightingale's staff who went to the Crimea at Lord Raglan's request in January 1855; after which she disconnected herself from Miss Nightingale). And while Dr. Hall could do with some extra nursing personnel in Balaclava, he did not want anyone owing allegiance to Florence Nightingale. In face

of this unbending opposition, and of Lord Panmure's tardiness in
defining her exact position, Miss Nightingale, on October 1,
1855, resigned the superintendency of the General Hospital at
Balaclava.[20]

General Codrington's decision was problematic also for Mother
Bridgeman, more especially as the rumours of a Sardinian occupation of Koulali had been recently confirmed. In August she
mentioned to Miss Hutton the possibility of volunteering for the
Crimea. Miss Hutton, though unwilling to part with the Sisters,
entered into Reverend Mother's views, and Mr. Robertson
promised to enquire into the nursing department in Balaclava.

" In the meantime," wrote Mother Bridgeman, " we made it
the subject of constant prayer that God's will might be done
in us. The more I prayed, the more did I become convinced
that the Crimea, surrounded as it might be with privations
and difficulty, was the place, the *only* place for us, if God still
willed us to remain out of our convents. And I resolved to try
all means of gaining information and of removing the
*mountains* (*sic*) that lay between it and us. If we should
succeed in surmounting these difficulties, I would take that
and the course of events to follow as manifestations of the
Divine Will, which alone we sought in this all-important step.

Indeed, what other means had I of ascertaining God's
will? I had no Superior out here. I had long since written
to those at home, by whom I should have been directed, and
had no reply on the subject."[21]

A communication duly arrived from Bishop Delany in the
form of a letter written by him on July 28 to Mother M. Anne
in Kinsale, and by her forwarded to Mother Bridgeman. For
some unaccountable reason there appears to have been considerable delay in the delivery of this important letter, which reads:

" Dear Mother M. Anne,

When I expressed an objection to the Sisters leaving
Constantinople for the Crimea, matters were different from
what they now are. I then contemplated the possibility of the
Russians making some successful attack which might cut off
Balaclava from the lines of the Allies; in which case the good
Sisters might get a vacation they would little care for, by
being made Russian prisoners. But there seems no longer
room for fearing such a contingency, and therefore there is
no remaining objection except on the score of climate.

" This however, though not insignificant, as well as I can judge, is by no means insuperable. And if Reverend Mother thinks it advisable to proceed to the Crimea, I would not think of opposing it. She can therefore proceed. I beg of you to send her and the heroic Sisters my kindest regards and most earnest blessing.

✠William Delany."[22]

Whatever might be the views of Archbishop Cullen on the matter, Mother Bridgeman was gratified that at least she had her own Bishop's permission for her projected mission to Balaclava. While awaiting instructions from Mr. Robertson, her thoughts turned naturally to the four Sisters at the General Hospital, Scutari. There were " potent reasons for not abandoning them," and her own " frequent presence and constant direction were so very essential to them, that none of them would consent to remain there " without her.[23] She was only too painfully aware that any effort at removing them would be bound to aggravate matters between herself and Florence Nightingale. Her next move would require careful diplomacy.

It was precisely at this crisis of the mission that fate dealt Mother Bridgeman another blow. Father Ronan's ill-health obliged him to return home. He left Koulali on September 2, 1855, having placed the Sisters temporarily under the direction of Father Woollett, a fellow-Jesuit, who came down from the Crimea for that purpose.

From Father Woollett Mother Bridgeman learned that Dr. Hall seemed " quite delighted at the idea of having Sisters immediately under his own direction and free of Miss Nightingale." He suggested that Mother Bridgeman should offer her services in writing so that her proposal might be submitted to the Commander-in-Chief. On September 2, Reverend Mother wrote the necessary letter, addressing it to Father Woollett, who was to be her intermediary with Dr. Hall and his colleagues in Balaclava.

" My dear Reverend Sir,
Through you I beg to offer the services of the Sisters of Mercy to the Medical Authorities in the Crimea, to attend the sick and wounded soldiers under their direction. As we have left our Convent homes for this work of Mercy, I am anxious to extend the sphere of our usefulness as far as possible, especially as few other than convalescents are now sent down to the Bosphorus. Indeed, it seems as if we are hardly doing the work for which alone we came so far.

If Dr. Hall accepts our services, I shall hope to get from home any number of Sisters he may consider necessary, with whom I would go and place ourselves under his direction. It may be well to add that I would not again undertake to work with Miss Nightingale, as I learned while I was at the Barracks Hospital, Scutari, how very different her notions of nursing are from ours. But if the Authorities wish to appoint a secular Lady Superintendent, I have no objection to work in the Crimea with the Protestant Lady Superintendent with whom I now act.

May I beg, Reverend Father, that you will ascertain as soon as convenient if our services will be accepted; as if Sisters from home are needed, it is desirable that they should come before bad weather sets in.

> Believe me to be, dear Reverend Father,
> Yours faithfully and respectfully in J.C.,
> Sister Mary Francis Bridgeman,
> Mother Superior."[24]

A week later, Father Woollett returned to the Crimea and was replaced as chaplain to the Sisters by Rev. Father O'Dwyer from Smyrna.

Father Ronan's departure was a personal grief for the Sisters. For the soldiers it meant the loss of a friend. For his fellow-chaplains it entailed extra labour, for as yet, the number of Catholic Chaplains in the British Army was totally inadequate; so inadequate in fact, that a review of the situation will furnish information at once revealing, and (by present standards), almost incredible.

CHAPTER 13

## ARMY CHAPLAINS

IN early August 1854 *The Freeman's Journal* in a re-published editorial from *The Post* drew attention to the shortage of Catholic Chaplains in the army and the consequent spiritual privations of the Catholic troops. The editorial reads as follows:

> "It would appear that the Roman Catholic soldiers are very ill-provided with Chaplains. The British forces in the East now number about thirty thousand, of whom one-third are said to be Irish Catholics. For these there are but *two* priests; and when it is considered how the men are scattered in different quarters . . . it is easy to conceive that many must fall sick, die, and be buried without the solemnities of their own religion. This is an unmitigated hardship and an inexcusable piece of cruelty. One priest to every thousand is the very lowest that ought to be allowed, if any real good is to be done to the souls of the men.
>
> The question of the relative truth, theologically considered, of Popery and Protestantism, cannot be entertained for a moment. A military camp is no place for proselytising one way or another. A man in the last stage of fever, or riddled with gunshot, has spiritual exigencies more pressing than the controversy between the two Churches; and it would be absolute cruelty to leave him no other resource, at the climax of his greatest need, than the ministrations of a clergyman whom all his life he has been taught to believe in deadly error.
>
> "We are not, of course, advocating the extension of any Popish element in the Army ; but we say deliberately, that if we accept the services of the Roman Catholic soldiers to fight our battles, we are bound, in return, to leave no reasonable necessity of theirs, either for flesh or spirit, uncared for."

For the period preceding the Crimean War there are but scanty references to the provision of regular chaplains for the troops. Such references as are available deal almost exclusively with the allocation of Protestant clergymen. One reads, for instance, that while George I in statute forbade Catholic chaplains in the Navy, special Protestant chaplains were recruited for each corps of the Ulster Volunteers. Applicants were few ; the office of chaplain apparently held little in the line of emoluments to recommend it. The Wellington era saw a further reduction in the chaplains' department, which was so whittled down that by 1845 the religious care of the army had devolved upon four elderly commissioned chaplains and a number of officiating clergy. The latter were of two kinds: clergy paid for duties to the troops undertaken in addition to parish duties ; or those who, while engaged full-time in duties with the forces, were not commissioned and had no rights as to pensions, preferments etc. The position was somewhat improved after 1845 by the Reverend George Robert Gleig who introduced a scheme for soldier curates at an annual salary of £75.

Even with this, there were only seven commissioned chaplains in England in 1853. The outbreak of the Crimean War made further legislation imperative. A small staff of chaplains, drawn from officiating clergy, was hastily selected—five of the Church of England, two Catholics and one Presbyterian. It was soon apparent that these numbers were inadequate, so the Society for the Propagation of the Gospel established a fund to subsidise the appointment of additional chaplains for the forces, of whom twelve were sent out between October and December, 1854. All twelve were Protestants. Between March and late summer of 1855 thirteen more chaplains were sent out by the same society.[1]

Similar facilities were not provided for the Catholic section of the army: ten thousand men depending on the ministrations of two chaplains. Non-Catholic sources represent these priests, Father John Wheble and Father Denis Sheehan, as " the very models of self-sacrificing devotedness, whose zeal and activity were almost superhuman."[2] Day after day they cheered and consoled and comforted the fever-stricken ; at night they might be seen with the fatigue parties accompanying the remains of Catholic soldiers to their resting pit. Yet with all their zeal, these two priests could not supply spiritual ministration to all who required their assistance. Of this they were only too keenly aware; for even if the Catholic section of the army had enjoyed the rudest health, two chaplains would be wholly unfit for even the ordinary duties entailed. And for the extraordinary—with cholera, fever and dysentery in every division and regiment; with the sick in thousands and the dying in hundreds, the insufficiency was more glaringly obvious. It was a situation crying out for remedial measures.

In London, Bishop Grant was untiring in his efforts to increase the number of Catholic army chaplains. After a youth spent in military surroundings, Dr. Grant was more than ordinarily aware of the spiritual wants of the troops. Letters from the Crimea were an added incentive. On August 8 Father Wheble wrote that " very many of our poor Catholics have departed this life without any religious attendance. How many have thus perished I cannot tell, but I am informed that sometimes the deaths were above a dozen a day in the General Hospital, Balaclava, besides those who died in the regimental hospitals." From Father Sheehan came news that " the advantage of spiritual assistance enjoyed by the regiments of the Light and of the Second Divisions is denied for the present to the Third Division, which lies in the neighbourhood of Varna. The hospital at Varna is likewise destitute of provision for the spiritual wants of the Catholic patients there."[3]

Bishop Grant was so far successful in his negotiations with the War Office that by October 1854 three more priests—Fathers Michael Cuffe, Michael Canty and Thomas Moloney—were en route for the Crimea. The appointment of Father William Ronan, S.J., as special chaplain to the Sisters of Mercy was a further concession; but it was grudgingly given, and for the entire period of his administration on the Bosphorus, Father Ronan was a target for criticism and acrimony. Notwithstanding which he retained his position until September 1855 when ill-health obliged him to return home.

The appointment of extra chaplains speaks well for Dr. Grant's diplomacy, and for the efforts of Manning who had the spiritual welfare of the troops particularly at heart. Still, in spite of such concessions, the number of Catholic chaplains was as yet far below the average of what an army so scattered as the Crimean Expeditionary Force demanded.

A second letter from Father Wheble, written on August 18 from Soombay Camp, speaks of the indifference of the authorities regarding the spiritual exigencies of the sick.

" The great complaint I have to make," he writes, " is that I am never sent for to the hospital, but I am obliged to find out as best I can where the most serious cases are. I suppose the reason is that the Church of England people think it unnecessary to trouble themselves about their own dying, so we are equally supposed not to care for ours. In the General Hospital, I found one poor fellow who burst into tears of joy when I approached him."[4]

Father John Wheble died at Balaclava on November 3, 1854. No soldier on the field could have met a nobler death than did this thirty-year-old priest who died thus prematurely in the service of his country. His name appeared on the honours list after the war when he was decorated with the Crimean Medal and with clasps for his services at the Alma and in Sebastopol.[5] His loss was a grievous one to the Irish Regiments. " His glorious grave at Balaclava," wrote *The Tablet* (9 December, 1854) " will forever stand a monument of the niggard and bigoted policy to which he has fallen a sacrifice." He was replaced on the chaplaincy staff by Father John Butt.

Speaking in terms of efficiency, and apart altogether from religious considerations, it is an accepted norm that if a regiment wanted even one sergeant of the full complement to make up its standard efficiency, the loss would soon be repaired. No commanding officer would allow his men to march without the regimental allowance of sergeants and subalterns; and rightly so. But at the beginning of the Crimean War three whole regiments were despatched on foreign service with *one single clergyman* to look after three thousand soldiers in health and in sickness, in the camp and in the field. " How it is these Catholic clergymen stand the work, I cannot imagine," wrote a correspondent. " They are from morning till night in the hospitals or burying the dead."

By way of appendix to the foregoing may be added an entry in the journal of Henry Clifford, V.C. Reporting from Sebastopol on November 27, 1854, Clifford mentioned that " Mr. Butt said Mass yesterday, the first Mass we have had since Monastir; and he preached a very *à propos* sermon on preparation for death while we yet have time."[6] The 16th Rifle Brigade to which Henry Clifford was attached, left Monastir for the Crimea on September 3; which meant that the brigade was almost three months without a priest.

A Protestant chaplain was permitted to accompany all exclusively English regiments; the same rule was discountenanced with regard to *mixed* regiments which were recruited in Ireland. In such cases a Catholic chaplain was obliged to undertake the care of Catholic soldiers in a number of regiments. The statute of George I forbidding Catholic chaplains in the Navy has been alluded to: by the time of the Crimean War this statute, still unrepealed, entailed that " for a priest to walk a British ship was contrary to the orders of a government for which so many Catholics were fighting."[7]

By the beginning of 1855 there were seven Catholic chaplains in the Crimea—Fathers Cuffe, Bagshaw, Butt, Canty, Doyle, Sheehan and Moloney. None of these priests were commissioned; they were ranked as officiating clergy. The death of Father Michael Canty on February 3, and of Father Denis Sheehan on

March 11, reduced the number to five. Shortly after Father Sheehan's death it was announced that a fourth chaplain was in a dying state, a fifth was debilitated and a sixth had to be invalided home. Once again the whole Catholic army in the Crimea reverted to the care of a single priest.

The circumstances surrounding the death of Father Sheehan were of a nature calculated to draw further attention to the chaplaincy shortage. Father John Butt was at the time recovering from a bout of fever, and though too weak to rise and too feeble to stand up, he had himself carried to the side of his dying colleague to raise his hand over him in final benediction. " It does good to see such deeds as this," wrote a contributor to *The Freeman's Journal* (20 March, 1855). " It helps to teach men that virtue is a fact and religion a reality." Dr. Thomas Longmore's tribute is also worthy of record : " Father Sheehan was worth ten doctors amongst the poor wounded men; he died a sacrifice to his profession and his duty."[8]

References to Father Canty in the journal of Henry Clifford reveal some of the hardships endured by the Catholic military chaplains of the Crimean War period. Father Canty suffered terribly from the cold. " He comes and heats himself at my fire and I make him tea and chocolate, and fry ham for him," said Henry Clifford. " Protestants and Catholics all like him, and the officers respect him so much. He is so good and suffers so much. I fear he will be knocked up by this hard work and bad weather." Clifford maintained that Father Canty died of fever brought on by hardships encountered when visiting the sick. A number of Protestant officers and the Protestant clergyman attached to the division accompanied his remains to the grave.[9]

Another entry in the Clifford journal is equally revealing:

> " Rev. Mr. Butt who is with the Light Division is the only Priest up here in Camp. There is one in Balaclava. Mr. Butt is almost knocked up and now he has to do duty for *five Divisions*, he cannot hold out much longer. It is such a contrast to see the work our Priests do, and the Protestant Clergy, though some of them do all they can ; but after all they have so little consolation or means of helping the sick and those on their deathbeds."[10]

Death also claimed its own toll from among the Protestant clergy, two of whom—the Rev. W. Whyatt and the Rev. G. H. Proctor—died in the Crimea between November 1854 and March 1855. Exaggerated and groundless statements have been made of contention and denominational differences between the several chaplains of the Crimean War period. The contrary, rather, is the case; for personal intercourse and the mutual sharing of hardships tended to soften down many asperities and to tighten the bonds of charity and loyalty among them. Mr. Whyatt watched by the bedside of the dying Father Canty a few weeks before his own death. The Sisters of Mercy shared in the general goodwill by laundering neckties for certain Protestant chaplains in Koulali and at Balaclava. And there is an entry in Mother Bridgeman's *Diary* referring to an offer of service made to the Sisters by the Reverend Mr. Holt, who "felt that their own chaplains were not properly acquitting themselves of their duties in that direction!"[11]

In later years, when reporters in *The Times* exaggerated the denominational differences which inevitably arose in the chaplains' department, the Reverend Henry Press Wright made the following spirited reply:

> "Should we ever have another war in the Crimea (which God forbid), and the critics will join the chaplains' department of our army, they will find the thermometer at 7° below zero an effectual cooler of all 'wretched theological disputes,' and a dripping bell-tent peculiarly calculated to put a damper upon all unkind feeling."[12]

It was only natural that a certain degree of tension should exist between the ministers of the rival Churches. The interference of some of the Anglican clergy with the Sisters of Mercy in Koulali is sufficient to illustrate the point. Nor must Florence Nightingale's aggravation of the situation be lost sight of. Matters, however, did not become really serious until John Edward Sabin was appointed Senior Chaplain to the forces in the Crimea.

There was no precedent for the exact status of a principal chaplain in wartime, and it was a matter of some delicacy to establish it. Administratively speaking, the Catholic clergy were normally subject to the military authorities direct, but they were obliged to make certain statistical returns through the principal or senior chaplain. The only group with which the principal chaplain had personal dealings were members of the Church of England. He was responsible for their allocation to the camps in the Crimea, and—with the sanction of the military commandant at Scutari— to the base hospitals. He had a marquee near headquarters and a soldier-clerk to assist him.

Friction was inevitable between Mr. Sabin and the Catholic chaplains when he interpreted his own authority in a manner to which they found it impossible to submit. By mid-summer of 1855 there were three Jesuits in the Crimea, Fathers Woollett and Strickland having volunteered for military service following the appointment of Father Ronan as chaplain to the Sisters of Mercy. Before the end of the year a fourth arrived, Rev. Michael Duffy, and he was later followed by a Vincentian, Father Michael Gleeson. Each of these priests proved himself a staunch supporter of the Sisters in the later days of their sojourn on Crimean soil. Their appointment helped also to restore the depleted ranks of the Catholic chaplains. Unfortunately, their arrival was more than balanced by sickness and death ; all of which goes to prove that the number of priests actually fit for duty was always fluctuating, and that a proper standard of service was never maintained.

Mr. Sabin did not take kindly to the enlistment of so many Jesuits as army chaplains. In an effort to counteract their influence, and the more surely to keep an eye on their activities, he wrote on June 1, 1855, to Father Michael Cuffe, senior chaplain, making demands on the Catholic chaplains almost identical with those which Florence Nightingale wished to impose on the Sisters in the General Hospital, Scutari.

" Reverend Sir,
I have been instructed by the Chaplain-General to request from Mr. Ronan, Catholic Chaplain at Scutari, a report each month—*viz.,*

1. Place of administration, specifying hospital, ward, corridor etc.
2. Number of Roman Catholics under your care during the last month and at the present time.
3. Number of services given by you.
4. Any remarks or suggestions you may deem interesting or important.

If you prefer to forward to the Chaplain-General such reports from yourself and the other Roman Catholic Chaplains, they should be sent by an early post; or I shall be happy to forward such reports with those of the Chaplains of the Church of England and the Presbyterian, if you can let me have them by Monday next, in time for post.

Edward Sabin,<br>Senior Chaplain,<br>Scutari."

Father Cuffe replied as follows:
" Reverend Sir,
I am not aware of any military law which orders me, or any of my brother Roman Catholic Chaplains, to give in any

reports or returns to the Protestant Chaplain-General ; and until I am made aware of such a law, I must decline complying with the request made in your letter of this day's date.

Michael Cuffe,

Senior R. C. Chaplain."[13]

Though not a great admirer of the Jesuits, Father Cuffe acknowledged their labours among the troops. One of his letters to Bishop Grant announced that

" Mr. Ronan is in Koulali where he and the good nuns are much annoyed by the parsons. Their position is not comfortable though they are doing much good. In this consists their crime. It was not wise to send out a Jesuit, my Lord, for prudence must sometimes make us yield even to English prejudice, where no principle is sacrificed. The S.J.s gather constant storms around their own ears—storms, I fear, which will blow them home."[14]

Subsequent events belied Father Cuffe's prediction. Three Jesuit priests remained on with the army in the Crimea. In April, 1856, Fathers Woollett and Duffy returned to England with the troops evacuated from the seat of war. Father Gerard Strickland, S.J., was less fortunate. He died in September, 1855, just on the eve of his own departure. He was given military burial and his remains were placed beside those of his colleagues who had pre-deceased him in Balaclava.

Among the last contingent of Catholic chaplains to arrive in the east in November, 1855, was Father Augustine Maguire of Cork, curate in the Church of SS. Peter and Paul, and brother to John Francis Maguire, M.P., founder of *The Cork Examiner.* To mark the occasion of his departure, " an address was presented to this excellent clergyman by a large and influential deputation at the Reverend gentlemen's residence on Thursday, September 13, at one o'clock. It was accompanied by a purse containing one hundred and ten sovereigns as a testimony of regard."[15] Father Maguire reached the Bosphorus on November 3, accompanied by the Reverend Father Pauline, both of whom made Scutari their headquarters without ever moving up to the Crimea. A third arrival was one Father Mahé, who attached himself to the base hospitals at Smyrna and Abydos. In the course of his chaplaincy at Scutari, Father Maguire came within an ace of being drowned in the Bosphorus. A caique in which he was travelling collided with a hospital transport and capsized, leaving its occupants struggling helplessly in a backwash from which they were with considerable difficulty rescued and towed to port. After the war, Father Maguire returned to the diocese of Cork, where in later years he became Administrator in the Parish of Saint Finbarr's South.

Mr. Sabin was invalided home in June 1855 and was succeeded as senior chaplain to the forces by the Reverend Henry Press Wright who was later to become first Archdeacon of Columbia. Mr. Wright lost no time in representing to the Quartermaster-General the insufficiency of Protestant clergymen attached to the forces. At this time they numbered nineteen, as against six Catholic chaplains. Of these nineteen, some we are told, " had as many as five hundred sick to attend to, independently of such attention as they might be required or desirous to give to the healthy."[16] Mr. Wright having represented forty chaplains as the minimum required for the proper discharge of these duties, the Society for the Propagation of the Gospel, in response to his appeal, sent out an additional ten chaplains, the Government meanwhile sanctioning some extra appointments. By the close of 1855 the position regarding Protestant chaplains was declared satisfactory, thanks to the permission granted to certain religious societies to send out a specified number of ministers to the Crimea. Half the expense of their maintenance was to be borne by the Government, and half by the societies which submitted their names for the approval of the authorities.[17]

Liberality of a like nature was unknown to the Catholic section of the army. The situation in January 1855 was such that *The Tablet* (20 January, 1855) focussed attention on it by asking,

> " Why should not the English government send out a sufficient number of Catholic chaplains to the Catholic portion of the British Forces in the Crimea and at Scutari, and pay those Catholic clergymen out of the public funds? "

The question was a pertinent one ; but the War Office authorities were adamant, and only very reluctantly did they yield the point when disease and battle confirmed its necessity. Still, the number of Catholic chaplains seldom exceeded six, and the matter was so repeatedly in dispute that the War Office eventually relaxed its attitude. The remedy proposed was that the Treasury would contribute an equal amount to any sum which would be voluntarily raised in Ireland " *to defray the charge of additional Catholic chaplains in the East* "![18] The proposal, as such, was unsatisfactory. The case of Ireland was exceptional, and twelve paid chaplains, at least, should have been attached to the Catholic portion of the army.

The challenge of the Secretary at War was taken up in Ireland; its subsequent history is revealing. An application made by the Very Reverend Dean Meyler of Westland Row, Dublin, who received subscriptions to salary some extra chaplains for the army, was ignored by the War Office. A second application received similar treatment. One may imagine the good Dean's amazement to find shortly afterwards in the daily papers a statement to the effect that Protestants and Presbyterians had sent out extra chaplains to the Crimea, while the Catholics made no attempt to do so!

Governmental salaries and field allowances payable to chaplains of the Crimean War period are a further indication of the preferences extended to Protestant clergymen by the War Office. Generally speaking, such salaries and allowances were on a two-to-one basis. Catholic chaplains received £150 annually plus three-and-sixpence a day 'field allowance ; Protestants got sixteen shillings a day and an extra five shillings field allowance. All chaplains were allowed forage for one or two horses, but few Catholic priests could afford to buy a horse. Consequently, those billeted with the army before Sebastopol were obliged " to look after the General Hospital at Balaclava ; to visit the camp three times a week, some posts being nine miles distant ; to visit the transports when sent for—and all this on foot."[19]

Ministers of the Presbyterian Church were in the same category as the Catholic chaplains, but their duties were mainly nominal, they had not the same difficulties to contend with, and they were satisfied with matters as they stood. On the Catholic side, Bishop Grant was a constant agitator for the amelioration of conditions. His representations eventually paved the way for a reorganisation of the chaplains' department of the army in 1859.

The provision of reading material for the troops was an important duty imposed by the Regulations of the Service on the senior chaplain during wartime. This duty was interpreted with literal exactitude in the Crimea. Unlimited supplies of Bibles, tracts and prayer books were placed at the chaplain's disposal by the Society for the Propagation of Christian Knowledge, and these were replenished by an appeal through the columns of *The Times* for comforts and recreational reading. There was soon a Biblical harvest in the Crimea. Bibles and tracts were lavishly dispensed to all irrespective of creed, and the Ministers of the Established Church set on foot a determined campaign of proselytism.[20]

This development aroused grave disquiet in Catholic quarters ; yet for want of Catholic literature, it could not be counteracted. Writing from Scutari as early as December, 1854, Father H. Clarke explained that

" the poor Catholic *asks* a prayer book or instructive reading to relieve his many hours of pain, or to give him the support of patience and resignation ; and all the priest can answer is, ' I have asked from England. I have none to give.' Let me now, in the name of Charity, ask the good people of the Three Kingdoms to send papers, books and pamphlets to the Vicar General of Southwark for the hospital at Scutari."[21]

Five months later, a letter from the College of Propaganda at Smyrna, shows no improvement in the situation:

" I regret exceedingly I have no books to give my men ; neither prayer books nor religious tracts," wrote a chaplain. " What I had, I long since distributed. Oh, if it were possible to send me a supply, what a charity! The poor fellows are most anxious for religious books. What makes their case worse is that the hospital is literally inundated with anti-Catholic books of all sorts. Wherever you go, you have them scattered in every direction."[22]

Viewed in this light, England's duty to England's army left much to be desired.

" Catholics," said the Bishop of Meath, " were as willing as Protestants to risk their lives in battle ; but the Catholic soldier alone, of all those engaged in this conflict, was denied the privilege of preparing himself for the certain death that awaited him."

On May 5, 1855, *The Tablet*, in its leading article, once again drew attention to the situation by declaring that

" The Irish soldier does not fear hunger, cold, death itself. He is ready to brave them all, as he has done a thousand times before Sebastopol. He willingly risks his body, but naturally shudders at risking his immortal soul, as he must do when death approaches while spiritual succour is distant.

While the opportunity of preparing himself to die as a Christian is granted to the French soldier ; and while similar advantages are presented to the English Protestant, the Irish Catholic alone is denied the privilege of preparing himself to face his Creator ; not that he fights less bravely, but that the Empire he serves is brutally bigoted. A single chaplain, though he were gifted with the wings and energy of an angel, could not visit every lair on which a soldier lies gasping in a camp or leaguer, spreading over miles of rock and ravine, hill and vale.

The English Protestants have no commiseration for the mental agony, the distressing anxiety of the gallant Irish soldiers who fall in a distant land fighting for British interests. The Protestant soldier is treated as an immortal being ; the Catholic warrior experiences the indifference and neglect of the beast that perishes. Yet, if their valour be the same, why should not their privileges be similar?

What an amazing difference subsists between Catholics and Protestants! While *they* sternly and stingily refuse to salary a few Catholic chaplains, *we* lavishly and unthinkingly contribute to salary Protestant Bishops, Deans, Rectors, Curates and Sextons. In every village you will see some towering edifice which Catholic funds have contributed to construct. The very pews and pulpits are lined at the expense of Catholics.

We think it would be only just, it would be a very small return for the swarm of Protestant dignitaries and prebendaries whom we support in Ireland, if our Protestant Government would subsist a few Catholic Chaplains in the Crimea."

Other and similar criticisms followed, but for long, in vain. It was not until 1856 that the Government applied itself to the provision of proper religious service for the army. That it did so then was due to the representations of the Reverend Henry Press Wright, who while he was yet in the Crimea, submitted to the Chaplain-General, Reverend George Robert Gleig, a scheme for the permanent enlargement of the Chaplains' Department. Mr. Gleig submitted the plan, omitting only the section relating to salaries, to Lord Panmure who accepted it, with the result that on October 1, 1856, the Chaplains' Department was increased to twenty commissioned chaplains and thirty-five assistant chaplains. Crimean veterans were well represented in both categories.[23]

The Crimean appointment of assistant Catholic chaplains, however, came to an end with the war. Their suspension posed a new problem for Bishop Grant, who now sought to obtain from the Government a certain number of official appointments, securing to Catholic chaplains a fixed emolument with equivalent rank in the army. The struggle was long and wearisome, paved with difficulties and disappointments, but in the long run, successful. The War Office finally agreed to Dr. Grant's demands by appointing military chaplains on terms honourable to themselves and to the Church they represented.

" All our really successful negotiations with the Government for military chaplains and for navy chaplains, for mitigating oppressive laws, for Government prison chaplains, have been directly or indirectly due to Dr. Grant's tact and wisdom,"

wrote the Very Reverend William Bernard Ullathorne of Birmingham when eulogising the diplomatic achievements of Dr. Grant's episcopate.[24]

In 1858 Mr. Wright published a pamphlet entitled *England's Duty to England's Army*, which was tantamount to an open letter addressed to the Secretary of State for War on " matters affecting the Body, Mind and Soul of the British Soldier." In his pamphlet, Mr. Wright urged the need for providing chaplains for the troops in India in the proportion of one to each regiment. On this basis, chaplains of the Church of England would total ninety-two ; the number was to be balanced by a proportionate number of chaplains of the Church of Scotland (eight) and of the Roman Catholic Church (twenty-five).[25] The closing paragraphs of the pamphlet held out promises of commissions and pension facilities as an encouragement to clergymen to enlist.

Gradually the status and condition of soldier-curates began to improve. The ideas formulated in Mr. Wright's pamphlet were accepted, and in January, 1859, a new system of grading chaplains into four classes was adopted by the War Office. Henceforth, promotion and salary increases were accorded in proportion to length of service, and Catholic priests and Presbyterian clergy were given commissions. Seven Crimean veterans were commissioned after this enactment.

It is unnecessary here to enumerate the entire list, but certain names deserve special mention in connection with the present narrative . . . Father Michael Cuffe, Chaplain to the Forces from 1859-1884; Father Thomas Moloney, 1859-1879; and Father Thomas Unsworth, 1859-1869.[26] Of the others, two are worthy of note: Father John Mahé distinguished himself in the Hong Kong expedition of 1859, and Father John Vertue in the Yellow Fever epidemic of 1865 at Bermuda. Though no extant account of Father Vertue's Crimean service remains, it is beyond question that he was an assistant chaplain in 1855 and was commissioned in 1859. Father Vertue remained in the army until 1882 when he was appointed Bishop of Portsmouth. Another Crimean chaplain to be raised to the episcopate was Father John Butt, who in 1885 became Bishop of Southwark in succession to Dr. Thomas Grant.

## CHAPTER 14

## BALACLAVA

DOCTOR JOHN HALL was a graduate of the old school who had given forty-two years military service before his appointment as Inspector-General of the Hospitals in the Crimea. In the latter capacity he was, in the estimation of Sir Edward Cook, " the person most responsible, individually, for the state of things which had stirred so much outcry in England." Judged by modern standards, Doctor Hall would be labelled as incompetent ; according to mid-nineteenth-century reckoning, he was no worse than his colleagues. It appears that he was—partly at least—the victim of a false position. When the call came for him to go to the seat of war he was serving in Bombay, and he did not arrive on the scene in time to think out preparations properly. The difficulties confronting him were enormous ; and it was his misfortune that the system of administration in which he was involved was wholly at the discretion of Florence Nightingale, an outsider who was hopelessly out of her depth in dealing with the accidents and catastrophes attendant upon a war emergency.

Doctor Hall visited the Scutari hospitals just once—after the battle of the Alma, September 20, 1854—and his report to the Director-General was that the base hospitals were in as good a state as could be expected. A few weeks later the battle of Inkermann put such an unprecedented demand on the already slender resources of Scutari that Dr. Hall's report was questioned, criticised and condemned.

What followed is part of the Nightingale Legend : the story of the arrival of the Lady with the Lamp ; her horror at existing conditions ; her self-sacrificing endeavours to alleviate the sufferings of the soldiers, and the transformation she effected almost immediately after her arrival. Ostensibly, and by the strict letter of her original instructions, Miss Nightingale was only Superintendent of the Female Nursing Establishment. In time, she became a Purveyor to the hospitals, a clothier to the British Army, and as she put it herself, a General Dealer, with nursing relegated to the status of being the least of the duties to which she was committed.

Administratively speaking, Florence Nightengale was a reformer *par excellence*. Administration was her forte ; and in her sincere devotion to the welfare of the wounded British soldier, she will ever stand silhouetted as a water-shed marking the great divide between an outdated system characterised by neglect, incompetence, even cruelty, and a new and ever progressive era of efficiency, care and comfort. Her reforming administrative achievements during and after the Crimean War have been ably chronicled elsewhere ; while page upon page of blue-books in the War Office Library, not to mention the accumulation of her private correspondence with Sidney Herbert, are keys to her mental efficiency, her extraordinary grasp of detail, her foresight, and above all to the happy knack she had of getting things done. Her biographer, Sir Edward Cook, maintains that it was behind the scenes that her activity as a reformer was most powerfully exercised. And in fairness to Dr. Hall and his colleagues, the same biographer points out that their hostility and opposition were only to be expected, for " Miss Nightingale was no magician, and it would be ridiculous to suppose that by her exertions, either in a couple of days or a couple of months, she effected a complete transformation." It would likewise be unfair to attribute solely to her the gradual improvements which were, in fact, the result of the exertions of many people both at home and in the east.[1]

Florence Nightingale was soon to discover that Doctor Hall would be her greatest opponent in the military hospitals. He disputed her authority and resented her interference ; and in this he was backed by Dr. Andrew Smith, head of the Army Medical Department in London. The ambiguity in Miss Nightingale's letter of appointment caused considerable misunderstanding, if not ill-will, between her and Dr. Hall ; and until such time as her position would be clarified, the Inspector-General intended to exclude her from all hospitals on Crimean soil. Miss Nightingale's position *vis-à-vis* the Crimean hospitals and their nursing personnel is a matter of more than ordinary significance at this juncture ; and it is well to keep in mind the fact that the War Office in approving her appointment and in limiting her commission to *Turkey*, intended obviously to give her a " general superintendency but to relieve her of direct responsibility for the nurses in the Crimea."[2] Her appointment as Almoner of the Free Gifts in all the British Hospitals in the Crimea, while increasing her general prestige, did not at all clarify her position as Superintendent of Nurses. Dr. Hall's attitude is thereby explained. Florence Nightingale fought with Dr. Hall, and in the end she won ; even to the extent of preventing his appointment as Director-General of the Army Medical Service when that position became vacant in 1858.

In the fall of 1855, however, Dr. Hall was supreme. On October

1, as we have seen, Florence Nightingale resigned the super-intendence of the General Hospital at Balaclava, and informed Miss Weare, the acting superintendent, to "feel herself free from all obligation to her and her orders." Miss Weare accordingly placed herself and one other nurse at Dr. Hall's disposal, adding that she was ready to go wherever he wished, but that she would leave Balaclava "with regret, did she not know that, confided to the care of the amiable and good Mrs. Bridgeman," the hospital would not miss her presence.[3]

There was an interesting sequel to the above interchange. A second communication from Miss Nightingale ordered Miss Weare to leave the Crimea ; the latter having removed to the Monastery Hospital, disregarded the summons. Her insubordination formed the basis of a formal complaint lodged by Miss Nightingale early in 1856 in which Lord Panmure was told of the posting of two nurses to a hospital in the Crimea ; which posting she maintained, was sanctioned by Dr. Hall without previous consultation with her. It does not seem to have occurred to Florence Nightingale that she herself as well as the entire nursing personnel in the military hospitals was subject to the authority of the Inspector-General of Hospitals.

Doctor Hall's acceptance of Mother Bridgeman's offer of service arrived in Koulali on October 1. One statement in this letter would suggest that despite all Florence Nightingale's protestations to the contrary, Dr. Hall *did* consult her about "Miss Weare and two nurses whom she allowed to remain on" at his request, "when she had made up her mind to withdraw altogether from the General Hospital, Balaclava." The letter to Mother Bridgeman continues :

" If you feel disposed to make a trial of the General Hospital, it will be open to your kind ministrations at the beginning of October, and we will do our best to render your situation as little irksome to you as possible. The present superintendent, Miss Weare and one nurse, are anxious to remain in the Crimea, but their labours will in no way interfere with your ministration should you decide to come to Balaclava. Miss Weare, to whom I believe you are known, is an amiable, kind person, and it might be agreeable to you to meet her on your arrival. Should Miss Nightingale consent to her remaining, she will, in all probability, be employed at the Monastery Hospital."[4]

From Mr. Robertson came forewarnings of difficulties to be encountered in the Crimea which dwarfed those which had already threatened to engulf the Sisters. Mother Bridgeman was undeterred.

"Even should this be so," runs an entry in her *Diary*, "I concluded that difficulties were no difficulties in *His* way, whose work alone we sought to do. I also knew that privations could do no more than destroy health and life, and that these had been in constant danger since we came out. Yet the unseen hand which had so wonderfully sustained us weak ones against human power and prejudice, was as sure to be as omnipotent in the Crimea as on the stormy sea, in hostile Scutari, or on the banks of the beautiful Bosphorus."[5]

Doctor Hall had his reply by return of post.

"Dear Sir,
Last night's post brought me your favour of September 27, for which I am much obliged. We hope to leave for the Crimea in the beginning of next week. It may not be sooner, as the doctors will not allow a Sister who has not been well to travel this week. I take ten Sisters with me and two lay-Sisters, who are not usually employed in the wards, but who attend to the domestic requirements of the Sisters.

I trust you may find us obedient, useful, and anxious to contribute to the health and comfort of our suffering fellow-creatures. I shall be happy to renew my acquaintance with Miss Weare on my arrival in the Crimea."[6]

Florence Nightingale was next to be informed. To her Mother Bridgeman wrote as follows:

"My dear Miss Nightingale,
As it seemed to me our services should be more needed in the Crimea than elsewhere during the winter, I offered them to Dr. Hall, who has accepted them.

I shall therefore, be obliged to withdraw the Sisters from the General Hospital, Scutari. I trust my doing so shall cause no inconvenience. We hope to sail for the Crimea at the beginning of next week. We only got Dr. Hall's reply by last night's post."[7]

Florence Nightingale was dumbfounded. That the "Reverend Brickbat" should supersede her in Balaclava was unthinkable. She at once lodged a complaint with Lord Stratford de Redcliffe, only to be told that she should approach, not Lord Stratford himself, but General Storks who was military commandant on the

Bosphorus in succession to Lord William Paulet. To General
Storks Miss Nightingale pointed out the impossibility of carrying
on her work if interference with the control of her nurses was
permitted. She also maintained that if the Sisters *were* to go to
Balaclava, all arrangements should be made through herself alone.
In making her complaint Miss Nightingale quite obviously did
not take into account her resignation of October 1, or the fact that
she *never* had control over the nursing personnel in Koulali.*

Mother Bridgeman's letter was the signal for further contro-
versial exchanges with Miss Nightingale. Their correspondence,
hitherto unpublished, may be given almost verbatim:

" Concerning the departure of the Sisters from the General
Hospital, Scutari," wrote Miss Nightingale on October 4, " I
have referred the matter to the ambassador and await his
answer, as it is not in my power . . . to allow Sisters to have
their services offered, accepted and ordered elsewhere without my previous consent and knowledge.

At the same time, I am far from considering the measure
a bad one. I think it very advisable, for various reasons, that
the General Hospital at Balaclava should be in the hands of
Sisters. I will not answer your hope that 'their being withdrawn from Scutari will cause no inconvenience' in the
affirmative. This would be implying that they were useless,
which far be it from me to insinuate."[8]

Second thoughts convinced Florence Nightingale that the
implications of this new crisis could be seriously detrimental to her
already waning prestige. Doctor Hall must be conciliated at whatever cost: by 'permitting' the Sisters to go to the Crimea, she
might break through his opposition. Mr. David Fitzgerald, the
Deputy-Purveyor, was another for whose support she was angling:
a careful handling of the situation might lessen his antagonism
also. Finally, the Crimea then held large numbers of Irish troops,
and the disapproval voiced in certain quarters concerning their
victimisation by the Government might be silenced by giving them
in charge to the Irish Sisters. It goes without saying that Florence
Nightingale would have preferred to see the Bermondsey Sisters in
Balaclava: her authority over them was unquestioned. Some
weeks earlier, she had informed Mrs. Herbert that " the wisest
thing the War Office could do now would be to send out a few
more of the Bermondsey Nuns to join those already in Scutari,

* Miss Nightingale's biographers ignore altogether her resignation of
October 1.

and counterbalance the influence of the *Irish* ones who hate their soberer Sisters with the mortal hatred which I believe, only Nuns and Household Servants *can* feel towards each other."[9]

As to relations between the two groups of Sisters of Mercy in the military hospitals, it is difficult, even impossible, to plumb the depths of their differences. To generalize too quickly, however, can scarcely end in any but arbitrary conclusions, as unjust as they may be erroneous ; but lack of sufficient evidence on both sides suggests that neither party wished to discuss the matter. The Bermondsey Archives mention little about the Irish Sisters beyond their date of arrival and departure ; references to the Bermondsey Sisters are few and far between in the Irish sources. It would appear, however, that their mutual status *vis-à-vis* Florence Nightingale was the primary source of discord. The English Sisters were, by the decision of Bishop Grant of Southwark, subject entirely to Miss Nightingale's jurisdiction. The Irish Sisters, on the other hand, *and* by command of Archbishop Cullen, went to the military hospitals ' as a community under their own Superior.' Their connection with Florence Nightingale was merely of a co-operative nature ; her authority over them was limited ; the War Office authorities had endorsed that arrangement, and for Mother Bridgeman, it was a matter of principle that this autonomy should be maintained. Mother M. Clare either could not or would not appreciate this distinction as to character and status between the two communities. Difference of nationality, too, and the uneasy general atmosphere of the times, suggest another possible excuse for friction. Yet, animosity, such as it was, was rather dormant than active, and contacts between the two groups were not numerous. In fact, the author of *Leaves from the Annals of the Sisters of Mercy* makes it clear that

> " the Sisters who went originally from Bermondsey as a private charity, maintained their private character to the end. They never mingled with the larger and later group which followed, though both parties worked simultaneously in the military hospitals and for an almost equal period of time."

Another feature of the Bermondsey Archives is the absence of any definite reference to specific nursing duties in the military hospitals. It is significant too that Florence Nightingale mentions but one member of the Bermondsey group—Sister M. Stanislaus— as an excellent nurse. The obvious inference therefore is that the English Sisters, like so many others of Miss Nightingale's staff, spent the greater part of their time in non-nursing duties. *The Bridgeman Diary* and other Irish conventual sources mention the hospital kitchen and the free gift stores as Mother M. Clare's

sphere of employment: a circumstance which aroused grave disquiet in the mind of Mother Bridgeman, knowing as she did, that
Mother M. Clare Moore was one of Catherine McAuley's most
efficient helpers in nursing the cholera victims of 1832 in Dublin.
Mother M. Clare's companions in Scutari cannot be said to have
had much practical experience of nursing either, seeing that facilities for religious were almost non-existent in mid-nineteenth
century England, and that nuns could not appear in public in their
religious dress. All such considerations to the contrary, the
Bermondsey Sisters continued to be Miss Nightingale's most
valued helpers in the military hospitals, and she retained them on
her staff to the very last.

Mother Bridgeman's reply to Miss Nightingale was concise:

" Dear Madam,
I never gave up the right to withdraw my Sisters from
Scutari or elsewhere. So long as we are in a hospital under
your authority, we acknowledge you obedience in nursing
details. Were I about to place any of my Sisters in a hospital
under your control, I should, of course, have referred the
matter to you; but it is not so.
In Doctor Hall's official communication, he mentions that
you have given up the General Hospital in Balaclava, and to
it he invites us. I trust this will fully explain all."[10]

On October 4, Father Woollett, S.J., arrived in Koulali, having
been deputed by the Adjutant-General and by Doctor Hall to
conduct the Sisters to the Crimea. The picture he painted for
Mother Bridgeman was anything but heartening. Money, he said,
would not purchase lodging in Balaclava. The authorities there
were doing their utmost, but the only accommodation available
could scarcely house half a dozen Sisters in even comparative
comfort. Mother Bridgeman must use her discretion, but she must
act with promptitude, as it was essential that the Sisters should
take over in Balaclava without delay.

Monday, October 8, was settled as the day of departure. The
General Hospital, Koulali, was closed on the previous Saturday ;
all remaining patients were transferred to the Barracks Hospital
and final preparations for the forthcoming Sardinian occupation
were begun.[11]

Referring to the closing of Koulali, the Woodham-Smith
biography states incorrectly that " the lavishness there became
such a scandal that the Principal Medical Officer insisted that the
Scutari system must be adopted. The nuns then resigned, saying
their usefulness was destroyed."

Several reliable authorities may be cited in contradiction of this statement: three will suffice. General Storks, who succeeded Lord William Paulet as military commandant at Scutari, was, as we have already noted, quite forthright in declaring that " the cheapest of the four hospitals is Koulali." A Confidential Report submitted by Mr. David Fitzgerald to the War Office (and to be discussed at some length in a subsequent chapter) noted that economy was an outstanding feature of the Sisters' administration both in Koulali and at Balaclava. And Dr. John Hall, in a letter comparing the expenditure of Scutari and Koulali, informed Dr. Andrew Smith that " the contrast of expense, to say nothing of efficiency, between these quiet people and Miss Nightingale's establishment will astonish the authorities."[12] Nor was there ever any question of adopting the Scutari system in Koulali. Even after Mother Bridgeman's departure, Emily Hutton adhered faithfully to the methods introduced by the Sisters, methods which earned for Koulali its title of ' Model Hospital of the East.'

A letter from General Storks, with an enclosure from Florence Nightingale, coincided with the evacuation of Koulali. Miss Nightingale was affable. She considered it " exceedingly undesirable " that the arrangements made by Dr. Hall and Mother Bridgeman should be changed. At the same time, she had not the least intention of giving in to Mother Bridgeman, so she announced her decision " to go up with you myself on Monday." The letter concluded with the hope that Reverend Mother would be " pleased with this arrangement . . ."[13] Mother Bridgeman has not left her reply on record.

That General Storks was ignorant of the status of the Irish Sisters *vis-à-vis* Florence Nightingale is only too clear from *his* letter to Mother Bridgeman:

" Madam,

It appears to me that an irregularity has been committed which might lead to inconvenience if allowed to pass unnoticed. I allude to the request addressed by you to Doctor Hall for employment in the Hospital at Balaclava, without having, in the first instance, obtained my sanction and authority for such a proceeding. As you are aware, all the ladies in these hospitals are, as far as their distribution is concerned, solely under the direction of Miss Nightingale, and that all arrangements must have the sanction and concurrence of the General Officer here in the Bosphorus.

As the case now stands, it might cause inconvenience if the arrangements with Doctor Hall were not permitted to stand,

Convent of Mercy, St. Joseph's, Kinsale.

Convent of Mercy, St. Leo's, Carlow.

Convent of Mercy, St. Catherine's, Baggot Street, Dublin.

Convent of Mercy, St. Joseph's, Charleville.

and I, therefore, have arranged that passports be provided for you and the Sisters who are to accompany you, under the direction and superintendence of Miss Nightingale, who proceeds with you, on board the *Ottawa*, which sails on Monday for Balaclava.

I avail myself of this opportunity of expressing my sense of the services rendered by you and the Sisters of Mercy during the time you have been engaged in your work of charity and consolation in these hospitals."[14]

Mother Bridgeman was resolved not to place the Sisters under Florence Nightingale's superintendence. From the very beginning their relationship with her was purely co-operative, and Mother Bridgeman felt that co-operation was no longer due when the Sisters were originally rejected by Miss Nightingale. Compromise on so vital a point was impossible, and could end in nothing else but failure. For Mother Bridgeman it was entirely a matter of principle, and she was resolved that General Storks and all others concerned should know this as distinctly as did Doctor Hall and his colleagues in the Crimea. And even though General Storks was not commandant on the Bosphorus when she made her application to Doctor Hall, she decided " to risk his delaying the Sisters' departure to the Crimea, than by silence even *seem* to acquiesce in going up under Florence Nightingale's superintendence." As to her supposed breach of military regulations, Mother Bridgeman knew that General Storks' jurisdiction was subordinate to that of the authorities at headquarters: the latter approved of her negotiations with Doctor Hall, so there could be no irregularity in the transaction. She also knew that Florence Nightingale, on the face of things, could not afford to labour this point too heavily. It was with confidence, therefore, that she wrote to General Storks, taking care that her letter should be delivered to him on Sunday, October 7, early enough for him to prevent the Sisters' departure on the following day should he feel so inclined.

" Dear Sir,

I regret much to find that by some mistake or misrepresentation you have been led to believe us guilty of want of submission and respect to authority. Allow me to assure you that besides the respect due to your office, my esteem for your personal character should render me most anxious to remove from your mind any such impression; and for this, I trust a simple statement of fact shall suffice.

When the War Office sent us fifteen Sisters out nearly a year since, Miss Nightingale refused to accept more than five

Sisters, intimating that the remaining ten might return home, or in short, do what they pleased.

After passing a month between the Sisters of Charity at Galata and at Therapia, *unemployed,* Koulali was opened and the Sisters found work there. In the meantime I had a letter from Mr. Sidney Herbert authorising me to find work where we could, or return home. I suppose you are already aware that Miss Nightingale has no authority over Koulali nor over anyone in it.

Two of my Sisters were obliged by illness to return home, and only four of mine are at Scutari ; therefore over these four, *and only these,* has Miss Nightingale even a shadow of authority. I always considered myself and the Sisters free to withdraw from the work whenever we should deem it expedient. I believe we owe Miss Nightingale obedience merely in nursing details while we remain in a hospital under her control.

Were I about to place any of my Sisters in such a hospital, I should, of course, have referred the matter to her; but it is not so. Dr. Hall has informed me that Miss Nightingale has quite given up Balaclava General Hospital, and to it he invites us. May I trouble you with copies of my correspondence with Doctor Hall and my reply to Miss Nightingale? My letter to Doctor Hall was the result of a conversation we had with the Reverend Father Woollett, S.J. Mr. Woollett mentioned our willingness to go to the Crimea if required. Doctor Hall desired a written offer which he expressed himself willing to accept.

I had not thought of Balaclava (as I believed it in Miss Nightingale's hands) until Doctor Hall offered it to us. I believe my Sisters can be of more real use anywhere than in Scutari ; therefore it is I withdraw them.

I trust, dear Sir, this explanation will show that Miss Nightingale has no reason to complain. If we all thought well to return home—as so many ladies not nearly so long out have done—could we be prevented? At the time I first proposed going to Crimea, I hoped to get out more Sisters from Ireland. I should not at all have disturbed Koulali where ladies and Sisters have worked so cordially and happily together. But finding the General Hospital about to be given up, I saw that in Koulali there is neither accommodation nor sufficient work for the Sisters, and I resolved either to get the work we came for, or else return home.

May I hope my explanation shall satisfy you, and that you

will believe my only motive for exposing myself and my Sisters to the rigours of a Crimean winter is to work, to the best of our ability, the mission of mercy on which we came, and to afford all the help and comfort we can to our suffering fellow-creatures."[15]

General Storks accepted Mother Bridgeman's explanation and placed no further obstacles in the way of the Sisters' departure. Mother Bridgeman was not elated: she was " too weary and worn out " after the ordeal to which she had been subjected. Humanly speaking, it was " supreme folly " on her part to engage in new labours in strange and untried surroundings. But hers was a spirit ever ready to give and not to count the cost. She believed that " if God called us to the Crimea, He could and would supply the strength necessary to do His work. And at the worst, I felt that if health failed, as it threatened, I could but die or be sent home, and either would manifest God's will."[16]

The decision to quit Koulali in October was the signal for a renewal of the old struggle between Mother Superior and Lady Superintendent, which now entered upon its final and perhaps most vituperative stage. Letters of complaint began to go by almost every transport from Scutari to England, until at last, Florence Nightingale, exasperated by what Dickens so aptly called ' the Circumlocution Department ', demanded that Sidney Herbert call a parliamentary debate to decide the question and define her powers as against Mother Bridgeman. Mr. Herbert discountenanced the proposal. If such a debate were called, the history of the scheme for female nurses would have to be considered—and it had its weak spots. Some of the nurses had been convicted of innumerable irregularities. Others had been drunken and immoral. Not a few had written letters of criticism against the Government. The responsibility for all this would have rested on Miss Nightingale. She would likewise be held responsible for the indiscretions of Mr. Bracebridge who had castigated the administration in a way which it would be difficult to defend.

Florence Nightingale herself would also come in for no small share of criticism. Some of her actions would be hard to justify when described in the atmosphere of the House of Commons. She had broken regulations in emergency, and her behaviour, on occasion, could be construed as a defiance of orders—orders which in the last analysis, were approved by the House. Without condemning itself, the Government of the day could not sacrifice the military officials ; and Sidney Herbert foresaw that, whether or not Parliament supported Florence Nightingale, the scheme of female nurses might be discredited. Some other means of vindicating her position would have to be devised.

The departure of the Sisters on October 8 is described for us by Fanny Taylor: " Tears came into our eyes as we parted from them. From first to last the utmost cordiality had subsisted between all the ladies and the Sisters, and some of us felt we were parting from tried and warm friends." On their way to the jetty the Sisters were halted again and again by patients, orderlies, soldiers and non-commissioned officers, all crowding to say goodbye. Mother Bridgeman noticed too that " many of those who had served the Sisters most devotedly and had abstained from drink in special compliment to them, got drunk to drown their grief on this memorable day!" Everybody in the hospital was sorry to see the Sisters departing, " for their simple, holy lives had won the respect and good-will of all."[17]

They were accompanied on board the *Ottawa* by Father Woollett, S.J., and the Reverend T. Cooney, Protestant chaplain at Koulali, who insisted on escorting them to Balaclava. Already on deck they found Father Moloney, Miss Nightingale and the four Sisters from Scutari. Florence Nightingale and Mother Bridgeman exchanged courtesies, but neither alluded to the matter in dispute. Both got sick, and after the first day's misadventures, Miss Nightingale retired to her cabin when she did not again emerge until their destination was sighted on Wednesday, October 10.

Balaclava, according to the report of the Sanitary Commission, was a small land-locked port lying among lofty hills, the margins of the harbour formed, or deformed, with dead animals and filth of every description. Its upper end was a marsh which was used as a graveyard, and which contained thousands of carcases of men and animals, buried in water or scarcely covered with earth. Carcases floated everywhere among the shipping and the waters were reddened by the blood of cattle slaughtered on board. Inland, a rather motley scene presented itself: strings of mules and half-starved ponies splashing through the mud, besides numerous English, French and Turkish soldiers staggering along under some heavy load ; to say nothing of the ubiquitous British officer, his costume more civil than military, jogging along to camp on a lean pony, his saddle-bags and all his available pockets crammed with articles of food purchased on board ship.

The entrance to the inner harbour was a narrow channel navigable only by vessels in single file, and then only by a process of careful warping. Inside, the S-shaped bay was usually so cluttered with shipping as to be unable to accommodate new arrivals. Each vessel approaching the channel had to await a signal from an old

Genoese castle perched high upon the cliffs. When this signal was not forthcoming, the only alternative was to put out to sea again, the better to avoid destruction in the sudden squalls which were characteristic of the area.

Wednesday, October 10, was wild and stormy. Signals flashed from the *Ottawa* evoked no answering gleam from the castle. Father Woollett, taking advantage of the delay, directed the Sisters' attention to a spot on the distant hills, with the remark that " if we survive this storm and get to the shore, it will be only a matter of time until our coffins are borne by the soldiers to that mound in the distance!"[18] The Sisters had cause to remember Father Woollett's sinister prophecy when that very spot became the burial place for two of their little band.

Tiring of the delay, the captain of the *Ottawa* signalled for a tug, in which with luck, the Sisters might enter Balaclava ; but the tug could not approach the steamer. It was finally decided that if Mother Bridgeman wished to reach Balaclava that night, her only hope lay in going by a small boat to the tug, after which the channel might be safely negotiated. Mother Bridgeman decided to risk it. Accompanied by one Sister, she got into the boat with Father Woollett and Mr. Cooney. Miss Nightingale was still in her cabin, so the boat put off without her ; but in a matter of moments she was on deck announcing her decision of following Mother Bridgeman. The ensuing pageant is best described by the *Bridgeman Diary*:

" The sea was rough enough to swallow up the little boat which at every wave seemed likely to slip under the tug and quietly consign us all to a watery grave. After many dangerous and fruitless efforts to enter the tug by means of a ladder, it was suggested as the only means of success, that each time the boat should rise on a wave, one of us should stand up, extend her hands to two strong men in the tug and spring into it."

The experiment succeeded, but Mr. Cooney was so terrified that he sent his compliments to Miss Nightingale in the next boat begging her not to venture any further. Miss Nightingale, however, *did* venture, and she and Mother Bridgeman entered Balaclava together. Next evening the *Ottawa* berthed ; on the following morning Doctor Hall visited the Sisters and confirmed Mother Bridgeman as Superintendent of the General Hospital.

The hospital, once a Russian military school, consisted of two sections ; one, a stone structure containing seven wards well elevated from the ground. The second was a range of small apartments built against the slope of the hill. The buildings formed two sides of a parallelogram and were situated on the eastern side of the harbour. Two other buildings, used as stores and offices, completed the hospital. There were, in addition, some fourteen wooden huts, twenty-seven feet by fifteen feet inside measure, six feet high to the eaves, with ridged roofs rising to a height of twelve feet from the ground. Some huts were boarded, but the greater number had partially raised floors running along each side, and on these the men slept. These constructions, known as Portsmouth huts, were placed in rows on the sloping ground above the harbour and were used as wards for the sick.

One such hut was prepared for the Sisters: a miserable, dark, rat-infested compartment, once Miss Weare's domicile, and recently tenanted by a nurse with a broken leg and a goat as her companion.[19] There were only two windows in the hut—one at each end—but ventilation presented no problem, for the structure was so loosely held together as to be constantly draughty. The poverty of the interior was nothing if not Franciscan. A few cups and plates, a tin can, a sweeping brush, a small stove with a kettle on it, three beds and two backless chairs—such was the accommodation for thirteen Sisters of Mercy. Ten extra mattresses were sent up from the hospital, and these, laid out on the floor, were the only present amenities available. Cutlery was limited to three knives and three forks which, according to Sister M. Joseph Croke, " we passed from one to another, forgetting squeamishness and trying to take all in the spirit of our vocation—gaily and with much good humour ".

But it was soon discovered that something more than the spirit of a religious vocation was called for when it came to tackling the problem of rats which were shortly disputing ownership of the hut with the Sisters. One night Sister M. Paula awoke to find a huge rat licking her forehead. On another occasion Sister M. Stanislaus found a hole eaten right through the cloak which she had left folded at the end of her bed. So venturesome did the pests become that " they chased each other over beds and shelves; they rattled everything ; they scraped under the boards ; they chanted matins in the dead of night and danced quadrilles in the darkness." Thus did Mother Bridgeman sum up the situation. Father Woollett came to the rescue with a Russian cat, purchased for seven shillings from an old Russian woman. " The very sight of this powerful champion," wrote Sister M. Aloysius, " relieved us of some of our unwelcome and voracious visitors "; but, adds Sister M. Joseph Croke, " not before they sucked a hundred eggs and made off with some fine chickens on Christmas Eve!"

Mother Bridgeman's first impression of the General Hospital

exceeded her worst anticipations. She was confronted with dirt, confusion, quarrelling nurses, drunken orderlies, and a sad deficiency of proper cooking and washing facilities. The hut wards were a nightmare. The extra-diet kitchen, normally regarded as the principal concern of Miss Nightingale's department, and the administration of which she claimed to have reformed, was now administered by Mrs. Elizabeth Davis, " a hard-working honest old woman, but quite a character," whose largesse with the Free Gifts, already bordering on the ridiculous, made her name synonymous with extravagance in every quarter. Her kitchen was a wooden hut with " a stove inside, two charcoal braziers outside, filth and confusion at every side."[20] Methods of cooking for the sick were appalling. When fowl was ordered, each orderly got the quota for his own division *alive* from the store and brought them to his ward where they might be seen feeding until it should be thought convenient to kill them. The birds were then more often than not skinned instead of plucked, and they were boiled and eaten the same day. The doctors were constantly complaining, but hitherto without avail.

Mother Bridgeman refused to take any responsibility for the hospital kitchen until it should be given her in such a manner that she could re-model it according to her own ideas. For the time being it was arranged that Mrs. Davis should remain in charge until she should either join Miss Weare at the Monastery Hospital or else return home. She sailed for England in November.

The laundry so-called, was run by a soldier's wife, paid and supported by the Government. She had about six nurses at the Castle Hospital and three at the General Hospital to cater for, and she washed seven towels weekly for each ward. The rest of her time was spent in taking in washing for hire. In December she too left the Crimea and bequeathed her laundry to the Sisters.

Nursing arrangements in the hospital reflected the same inefficiency which characterised all other departments. In fact, all nursing seems to have been in abeyance in Balaclava for some considerable time before the arrival of the Sisters.[21] Of Miss Weare's assistants, we learn that one, a sergeant's wife, had a little nursing baby of her own. Miss Weare dared not risk the baby's health by allowing its mother into the wards ; so the nurse, like the mother of Moses, was paid for nursing her own child. The second nurse, Jane Evans, had the sole care of one cow. Any attention lavished on the sick was performed in the main by orderlies, who knew nothing about nursing and even less about hygiene, and who were never left long enough in the hospital to be taught even the rudiments of either.

The Sisters discovered that the soldier patients had had some little care bestowed upon them, but that the civilian corps had been neglected. Attached to the army as navvies or muleteers, civilians were looked upon as intruders for whom there was no quarter in a military hospital. Amongst the civilians then in Balaclava were Maltese, Greeks, Italians, Americans, Germans and Negroes ; and to these the Sisters endeavoured to show some special attention without in any way neglecting the soldier patients who were always their principal concern. Their decision must be regarded as a logical outcome of their dual character as religious nurses and Sisters of Mercy, who carried the nursing profession to the very peak of dedicated virtue, and whose every action proclaimed that they were the close associates of a Saviour whose very shadow brought health to the sick who lined His pathway. Because of their dedication, the Sisters wedded mercy to medicine, prayer to prescription and faith to service. Each was a splendid nurse because she was also a nun who drew her inspiration from the thought that

> " Mercy—the principal path marked out by Jesus Christ for those who desire to follow Him—has, in all ages of the Church, excited the faithful in a particular manner to instruct and comfort the sick and dying poor, as in them they regarded the person of our Divine Master, who has said: ' Amen, I say to you, as long as you did it to one of these My least brethren, you did it to Me.' " [Rule, Ch. III.]

As at Koulali, Mother Bridgeman set to work on the extra-diet kitchen, in the renovation of which she was assisted by Mr. David Fitzgerald, the Deputy-Purveyor. Though at first hostile (Mother Bridgeman found him " difficult to manage and most penitential to deal with ") Mr. Fitzgerald was at length won over by her tact and efficiency. The kitchen was enlarged, ovens were built, broilers set and charcoal stoves installed. A store room was added, and the Sisters were given access to the Purveyor's department—a permission which greatly facilitated their administration of the General Hospital.[22] What could not be supplied at Balaclava was sent up from Scutari by Mr. Robertson, the Purveyor-in-Chief. Again, as at Koulali, all stimulants passed through the Sisters' hands, a change which, to quote Sister M. Joseph Croke, " gave general satisfaction, except to those deprived of their daily whiff of spirituous consolation."

Florence Nightingale was meanwhile plying between the Monastery Hospital, the Castle Hospital and the General Hospital, where she made every effort possible to re-assert her authority. She seldom encountered Mother Bridgeman but she spent long hours conferring with Doctor Hall. He proved impervious to her entreaties, and was adamant in maintaining that the Sisters should retain charge of the General Hospital.[23] The improvements already introduced by them were a guarantee of what the hospital might yet become, and made Doctor Hall unwilling to institute any further change. Florence Nightingale was still urging her right of supreme authority when a copy of *The Times* for October 16, 1855, was circulated in Balaclava. It contained Mr. Bracebridge's tirade delivered at Coventry against the medical and military personnel of the army ; and as it was currently believed that Miss Nightingale was the instigator of the attack, everything asserted of her by Doctor Hall appeared to be justified.

" When one reads such twaddling nonsense," he wrote to Doctor Andrew Smith, " as that uttered by Mr. Bracebridge, and which was so much lauded in *The Times,* because the garrulous old gentleman talked about Miss Nightingale putting hospitals containing three or four thousand patients in order in a couple of days by means of the *Times Fund,* one cannot suppress a feeling of contempt for the ignorant multitude who are deluded by such fairy tales."[24]

Twelve months had elapsed since Florence Nightingale first received her appointment from the War Office. During that time she had become something of a national heroine, but the scheme for female nursing in the military hospitals was anything but an integral part of the army medical services. Mr. Bracebridge's utterances made matters more precarious than ever, and Lord Panmure's tardiness in clarifying Miss Nightingale's position played right into the hands of her opponents. These included Mr. (later Sir) Benjamin Hawes, permanent Under-Secretary, and head of an anti-Nightingale party at the War Office. To add to her troubles, Florence Nightingale was again taken ill and was forced to enter the Castle Hospital with acute sciatica. Within a week she was up and about once more, and in the leisure afforded by her convalescence, she concentrated her whole attention on the situation in the General Hospital.

She complained that though the Sisters worked well, they were lavishing their care on Catholic patients only ; that they were proselytising among the non-Catholics and that the latter fact was the source of all complaints lodged against them in Koulali. It should be remembered that these charges of proselytism were long since investigated and disproved: Miss Nightingale could not have been unaware of this fact, yet she " persistently ignored " Mother Bridgeman's protestation that the Sisters would consider it " a sin against God and a disgrace before man to violate the contract under which they were originally accepted by the government ".[25]

As yet, the Sisters had few friends in Balaclava, and it looked as if Florence Nightingale might at last succeed in jeopardising them with the authorities. Still, in this latest trial God raised up two stalwart champions whose testimony was sufficiently compelling to silence once and for all any further charges of proselytism and favouritism against the Sisters. That both were non-Catholics is a factor which gives their evidence all the greater weight.

Doctor Beatson, in a lengthy report to Doctor Hall, stated that he had worked in Koulali with the Sisters of Mercy from May to October 1855. At that time he was in charge of the south division of the hospital. In his daily intercourse with the Sisters he had been very observant of their work, and testified that " on every occasion their attention to the sick was unremitting, and they were careful to carry out and not deviate from any of the orders given by the medical officers." As to their supposed intervention in religious matters, he had heard " a loose assertion that the Sisters' object and aim was to proselytise "; but while he observed that the treatment given to Protestants and Catholics was equally good, he " knew of no instance " in which any assertion made against them was established.

" I am myself a Protestant, a Scotch Presbyterian," he concluded, " and I cannot, therefore, be supposed to bear this testimony from religious sympathy, but I do so from a sense of justice to these estimable women, believing that Christian charity and benevolence are the motives which influence them."[26]

Equally conclusive are the words of Mr. Cooney, then chaplain at the Monastery Hospital:

" During the five months of my officiating as chaplain in the hospitals at Koulali, my duties brought me daily in contact with the larger number of these Roman Catholic Sisters of Mercy who are now attached to the General Hospital, Balaclava. During that period, nothing ever came under my observation to induce me to attach the least credit to rumours which were afloat of their bent in proselytism. If any effort had been made with that object in view, it could hardly have escaped my notice."

As to the attention and care lavished by the Sisters on the sick, Mr. Cooney never noticed the " slightest line of demarcation " being drawn by them in regard to members of any faith. On the contrary, they displayed great kindness to all alike, " and in the universal love they showed to all, seemed to strive to bury any difference of faith which might exist among those to whom they were called upon to minister."[27]

## CHAPTER 15

## CRIMEAN GRAVES

BY late October 1855 there were in the Crimea fifty-one thousand British troops, a contingent of twenty thousand Turks, raised, trained and officered by Englishmen, and a German Legion of ten thousand men.[1] For the first time the army had a Land Transport Corps equal to the task assigned to it. The fleet had been greatly increased in force and in weight of guns, and even though it was already apparent that the Crimean War would end in nothing more than a negotiated truce, the British Government stood firm in its resolution of securing the best possible terms from that truce.

Among the so-called British troops then in the Crimea, William Howard Russell estimated that a large portion of the 41st Welsh were Irish; that the 77th, known as the East Middlesex Regiment, was almost exclusively Irish; that the 30th, or Cambridgeshire Regiment, contained " a very great number of Irishmen "; and that the 90th, or Perthshire Volunteers, had quite as many men from Tipperary as from the shire whence it derived its name.[2]

Numerically speaking, the strength of the army looked well enough on paper; there was little else to recommend it. Several regiments had been more than thrice renewed, and the new material could bear no comparison with the old. Under the circumstances, then, it was fortunate for England that the second winter in the Crimea was to be a time of comparative rest for the greater part of the army. There were no more major engagements. Uncomfortable anti-climax set in. Even the newspapers, having had their headlines, were gradually relapsing into ordinary print.

An outbreak of cholera within a week of the Sisters' arrival in Balaclava was Mother Bridgeman's opportunity for introducing her stuping remedy which, modified by the administration of chloroform, had saved so many lives in Koulali. Hitherto, for lack of proper nurses, the Crimean doctors were dubious as to the introduction of chloroform. Its administration required nurses at once careful, vigilant and thoroughly reliable as to obedience— qualities as yet unknown in Balaclava. It is not surprising then that the Sisters were asked to undertake night duty: this in itself was a break-away from the Nightingale system which discouraged night nursing and limited nursing duties to the daylight hours.

211

Mother Bridgeman's ruling on night duty was that "the Sisters should never stay up but by the wish of the doctor, expressed by him to the Sister herself, or in writing, in a book for directions left in each ward."[3] When night nursing was undertaken, the Sisters remained up in pairs and went about together. The rule of companionship was relaxed during the day, for the hospital huts were scattered on the side of the hill above the harbour. These divisions became the bounds of the "enclosure" through which the Sisters went freely alone. Actually, they were seldom on their own, for it was quite a normal spectacle during those days in Balaclava to see a Sister of Mercy surrounded by a bevy of admiring Redcoats on the slippery heights above the General Hospital.

One of the earliest victims of the cholera epidemic was Sister M. Winifred of Liverpool who died on October 20. *The Bridgeman Diary* describes the death-bed scene as

"a touching, though to human eyes, a desolate picture. The wretched wooden hut, damp and unfurnished, with the wind playing freely through the open chinks. The poor uncurtained bed; the Sister of Mercy extended upon it, dying of that fearful disease far from her Convent home and community, surrounded by her Sisters, while the Jesuit priest prayed the prayer of faith and confidence for her."[4]

Miss Nightingale sat by the bedside and joined in the prayers, and while praying, she killed with her umbrella a huge rat which every now and then made towards the bed on which Sister M. Winifred lay dying.[5] Mother Bridgeman was touched by Miss Nightingale's obvious solicitude, and "found her manner kinder than ever before."

The struggle was over at 3 p.m.

"It was strangely touching," wrote Fanny Taylor to her mother, "to think of the Sisters turning from the terrible scene of the cholera patients in their agony to her who lay so calmly there, arranged for burial, holding the parchment on which were written the Vows she had made to devote herself to God and her suffering fellow-creatures. She had finished her work; theirs lay yet before them."[6]

Reverend Mother wished to have Sister M. Winifred buried alongside Father John Wheble, the first Crimean martyr. Permission to do so was granted by the Commander-in-Chief, but Doctor Hall, fearing that this particular spot might be desecrated, advised another site. So, on the hills of Balaclava, a little to the right of the General Hospital, Father Unsworth, newly-appointed chaplain to the Crimea, selected a plot of ground between two rocks with just room for about two graves. It was the very place pointed out by Father Woollett on the day of the Sisters' arrival. Here, borne by the Sappers and Miners, who claimed the privilege, Sister M. Winifred was laid to rest. Three priests attended the funeral—Fathers Woollett, Unsworth and Moloney. The Sisters clad in Church Cloaks and each bearing a lighted candle, followed the cortége, and psalms were chanted in the usual manner while the procession, headed by the Cross, moved up the hill accompanied by " soldiers, doctors, officers and officials, Florence Nightingale included." It was, said Mother Bridgeman, " an edifying sight to see the Sister of Mercy carried to her grave by the soldiers she came to serve, accompanied by the beautiful prayers and ceremonies of the Church."[7]

Father Michael Cuffe, who disapproved of the withdrawal of the Sisters from Koulali, made of Sister M. Winifred's death a new peg on which to hang complaints in his reports to Bishop Grant. He was convinced that " the nuns acted unwisely in leaving their comfortable quarters in Scutari and Koulali, where they were doing much good, and in settling down in Balaclava, where they can do but very little good and enjoy but very little comfort."[8] Dr. Manning appears to have been similarly misinformed, and both he and Bishop Grant remained under this misapprehension until Miss Hutton, on her return to England, lifted the veil from their eyes, revealing to them the true state of affairs in the military hospitals, and possibly surprising them at the extent to which she, an orthodox Protestant, wished to identify herself with the Sisters of Mercy and their Superioress.

" Dear Mother," she wrote to Mother Bridgeman, " how little do the malice and evil-speaking of some and the misjudgment of others matter, when set against the real good accomplished. I will not have *my* Reverend Mother and Sisters misrepresented; and I am vexed that this has been the case even among Roman Catholics."[9]

Emily Hutton was as good as her word. At a later date she defended the Sisters before no less a personage than his Eminence, Nicholas, Cardinal Wiseman.

Florence Nightingale offered to erect a Cross over Sister M. Winifred's grave. Mother Bridgeman declined the offer, having previously consented to a like request from the 89th Royal Irish Regiment. The monument, purchased in Constantinople, was of white marble, simply engraved, and testifying that it was " erected

by the soldiers of the 89th Regiment in memory of Sister Winifred
Sprey, Sister of Mercy, who died of cholera at Balaclava on
October 20, 1855."[10]

Sister M. Winifred's death and Mother Bridgeman's refusal to
accept a headstone from Florence Nightingale was duly reported
by the latter to Sidney Herbert. " Mother Brickbat's conduct
has been neither that of a Christian, a gentlewoman, or even a
woman," she wrote. " I have even offered to put up a cross to
poor Winifred to which she has deigned no reply . . ."[11] The
following copy of Mother Bridgeman's reply to Miss Nightingale's
offer is taken from the Archives, Kinsale:

> " Thank you for thinking of erecting a Cross over the
> remains of our dear Sister Winifred, but as I had already
> consented that another party might undertake this, I shall
> not trouble you.
>
> Believe me to be, dear Madam,
> Very sincerely yours in J.C.
> Sr. M. Francis Bridgeman."

The virulence of the cholera epidemic was such that Sister M.
Winifred was scarcely laid to rest when a request came for two
Sisters to remain up that very night. The varied nature of these
requests is a pointer to the extensive services rendered by the
Sisters of Mercy to the cosmopolitan assemblage of patients
then in the General Hospital. At one time a doctor might ask
that " a Sister would sit up with the Dutch patient in No. 9
Ward." Another would request the Sisters " to sit up with the
Maltese and the Arab." A third would inform the Sisters that
their " kind attendance on Jones every night would be necessary
until a notification to the contrary be given." The Sisters
appointed by Mother Bridgeman for the night watching would
find various written instructions awaiting them in their wards.
" Blackman may have one gill of brandy beaten up with an egg,
or any other stimulant the Sisters may suggest." " Elliott to be
watched all night; the powder every half-hour; wine in small doses,
if necessary." In the case of frost-bitten patients, the usual
direction was that the " stump " should be kept moist. The
Balaclava orderly upon whom the care of the stump devolved at
this period was evidently somewhat of a character. One day, a
Sister wishing to ascertain the doctor's directions regarding a
newly-admitted patient, asked, " Do you know, Thomas, if this
man's leg is to be amputated?" " O Lord, no Ma'am," came the
reply, " it's only going to be cut off!"[12]

Reformation of the orderlies was outstanding among the

achievements of the Sisters in Balaclava no less than at Koulali. At first, the going was rough. The orderlies, so long their own masters, did not take kindly to discipline; but Mother Bridgeman, who ever made her own the observation of St. Francis de Sales, that a spoonful of honey is more potent than a barrel of vinegar, set herself to win them over by patience rather than by punishment. She made it a point never to complain anyone, or to risk getting anyone into trouble, but arrived at success by establishing her influence, " gently, and as it were, imperceptibly."[13] As superintendent in Koulali and Balaclava she never once came into conflict with the authorities under whom she worked. Perfect harmony characterised the relations between the personnel in these hospitals, Mother Bridgeman being a living exemplar of the dictum of Catherine McAuley that " wherever a religious woman presides, peace and good order are generally to be found."

Never did hospital matron have in her service such zealots as had Mother Bridgeman in the Balaclava orderlies. One word of admonition from her or from the Sisters was far more effective than a flogging from a military superior. Such admonitions were of frequent occurrence during the early days; but methods of delivering reprimands were always of a nature calculated to rob them of all traces of asperity. On one occasion, for instance, Sister M. Stanislaus, finding it necessary to correct an orderly, prefaced her remark with, " Perhaps, James, you do not wish me to speak to you a little severely—" " Troth, Sister," interrupted James effusively, " I *glory* in yer speakin' to me. Doesn't it show ye take an interest in me? Sure the day I came to Ballyclava, I cried with joy when I saw yer face."[14]

One day an orderly, showing visible signs of intoxication, was so mortified on meeting Mother Bridgeman, whom the soldiers were wont to call their Commander-in-Chief, that he wept and sobbed like a child. Another under a similar difficulty, was so terrified of a like encounter " before his senses came back entirely," that he hid for several hours between the shelves of the linen-press. He had never hidden from the enemy; a medal with three clasps bore testimony to his bravery at the Alma, Balaclava and Inkermann, but the period of probation imposed upon him for his delinquency was so unbearable that within a few days he was imploring of Mother Bridgeman, " Speak to me, Ma'am; the words out of yer blessed mouth are like jewels fallin' over me."[15]

To these orderlies was entrusted the task of keeping the wards in order, a task which was always supervised by the Sister on duty. In the kitchen, Sister M. Aloysius was helped by " three first-class orderlies and a party of fatigue-men who came down from the front every day." The latter carried meals from the kitchen to the various wards and huts over which the Sisters had charge. That meals be served while hot was a strict regulation with Mother Bridgeman; hence her insistence on speed and efficiency in the orderlies.[16] Loiterers were not welcome in Balaclava.

Invalid cooking was entirely in the hands of the Sisters; and though some minor culinary duties were entrusted to the orderlies, the General Hospital at Balaclava was unique among the Crimean hospitals for the personal attention given by the Sisters to this most important feature of proper nursing. With the laundry under the same supervision, and the stores at the Sisters' disposal, an all-round improvement was soon apparent, and acknowledged even by those who at first were prejudiced and suspicious in their appraisal of nuns. And there were many of the latter, as the following excerpt, written from Sebastopol on October 20, will show.

" The nuns at Balaclava . . . give great satisfaction to the official authorities, and their presence commands respect from all who can appreciate their purity of character and the angelic dispositions which animate their actions . . . Surely the tongue which could whisper an insinuation against their usefulness must be steeped in impious venom, and the imagination which could conceive aught but what is pure, holy and good of such beings, must indeed be warped by bigotry and immensely wicked."[17]

An outbreak of cholera at Scutari in November necessitated Miss Nightingale's return to the Bosphorus. Her departure ushered in an era of tranquillity and peace for all in Balaclava, more especially for the Sisters who at last felt free to work their reforms without trace of discord or interference. Their subsequent achievements in this line were such that the doctors were " delighted and loud in their thanks and approval," the Purveyor was " proud of the Sisters," and the patients were " grateful and content." The ministers associated themselves with this general manifestation of good-will; and it was not at all unusual for a newly-arrived Anglican chaplain to be presented at the Sisters' quarters for an introduction. In fact, one of the first callers to the hut was a Protestant Minister who, like his colleagues at Koulali, wished to have his collars laundered in true conventual style.[18]

Improvements in the hospital were, unhappily, not matched

by any amelioration in living conditions for the Sisters. Until well after the date of Sister M. Winifred's death they were still housed in their single Portsmouth hut; besides which they were in constant danger of accidents as day and night they trudged the muddy slopes between the huts and the General Hospital. At times hunger was their lot. An entry in the *Croke Diary* for October 25, states,

" We had nothing at supper this evening except a cup of tea; no bread could be got. No food either this morning. When the Purveyor discovered we had no breakfast, he could not rest until he made out some sea-biscuits which, though very hard, we were very glad to get."

The greatest privation of all was the want of daily Mass. Father Unsworth could only celebrate the Holy Sacrifice in Balaclava twice a week besides Sundays, " but this was so late that it interfered with the Sisters' duties in the wards," and they had no other option but to forgo their greatest privilege until towards the end of the year when Father Michael Gleeson C.M., was appointed chaplain to the General Hospital by order of Colonel Pakenham.[19]

In time, Mr. Fitzgerald had a row of steps cut out on the hill and ordered two additional huts to be erected for the Sisters— an improvement which drew from Sister M. Joseph Croke the quip that " we shall soon have as many palaces as the Sultan!" One hut was screened into compartments, giving each Sister a cubicle of her own. The second hut was partitioned to form a refectory, a small infirmary, and an oratory where the Blessed Sacrament was reserved. Nearby, a vacant hut was converted into a Chapel of Ease, mainly for the benefit of the soldiers who could henceforth attend daily Mass and go more regularly to confession.

The apartment in the General Hospital vacated by Miss Weare was next given over to the Sisters, and by them converted into a store where private gifts of clothing were kept. It served also as a reception room where the Sisters might receive visitors, and whither they might retire when not engaged in their wards. The small closet attached to the room was used as a refectory; and in a letter to Kinsale shortly before Christmas, Mother Bridgeman reported that " we have now much more ample accommodation than we ever had since we came out . . . Our position is in every way more suitable, and we are more of a religious community than ever."

The peace was short-lived. The cold war against the Sisters

was, in early December, renewed by Florence Nightingale who transmitted to Mother Bridgeman a document issued from the War Office on November 5, to the effect that Lord Panmure considered that " Mrs. Bridgeman was not justified " in removing, except by Miss Nightingale's consent, any of the nurses engaged under the latter's control in the hospital at Scutari, " nor in offering the services of the Roman Catholic Sisters at Koulali to the Principal Medical Officer in the Crimea without having previously obtained the consent and sanction of the Secretary at War."[20]

Mother Bridgeman regarded the foregoing as " a cheap way of mollifying Miss Nightingale," seeing that it neither incriminated Dr. Hall, nor did it give Miss Nightingale any authority to undo what had been done. If anything, it proved that her jurisdiction extended only to those nurses immediately " under her control in Scutari." This being so, and the better to clarify the position once and for all, Mother Bridgeman resolved to lay before Florence Nightingale certain written statements of her own which might help to put an end to the unhappy rivalry between them and which threatened to become more and more accentuated with the passage of time. She reminded Miss Nightingale of her refusal to accept more than five of the fifteen Sisters who arrived in Scutari in December 1854; of her denial of all authority in the disposal of the remaining ten; of her concession as to the withdrawal at any time of the five who were actually under her control. In support of these reminders Mother Bridgeman quoted from Miss Nightingale's letter of Christmas Day 1854, which stated, among other things, that

> " I have no power to dispose of those who do not come here. None are consigned to me. You must consult with Dr. Meyer and Miss Stanley. I shall be glad to give advice if called upon . . . As far as my office goes, I can recognise the right of any person to interfere in the way only of giving advice to anyone placed here. If you should advise a Sister to withdraw at any time, she can do so."[21]

Mother Bridgeman concluded her own letter to Florence Nightingale as follows:

> " No doubt the authorities in London are ignorant of the existence of such a letter as this, and of many other circumstances which might induce them to view matters in a different light. But to save further discussion on the subject, I wish it to be clearly understood that we will not continue in the service of the Government under any other conditions

than those accepted by Doctor Hall previous to our coming here. If the War Office is not satisfied, it has but to recall us, and we shall, of course, obey."

Before despatching the above to Florence Nightingale, Mother Bridgeman submitted it to Doctor Hall for approval, with the request that if he preferred any other style of reply, he would suggest it. Doctor Hall advised that Reverend Mother should not enter into any explanations with Miss Nightingale; she should merely acknowledge her letter and decline all further discussion with her. Mother Bridgeman therefore informed Florence Nightingale that " if called upon by the War Office " she would be " happy to give such explanations as would prove satisfactory to the authorities."²² The explanations were never sought. The War Office authorities considered it unnecessary to investigate the matter, even though the misrepresentations of Florence Nightingale affected the reputation of the highest-ranking official of the medical corps of the army in the Crimea. Despite such misrepresentations, Doctor Hall was awarded the K.C.B., in January 1856. Miss Nightingale's remark on the decoration was that it could only signify " Knight of the Crimean Burial Grounds."

Doctor Hall kept the original of Mother Bridgeman's undelivered letter to Florence Nightingale. Its ultimate fate is uncertain, but its omission from Doctor Hall's biography suggests that this document, like so many others of a similar nature, was destroyed or remained the secret of the War Office and other archives. Thus it happens that the Sisters of Mercy appear only on the margins of all histories of the Crimean War period; which is exactly where they would have chosen to be, for despite the many controversies which raged round her reputation, Mother Bridgeman directed that the contents of her *Diary* should not pass outside the walls of her convent during her own lifetime and the lifetime of those whose names she had occasion to record. The misrepresentations still afloat show with what exactitude her request was honoured.

It was no small consolation to the Sisters that other communications from the Bosphorus differed greatly in tone and sentiment from those of Florence Nightingale. Former patients were profuse in voicing their appreciation. Letters came by devious routes to Balaclava; the following inimitable production, dated " Scutari, November," being a fair example of all such literary effusions:

" Dear Sister,
    I write to send my best respects to you, hoping they will

be acceptable. For me to draw any inference from how good and civil you were to me, it is that makes me think you will not be vexed with my audacity in enclosing a note for you. But if it displeases you, all you have to do is to tell Tom Connors that I should not enclose a note for you and you will be obeyed.

Dear Sister, I cannot congregate my good wishes for you as a very Noble Lady.

Dear Sister, the Sergeant of the Rifles and myself unite in sending you our best respects. Our feelings on this point are incomprehensible. We cannot express how lonesome we are since you left Koulali. Please do us the honour to write to us.

> Dear Sister, I have the honour to be,
> Your obedient humble servant,
> John James Hopkins."[23]

Even after their departure from Koulali, strong interest and affection continued to be expressed there for the Sisters, and this quite as much by those who differed from, as by those who were one with them in religious belief. All voiced appreciation of their constant and gentle courtesy, their amiability and their obvious devotion to their work. Their obedience formed a topic for endless discussion ; their tireless energy was repeatedly under consideration ; above all, their experience in hospital management and nursing skill aroused the query as to how such skill and experience had been acquired. A brief glance at the status attained by the Congregation of Our Lady of Mercy by the year 1855 will best provide the answer to this query.

The transformation of the General Hospital at Balaclava into a Mercy Hospital was but one of many glorious incidents in the great saga of Mercy which in 1831, at Catherine McAuley's bidding, began to emanate from Lower Baggot Street, Dublin. If the nineteenth century is the century of religious women, it is the century *par excellence* of the Sisters of Mercy, who stand out as a most effective group, perhaps unsurpassed in the English-speaking world, and a very efficient unit in the forces of the Militant Church. The rapid expansion of the congregation to the far corners of the English-speaking world is nothing if not phenomenal. It rivals the rise of the Benedictines of Cluny in the eleventh century, of the Cistercians in the twelfth, of the Franciscans and Dominicans in the thirteenth, of the Capuchins and the Jesuits in the sixteenth, and of the Sisters of St. Vincent de Paul in the seventeenth. Twelve foundations were launched by Catherine McAuley herself in the short space of ten years. By 1855 there were thirty-one

Convents of Mercy in Ireland, fourteen in England, one in Scotland, twelve in America and three in Australasia.

The immediate impact of Catherine McAuley's creation on the English-speaking world was striking. In 1840 while he was still an Anglican and Mother McAuley still living in Dublin, John Henry Newman voiced the opinion that there was no reason why the Church of England should not supply from among its members those requisites necessary for the life and character of a Sister of Mercy. His suggestion led to the establishment of the Sisterhood of the Holy Cross, a congregation based on the Rule of the Sisters of Mercy. Later again, in 1848, Priscilla Lydia Sellon (Mother Lydia), founded at Devonport another order of Anglican religious whom she called the ' Sisters of Mercy '.[24] These Anglican Sisterhoods were amalgamated in 1856, and were thereafter known as the Sisters of the Holy Trinity ; but the fact remains that within seventeen years of its inception the Congregation of Our Lady of Mercy had its imitators in the Church of England. The Sellonites were never really prolific: confined within the narrow limits of Anglicanism, they remained rather insular and conservative, leaving to the daughters of Catherine McAuley the glory of spreading the mantle of Mercy across new, and in many instances, uncharted seas of charity. Everywhere, in the popular mind and in the tradition of their Foundress, they proved themselves to be exactly what their name implied: Sisters of Mercy, devoted to the works which most characterised the Saviour as He walked the earth.

Social service and educational endeavours were the twin pivots on which the life of the Sisters revolved. Expansion of the Congregation was accompanied by an increasing efficiency among its members ; an efficiency most apparent in the field of nursing where we learn that " the Sisters acquitted themselves with signal excellence and with continuous progress in method and in scope."[25] The question therefore arises, as to why historians fail to give more than a mere nodding recognition to the work done by Catholic Sisterhoods in salvaging the last remnants of the nursing profession in the eighteenth and early nineteenth centuries. The answer lies in the fact that the majority of historians erroneously assume that nursing, be it modern or otherwise, originated with Florence Nightingale. Such is not the case. Nursing, like medicine, began with disease, long before the first chapters of human history came to be recorded. The advent of Christianity gave an important simulus to nursing by raising and ennobling its ideals, while the development of nursing orders in the Church ensured its continuity as a profession to the present day.

The present work is not concerned with the history of nursing as such. Suffice it to say that Catherine McAuley, through the congregation she founded, ranks with the greatest of the Church's great ones. Among others, with the early Augustinian Nuns of France, whose hospital, the Hotel Dieu, dates from the year 650 ; with St. Elizabeth of Hungary, the hospital patron, in whom royalty served humanity ; with Louise de Marillac, friend and collaborator of St. Vincent de Paul in his twin creation of Sisters and Ladies of Charity ; with St. Francis of Assisi who could see the image of Christ himself in a leprous beggar whom he kissed on the roads of Umbria ; with St. John of God, whose life is a splendid record of selfless service, and with St. Camillus of Lellis, for whom ill-health became an inspiration which expressed itself in a military nursing order, the members of which were given papal approval in 1586, with permission to wear a cross of red cloth on their cassock or mantle.

Thousands today wear this emblem of the International Red Cross. How many of them realise that a Pope had a hand in its selection and that it was recognised as a token of nursing for more than three centuries before Henri Dunant, impelled by the carnage of Solferino, established his world-wide voluntary nursing service, and in so doing acknowledged a certain indebtedness to Florence Nightingale?

For Catherine McAuley to love the poor was to help them, to improve their condition of soul and body ; in other words, to nurse them. To realise how well the first Sisters of Mercy imbibed the spirit of their Foundress, one has but to read the eulogy accorded them by Lavinia Dock in her four-volume treatise on the evolution of modern nursing:

> " The order of the Sisters of Mercy . . . early attained brilliant prestige in nursing. Its foundress, Mother Catherine McAuley, was a beautiful, benign, and highly-cultured woman of great gifts for leadership. From this (Irish) order went, in all, ten* nuns to the Crimea. They must have had hospital training at an early date, for they had skilled nurses when the Crimean War broke out, and in the same year, 1854, we find them taking over the nursing in the Jervis Street Hospital, while in 1857 they assumed that in the Mercy of Cork, under Mother Mary Josephine Warde . . .
>
> The extension of the Sisters' labours forms a unique phase of their history. It brings them into close and direct relation with the modern nursing movement ; it knits common interests

---

*This is incorrect; *fifteen* Irish Sisters of Mercy served in the Crimean military hospitals. Even as applied to the Bermondsey Sisters, the number is still incorrect.

between the Convent Sister and the self-supporting nurse in the world ; and it brings harmony, mutual interest and regard, where before there was wide separation and complete absence of acquaintanceship."[26]

Such recognition was won only through steady perseverance in face of prejudice and bigotry, for no great Catholic enterprise is ever accomplished but by overcoming a multitude of inconveniences. Yet these very inconveniences were the circumstances through which the Sisters of Mercy early learned that their congregation was "established on Calvary, there to serve a crucified Redeemer." For Mother Bridgeman, perhaps more than for any other of her contemporaries, this quotation was no mere platitude. Few foundresses have had to deal with a campaign of mendacity and misrepresentation comparable to that which encompassed her. Fewer still could have steered their course so successfully and with such unerring dexterity; for succeed she did, though perhaps not according to the standards of human reckoning.

In January, 1856, there arrived in Balaclava one Colonel Lefroy, Confidential Adviser to the Secretary at War on scientific matters. His mission, a secret one, was to draft a truthful and accurate report on conditions in the military hospitals. While at Scutari— he arrived there in October, 1855—he appears to have conceived the greatest admiration for Florence Nightingale ; and she, perceiving in him the champion who might take up her cause at the War Office, made certain representations to him in which she spared neither Doctor Hall nor the Sisters of Mercy. Not unnaturally then, Colonel Lefroy was prejudiced. Miss Nightingale impressed upon him that " the Sisters were too great an expense on the establishment, and far too numerous in proportion to the number of patients then in hospital," which accounts for his asking on arrival at Balaclava if twelve ladies were required for two hundred and fifty beds.[27]

*The Bridgeman Diary* supplies the best answer to Lefroy's question: " Far from wanting occupation in Balaclava, we had often harassing labour. The number of patients though seemingly small, generally included several acute and critical cases, one or two of whom would give more employment and require more care than a ward full of those we had latterly been attending in the south." The General Hospital at Balaclava was, to use Mother Bridgeman's own phrase, " a current ", with such frequency of admissions and discharges that the number of beds could give no fair test of the work entailed if compared with the hospitals on the Bosphorus. Admissions as catalogued by Mother Bridgeman for the General Hospital were: October (1855), two hundred and thirty ; November, three hundred and one ; December, three hundred and forty-nine ; January (1856), two hundred and sixty-eight ; February, two hundred and ten. Miss Nightingale when questioning the numerical proportion of Sisters as compared with patients, made no allowance for hospital methods other than her own. It meant little to her that " all extras, food as well as stimulants, passed not through the orderlies' hands but through those of the Sisters to the patients "; that the food was prepared by the Sisters, and that they engaged in night watching " by the express desire of the medical officers," who required the " constant attendance of the Sisters for those patients needing frequent doses of medicine or stimulants." In Balaclava such patients were always numerous. Reverend Mother's final argument was that " we have here neither servant, nurse, nor laundress, and our domestic requirements and arrangements, simple though they be, must have hands to do them."[28]

Personal observation gradually inclined Colonel Lefroy to a less critical attitude towards the Sisters, and despite Florence Nightingale's strong urging for a reduction of their numbers, he did not press the issue. The text of his report to the Secretary for War was that

" With reference to the female nursing establishment at the General Hospital, Balaclava, which I was instructed to review, the reasons given by the Principal Medical Officer for retaining the whole number of ladies there under Mrs. Bridgeman were such as to decide me not to press for any reduction of them."[29]

The financial aspect of the complaints submitted to Colonel Lefroy was dealt with by Mr. David Fitzgerald. He presented Colonel Lefroy with a balance sheet on which the expenditure of the paid nurses for one month was compared with that of the Sisters for the same period. The month selected for the nurses was June, 1855, " because during that period the establishments were most effective and the system of drawings settled." There were at that date six of Miss Nightingale's nurses at the Castle Hospital and seven at the General Hospital. Expenses in the former establishment amounted to £56-5-0;* in the latter they totalled £128-1-10¼†. Applying the same test to Mother Bridgeman and her community of eleven for the period dating November 23-December 22, the balance registered was only £41-10-1.[30]

In view of these revelations, one finds it hard to credit that Colonel Lefroy on his return to England in February, 1856,

---

*Divided as follows : Provisions, £41-5-0; Salaries, £15-0-0.
†Divided as follows : Provisions, £110-1-10¼; Salaries, £18-0-0.

brought with him a letter from Florence Nightingale to Sidney
Herbert, the tone of which is significantly expressive of her determination to condemn all parties in the military hospitals whose
presence was an obstacle to her own authority.

" I am now fighting for the very existence of our work,
and whether peace is to come or not, I desire for the sake of
that work, that it should be placed in ' General Orders ', so
to speak, before the next move, whatever it is, takes place.
Colonel Lefroy will inform you of the attempts which are
being made to root me out of the Crimea ; of Doctor Hall's
official letters to him ; of a Purveyor's ' Confidential Report '
against me. Might I ask you, my dear Mr. Herbert, to crown
your enduring kindness to me by . . . urging upon the War
Office to *telegraph* my powers to the military and medical
authorities in the Crimea and to myself. The hospitals wait."[31]

Sidney Herbert accepted the letter at its face value. He assured
Florence Nightingale that she need have nothing to fear from the
Confidential Report, and he began at once to negotiate for the
inclusion of her name in army orders.

It was precisely at this juncture that death claimed another of
Mother Bridgeman's community: Sister M. Elizabeth Butler of
Liverpool, the senior of the group and beloved by all for her
" extraordinary sweetness of disposition." She caught typhus in
the wards and died on the night of February 23.

" It was a wild, wild night. The storm and winds penetrated the chinks, extinguishing the lights, and evoked many
a prayer that the death-bed should not be left roofless. It
was awful to kneel by her bed and to hear the solemn prayers
for the dying mingled with the howling of the winds and the
creaking of the frail wooden hut. O never, never can any of
us forget that night. The storm disturbed all but her, that
happy being for whom earth's joys and sorrows were at an
end, and whose summons home had not caused her one pang
or one regret."[32]

The death was announced by the chaplains of the different
divisions after Mass next morning. By special permission the men
of the 89th Royal Irish Regiment were excused from parade in
order to attend the obsequies which were fixed for 3 p.m. Detach-
ments from every regiment joined them, as did also the Medical
Staff Corps which was formally paraded by order of the Principal
Medical Officer. Before the funeral, five Sisters of Charity came
with messages of condolence from the Sardinian camp. The soldiers of the 89th Regiment carried the coffin, followed by the
army chaplains and the Sisters, a Sister of Mercy and a Sister of

Charity side by side. The cortége passed through a double file of soldiers who fell into step behind as the procession moved slowly up the hill. The rocks above the grave were studded with men, and "in all that thronging multitude there was not a single head covered until the body was lowered into the grave." [33] A second marble cross was erected on this spot by the Medical Staff Corps of the General Hospital. The epitaph was simple: " Sacred to the memory of Sister Mary Elizabeth Butler, Sister of Mercy, who died of fever at Balaclava on February 23, 1856."[34]

There is no monument to Florence Nightingale in the Crimea ; but the graves of two Sisters of Mercy from Liverpool continued to be tended with loving care when those of more distinguished individuals were either forgotten or neglected. A chaplain on a visit to Balaclava long after the remaining Sisters had sailed for home, found the graves enclosed by a high iron railing set in cut stone, the whole being visible from the Black Sea underneath. They were decked with beautiful flowers and evergreens, and on the arm of the Cross on Sister M. Winifred's grave, the priest found a paper containing the following lines, composed, as he afterwards learned, by one of her orderlies:

" Still green be the willow which grows on the mountain
   And weeps o'er the grave of the Sister that's gone ;
More blessed its lot than to droop by a fountain
   And bespangle its green leaves with gems not its own.
Much more glorious its lot to point out to the stranger
   The hallowed remains of the sainted and blest ;
For those Angels of Mercy had dared every danger,
   To bring to the soldier sweet comfort and rest.
They left their own home when war's trumpet was blowing,
   When hunger and cold laid our brave comrades low ;
Their pure hearts were filled with Heaven's brightest of glories,
   As they came here to banish fell sickness and woe.
Still be hallowed their memories, they'll ne'er be forgotten,
   Though their bones lie so far from their green island home ;
And should e'er these wild hills be by Erin's sons trodden,
   Thou'lt point out, green willow, who sleeps here alone."

Nearby, another and a larger cross was subsequently erected " to the memory of the heroic dead, and to those Sisters of Mercy who perished in their service."[35] Bearing the inscription, " Lord, have mercy on us," this Cross was another addition to the Grave of the Hundred Thousand, the monuments of which were soon the only traces left of an unnecessary war in which three mighty nations stood breathing hatred and defiance at one another on the shores of the Black Sea.

CHAPTER 16

## THE CONFIDENTIAL REPORT

OF the four Parliamentary Commissions appointed to investigate the circumstances which during the greater part of the Crimean campaign involved the virtual annihilation of the British Army, none gave any detailed exposition of the experimental scheme for female nurses then on trial in the military hospitals. In December, 1855, Mr. David Fitzgerald, with the title of Deputy-Purveyor-in-Chief, was deputed to make such a survey; and Mr. Fitzgerald, after a detailed and exhaustive study of the systems under which the base and field hospitals were administered, embodied his findings in a Confidential Report. Early in 1856 the Report was forwarded to the War Office, where it was discussed, and red-taped, and thereafter so effectively pigeon-holed that not even Florence Nightingale was permitted to see it. Mr. Fitzgerald gave a copy of the report to Mother Bridgeman, and though nuns are reputedly bad archivists, this document has been preserved intact in Mother Bridgeman's own convent in Kinsale. Miss Nightingale knew of its contents only by hearsay; but taking Mr. Fitzgerald's revelations as a direct personal attack upon herself, she condemned the report as " a tissue of unfounded assertions, wilful perversions, malicious and scandalous libels " calculated to undermine her prestige in certain official circles.[1]

The opening pages of the Confidential Report, containing a survey of the nursing system introduced into the Crimea on January 23, 1855, expose the appalling lack of discipline, decency and decorum in the nurses which from the start had alienated the medical staff in the military hospitals. Of the original staff of nurses serving in Balaclava, the report mentions only two—Mrs. Shaw Stewart and Miss Clough—as being even relatively efficient. Of the remainder, some gained notoriety for their habits of intoxication ; others were insubordinate ; others again had to be removed for promiscuous conduct within the wards. Florence Nightingale contested these allegations, maintaining that her nurses were the very embodiment of integrity, efficiency and obedience. Here again a perusal of her private correspondence with Sidney Herbert reveals a totally different story. In places, this correspondence amounts to what can only be termed a crescendo of abuse ; as, for instance, when Miss Nightingale complains

227

of certain nurses breaking out and coming home ' dead drunk ';
of those whose characters were such as to make her legislate
against their entering the wards after 8 p.m.; of the many who
withdrew from the work to get married ; and of the constant insubordination which she never succeeded in effectively controlling.[2]
In fact, insubordination became such that Miss Nightingale on one
occasion was compelled to turn down a request made to her by
the chaplains : she refused to allow certain of her nurses attend
evening service lest they be afforded too many opportunities of
meeting the patients there.[3]

From the next section of the report it appears that misunderstandings between Mrs. Shaw Stewart and Miss Clough disrupted
an already delicate situation in Balaclava. Miss Clough ' deserted '
to the Hospital of the Highland Division where she maintained
herself in defiance of Miss Nightingale and the Principal Medical
Officer. Miss Nightingale's subsequent appointment of Miss Weare
as superintendent at the General Hospital failed to ease the
situation, for " whether from a disinclination to serve under
another, or by pre-arrangement with Miss Nightingale, Mrs.
Stewart left and went to the Castle Hospital ". There were then
one superintendent and six paid nurses at the General Hospital,
one superintendent and five paid nurses at the Castle Hospital,
and Miss Clough with the Highland Brigade. Most of the paid
nurses were sent home, only to be replaced by others who were
similarly discharged, so that " for some months before the arrival
of the Sisters of Mercy the nursing in Balaclava was in suspension
or abeyance ".[4]

À propos of the foregoing, Mr. Fitzgerald cited as the principal
drawback in the nursing system then in practice the undue interference of the superintendents with the general management and
economy of the hospitals, and the consequent unavoidable col-
lisions with Medical Officers and Purveyors.

" It should be the duty of the Superintendent to obey the
instructions of the hospital authorities and not to criticise or
contravene them," runs the report. " The Superintendent
should limit her control to a vigilance on the actions and conduct of her subordinates. Further, the Superintendent should
be exclusively under the orders of the Principal Medical Officer
of the Army, or his subordinates or local representatives. The
existence of a Supreme Superintendent is incompatible with
local control, action, obedience and co-operation—the local
Lady Superintendent considering herself not a subordinate
of the local hospital authorities, but of the supreme Lady

Superintendent ; and this has pre-disposed to unwarrantable meddling and unpleasant feeling."

It is scarcely necessary to observe that in this able report Mr. Fitzgerald was agitating against sanctioning Florence Nightingale's claim to be the Lady Superior of all the Crimea nurses. Equally clear is his pin-pointing of one of Miss Nightingale's greatest failings: an undue interference in matters outside her jurisdiction and a disinclination to delegate even a minimum of authority to any of her subordinates. She had, said the Reverend Sidney Godolphin Osborne, " the failing common to many ' Heads ', a too great love of management in the small details which had better perhaps have been left to others ".

In an effort to vindicate her position against the disclosures of the Confidential Report, Florence Nightingale wrote at white heat to Sidney Herbert complaining of encroachments on her department by the Principal Medical Officer, and of the efforts made by other officials to traduce her behind her back. The War Office, she felt, was not adequately supporting her. " It is profuse," she said, " in tinsel and empty praise which I do not want, and does not give me the real business-like standing which I do want." She again begged Mr. Herbert to move in the House of Commons for the production of correspondence, that the public might be able to judge between her and those who were traducing her and trying to thwart her work. But Sidney Herbert was all for soft-pedal tactics. In a careful reply, marked alike by common sense and good feeling, he ventured to scold her. " You have been over-done," he wrote, " with your long and harassing work. You see jealousies and meannesses all round you. You hear of one-sided, unfair, and unjust reports of your proceedings and of those under you.  But you overrate their importance; you attribute too much motive to them, and you write upon them with an irritation which detracts very much from the weight which would attach to what you say."[5]

Other letters show that this was also the confirmed opinion of the more sagacious among Miss Nightingale's closest friends. To move for papers would, in Sidney Herbert's opinion, be very injudicious. The publication of such correspondence as that demanded by Miss Nightingale, would focus attention on disputes of which the public in general were at the time completely ignorant. The less publicity the better ; and in any case, it was still true that the Lady with the Lamp continued to enjoy the ear of the Cabinet, and that " her many friends in England were powerful enough to carry her through, *right or wrong* ".[6]  Florence Nightingale might fume at the delays of red tape, but there could never be any doubt as to the eventual outcome of her struggle.

Pages nine to fourteen of the Confidential Report deal exclusively with the expenditure entailed in the upkeep of the Balaclava hospitals. An outstanding feature of these pages is the enormous quantity of liquor invoiced for the paid nurses as against requisitions for the patients. Miss Weare lodged several complaints against the nurses under this head, but fearing to retrench, she referred the matter to Doctor Anderson. He recommended that each nurse be limited to four glasses of wine *per diem*, without porter or else two glasses of wine and one bottle of porter. But the days of Sairey Gamp were not yet run out. The nurses rebelled, and Miss Weare was obliged " to yield the limitation to their clamours ".

In tribute to Mother Bridgeman's managerial superiority Mr. Fitzgerald reported that " the expense of the twelve Sisters is far lower than either of the other hospital systems. Conventual rules prohibit extravagance, and conscience and propriety repress waste or excess or abuse of anything."[7] Sufficient proof this to scotch the suggestion that Mr. Fitzgerald confided to Florence Nightingale his hope that the Sisters would not bring their extravagant habits to Balaclava.[8] As already pointed out, Mr. Fitzgerald was not at first an admirer of the Sisters ; but he was open to conviction, and he altered his views when personal observation showed him to be in error. His opinion of Florence Nightingale remained unchanged. He resented her interference in his department and so effectively did he resist her overtures that " her labours were shorn of much of the newspaper gilt that had formerly attached to them ; and this," said Doctor Hall, " gave great dissatisfaction."[9]

The Confidential Report concludes with a eulogy on Mother Bridgeman and her community :

> " The superiority of an ordered system is beautifully illustrated in the Sisters of Mercy. One mind appears to move all, and their intelligence, delicacy and conscientiousness invest them with a halo of confidence in the extreme. The medical officer can safely consign his most critical cases to their hands. Stimulants and opiates ordered every five minutes will be faithfully administered, though the five minutes' labour were repeated uninterruptedly for a week.
>
> The number of Sisters, without being large, is sufficient to secure for every patient needing it, his share of attention. A calm resigned contentedness sits on the features of all, and the soft cares of the female and the lady breathe placidly throughout.

Lady nurses of the disposition and experience of Miss Weare and Mrs. Stewart would be equally useful, if the pride of will and independence of action of former years could be silenced, and humble obedience connect and maintain an amiable union between large numbers."

There is a relevant supplement to the Confidential Report: a reply to a query voiced by Colonel Lefroy regarding the exclusion of Miss Nightingale from the Crimea and the failure to consult her on the appointment of Miss Weare to the Monastery Hospital. Mr. Fitzgerald's explanation was that Miss Weare refused obedience to Miss Nightingale owing to the latter's resignation of October 1, 1855; and that a similar repugnance to Miss Nightingale's " control, supervision or interference " was more strongly expressed by Miss Weare's successor, the Superioress of Mercy.

"Resistance of such control has become a principle with them," wrote Mr. Fitzgerald. " They exist, they declare, as nurses free from interference, and cease as nurses the moment Miss Nightingale's supremacy is decided to rule or interfere with them."[10]

Mr. Fitzgerald took occasion also to inform Colonel Lefroy that Mother Bridgeman offered her own services and those of her Sisters to Miss Nightingale on arrival in Scutari in December, 1854, but that they were declined, " excepting five, who were provisionally engaged, with the power of withdrawing when they pleased," which they did when Mother Bridgeman transferred their services to the sick of the Crimea " under the immediate and undivided direction of the Principal Medical Officer of the Army."[11]

Shortly after the despatch of the Confidential Report Mother Bridgeman received a copy of certain " Observations on the Female Nursing Establishment of the Army" which had been compiled by Florence Nightingale for the War Office. Measured against Mr. Fitzgerald's disclosures, this document shows how far Florence Nightingale was prepared to go in her determination to secure that official and parliamentary sanction which she knew was essential to the success of her nursing enterprise in the military hospitals. The subsequent publication of her findings reveals the extent to which the ' Nightingale power ' had percolated through practically every facet of England's political structure. A few of Miss Nightingale's most serious misrepresentations will serve as an assessment of the whole tenor of her ' observations '.

Nurses are represented as having been invalided home, when

actually they were dismissed for misconduct. The Protestant Sister Elizabeth Wheeler is reported as " having withdrawn "; Mother Bridgeman recorded that she had been " summoned by Miss Nightingale before a special Board and dismissed for having written a little of the truth to England ". The ladies, nurses, and Sisters who went to Koulali, where they were free from Miss Nightingale's control, were " so mingled with those in Scutari as to make it difficult, even impossible for those who knew the details, to unravel them ". The Sisters in Balaclava are reported by Miss Nightingale as " feeling bound by their consciences to convert ", and she declared it contrary to her experience " to suppose twelve women to be necessary to nurse one hundred and sixty patients—which generates many evils ".[12]

Overlooking the fact that Florence Nightingale knew nothing of the actual numbers in Balaclava Hospital, the charge implied in the foregoing statement was as a knife-thrust to Mother Bridgeman's heart. It is quite true that as the work of the nurses decreased there was a corresponding upcurve of immorality among them.

> " But does Miss Nightingale's experience warrant her applying the same rule to the Sisters of Mercy?" asks Mother Bridgeman. " One would naturally conclude from this paragraph that it does. But we must place it in God's eternal treasury, with all the other exercises of patience and humility this Heroine of Charity has given us ; and I trust *it* and the rest will prove a lasting warning never again to place Religious in such a position."

Concluding her observations, Miss Nightingale, in Article 15, taking upon herself the entire credit for the " regularity and simplicity enforced among the nurses," pronounced the " experiment of sending nurses to the East " as having been " eminently successful ". It was an extraordinary pronouncement ; one with which few would have concurred, all the more so as it was becoming daily more apparent both in England and at the seat of war that the experiment of the Female Nursing Establishment of the army was far from successful, and that " no class of people could have been more disliked or despised than was the paid class of nurses in the East ".[13]

And while it is true that three figures—the soldier, the war correspondent and the nurse—emerge from the Crimean War as heroic, it is equally true that the nurse thus enhaloed is exemplified, not by the tipsy harridan of the hired category, but by Florence Nightingale herself, the Victorian lady of gentle birth and cultured upbringing, who owed much of the experience she possessed to

M. Prescote

Miss Nightingale complains of more interference with her control over the nurses—

It appears that Dr. Hall has, through the Senior Purveyor in the Crimea, obtained the services of two of the nurses about to be reduced from Smyrna. This Miss Nightingale did not hear of until after it was done—and resents as an interference with her rights of control—

It really has come to this point—Is every woman who can aid the sick and wounded, to be forbidden to enter the Crimea, even at the request of the distinguished head of the Medical Department of the Army in the East, unless with the consent first obtained of Miss Nightingale? I trust this will not be decided to be the case—at any rate Dr. Hall must, I conceive, be freed from any blame in the matter, as he has never—as far as I am aware—been officially informed that Miss Nightingale is supreme in his hospitals as far as regards the "female element"—

I confess I think it is time that we curbed the pretensions of Miss Nightingale to unlimited & almost irresponsible command over the nurses attached to the army in the East. When it suited her views, she threw over all those stationed at Kulali—and

Marginal Addendum to Nightingale Letter in Public Records Office, London.
*vide* p. 242.

Kululie W Hospital
March 55

My dear Miss Stanley

I am not aware that
any of the sisters of Mercy have interfered
with the protestant patients regarding
their religion; but I have seen on several
occasions the greatest kindness & attention
shown by them to protestant patients
under my charge & may also add that
any change regarding the sisters doing
duty here would be highly injurious
to the present perfect state of this
Hospital

faithfully yours
Fred K Gust Hamilton

Letter of Frederick Gustavus Hamilton, Medical Officer at Koulali.

vide p. 144.

Catholic Nursing Orders, and who was indebted in no uncertain manner to Mother Bridgeman and the Irish Sisters of Mercy, whose methodical efficiency caused her at last to modify her own ideas of nursing in Balaclava.

As early as January, 1856, there were unmistakable signs that the Crimean War was at last staggering to its inglorious conclusion. The losses of Russia, her financial exhaustion, and the critical state of her economy made peace particularly desirable. The war had taken a heavy toll of human life, a toll which no territorial compensation could counter-balance. Thus it was that Russia, after three years of useless conflict, found herself face to face with both human and material bankruptcy.

For the Allies, the cost of the Crimean War had been equally staggering. The French were exhausted, but censorship of the press by Napoleon III hid the extent of their losses. English casualties alone totalled over forty-five thousand, and the national debt was increased by several millions.

The real impact of the Crimean War, however, was its exposure of the radical weaknesses of contemporary Europe's professional armies. It revealed more particularly the ineptitude of the entire army organisation of England. Certain points are noteworthy. A staff college had been established in England more than half a century before the Crimean War, but in 1854 the majority of the staff vacancies were given to outsiders who had not taken the course.[14] This brought its own retribution. Wealth and birth were the basis on which promotion was awarded: merit, experience and seniority counted for little. Stemming from this was the natural jealousy which generated feuds between generals and nullified co-operation between units on the field. In the Crimea itself, allied co-operation was poor; ignorance of the Crimean terrain was accentuated by lack of adequate maps and tactical blundering led to one of the most famous military disasters of all time, the Charge of the Light Brigade, " which was magnificent, but it was not war ".* Supply organisation faltered and even collapsed. Horses were landed without sufficient fodder because of shortage of transports. Nobody thought of planning a railway to carry supplies from the port of Balaclava to the front just five miles away. . . . Instances might be multiplied to show that where care, skill and foresight ought to have been expected, there prevailed instead presumption, ignorance and inefficiency. The resultant sufferings could only be paralleled by the horrors of the Russian campaign of 1812, or by those of the Irish Famine of 1845, '46, '47.

---

*General Bosquet's remark: "C'est magnifique, mais ce n'est pas la guerre."

It was only because Russia lacked the necessary military strength to take advantage of the weaknesses of the invaders that the war was to eventuate in an unsensational victory for the allies. On February 25, 1856, the envoys of the belligerent powers met in Paris to frame a definitive treaty of peace, and in the ensuing negotiations Lord Clarendon, the British Foreign Secretary, contrived to effect a settlement sufficiently glorious to bring credit on the British Government. Over a month was to elapse before the final draft of the treaty was ratified. It was an anxious period for Mother Bridgeman, knowing as she did, that the final reckoning between herself and Florence Nightingale could be now only a matter of time.

Notwithstanding the trials which continued to multiply around them, the Sisters found " many, very many causes of gratitude to the good God " for all He had done for them in the course of their mission. The respect and reverence accorded them in Balaclava was by this time almost ritualistic in its manifestation. " I belong to ye'es, Ma'am ", or " to you, Sister "—this, to the accompaniment of a profound bow, was the invariable salute of the Catholic soldiers. Protestants convalescing at the General Hospital were equally enthusiastic. The soldiers in camp, not content that their wounded comrades should entirely monopolise the Sisters, tried by every device and stratagem to manage a few words with them also. " Please Sir," they would say to the chaplains, " do send us on an errand to the hospital to get a sight of the nuns."[15] The *Croke Diary* records that on one occasion an ex-patient from Koulali walked seven miles from his camp, ostensibly for water, but in reality to meet Mrs. Bridgeman " and her ladies ".

A letter from Bishop Delany in late January was of considerable encouragement to the Sisters. When assailed by renewed charges of proselytism, Mother Bridgeman had asked her Bishop's advice as to procedure, more especially when Florence Nightingale first urged that the Sisters be restrained from introducing religious topics even with Catholic patients. Dr. Delany's reply re-echoes the sentiments of Archbishop Cullen's earlier letter from Rome which exhorted the Sisters to " hold their ground until they should be sent away by force ". It recalls also the directions sent to Mother M. Clare Moore by Bishop Grant of Southwark, whose fear was that Miss Nightingale's legislation would reduce the Sisters to the status of " mere nurses ", thereby detracting from their true character as nursing Sisters of Mercy.

" Your work is so manifestly the work of God that we must expect various contradictions as a matter of course," wrote

Dr. Delany. " Whatever they may be, there is always one even course to be followed: bear up cheerfully and happily against them all, be firm in your just rule of acting, and do not leave your post. It is only when you have returned to your native home, full of merit before God, that you can begin to enjoy fully the happiness of your present mission. But there will be results, and from what I hear, they are even now beginning, which will be glorious to religion and beneficial to Catholicism in the minds of our fellow-subjects. . . .

" It is scarcely necessary for me to say anything in confirmation of the duties and calling of a Sister of Mercy. Noble as benevolence undoubtedly is, you are not mere philanthropists in the restricted sense of the term, though in its true meaning, the philanthropist is one who would minister to the comfort, the true and great comfort, of the soul no less than to the wants of the body. Your calling is from God, and principally for the salvation of souls; and you cannot undertake the mere task of nurse-tending unaccompanied by the higher functions of your Order. . . .

" I thank God most frequently for the manifest protection afforded you in your many trials, and hope to see you all return home soon and happily.

I remain, dear Reverend Mother,<br>
With sincere regard, yours very truly,<br>
✠William Delany."[16]

The publication of the McNeill—Tulloch Report in January 1856 so jolted public opinion in England that Lord Panmure ordered that a Board of General Officers be assembled at Chelsea to " allow the officers adverted to in the report to have an opportunity of defending themselves ". Among others, Lords Cardigan and Lucan (of Balaclava fame) and Sir Richard Airey, Quartermaster-General, were arraigned by the commissioners ; and while the Chelsea Board went a long way towards exonerating these officers, it still remained true that the mud and quagmires of Balaclava tarnished many a good English reputation. Now that the war was practically over, it was necessary that some step be taken to restore the national confidence. The effort at so doing resulted in the emergence of Florence Nightingale as a heroine, canonised by popular acclaim, the most outstanding woman of her day, the soldier's friend and the founder of modern nursing.

The orgin of this development dates from the time of Miss Nightingale's first illness at Balaclava. An influential committee was then formed in England, the members of which decided to raise a fund for the establishment of some school for nurses, under

a Council to be nominated by Florence Nightingale. A public
meeting was called for November 29, 1855, to " give expression to
a general feeling that the services of Miss Nightingale in the
hospitals of the East demand the grateful recognition of the British
people." [17] The form taken by the memorial thus inaugurated was
the establishment of a " Nightingale Fund ", to enable Miss
Nightingale to establish and control an institute for the training,
sustenance and protection of nurses, paid and unpaid. The existence of the Fund was notified in General Orders to the army, with
the suggestion that contributions from all concerned should take
the form of a day's pay. The announcement was coldly received
by the doctors. " I hear," wrote Mr. Robertson at Scutari to Doctor
Hall in the Crimea, " that you have not (any more than myself)
subscribed your day's pay to the ' Nightingale Fund '. I certainly
said, the moment it appeared in Orders, I would not do so, and
thereby countenance what I disapproved. . . . I believe the subscriptions *in the hospital* are not many or large." [18]

A sum of £9,000 sterling, represented subscriptions from the
troops. A letter directed to *The Tablet* on February 29, 1856,
discloses the method by which this enormous sum was raised. . . .

" You are aware," writes ' One of the Service ' " that a
large sum of money is being collected for what is called the
' Nightingale Fund '. When asking the contribution of the poor
Catholic soldiers, the expression used by the collectors is,
' Your subscription is expected for Miss Nightingale and the
Sisters of Mercy '. . . . Now Sir, will you in your journal . . .
inform the Catholic soldiers whether the Sisters of Mercy or
Charity will have any part in this collection? And you will
oblige me, and perhaps check a fraudulent scheme, by
informing the public whether this fund is for the purpose of
personally complimenting Miss Nightingale or for the establishment of a Protestant charitable institution? If for either
object, the present manner of collecting the Fund is a
swindle—an obtaining of money under false pretences."

The misgivings of the unknown member of the service were
apparently not altogether without foundation. The first remittance
of £4,000 from the army was described as indicative of the
" universal feeling of gratitude " existing among the troops in the
Crimea for the care and attention bestowed upon them by " Miss
Nightingale and the other ladies associated with her ". [19] The
" other ladies " were soon forgotten. Even Mother M. Clare Moore,
once referred to by Florence Nightingale as " my right hand " was
ignored. A woman of superior gifts and talents, and no mean
organiser, Mother M. Clare has not emerged as a personality from

the Crimean War. Lost in the shadow of the Lady with the Lamp, she was never given opportunity to generate any illumination on her own. History has been kinder to her, though, than to Mother Bridgeman. Both were denied recognition for their services in the military hospitals, but Mother M. Clare returned unscathed, if invalided, from the Crimea.

The obvious and invidious neglect meted out to the Sisters by the organs of public authority and the combinations of private individuals on the one hand, and on the other, the national effort to immortalise the " heroic devotion'" of Florence Nightingale was—said a contemporary newspaper—a public if unintentional admission of the fact that such devotion which is the ordinary routine of Catholicism was " a new and wonderful effort of Protestant charity."[20] Many of the Irish Sisters who served in the Crimea were as well born as Florence Nightingale; all of them were as well educated, and each of them more devoted than she to the personal service of suffering humanity. The devotion of the young and bright was not then, any more than it is now, something new to Catholic society, where long years of obscurity and self-chastisement for a higher measure of obedience and usefulness are everyday matters. Bearing this in mind, therefore, it cannot be too often repeated that the studied silence with which the Sisters were treated, while portraying an element of dislike for all things Catholic, was also in some degree an unintentional admission of the fact that the work accomplished by the Sisters of Mercy in the Crimea was nothing extraordinary for Catholic Nuns.

On the other hand, states an article in *The Lamp*, March 29, 1856, " it behoved the aristocracy of Victorian England to erect a monument which would prove to future generations that Anglicanism in the space of three hundred years had produced one truly great and charitable daughter." Aptly and elegantly did Cardinal Wiseman in his Lenten Pastoral of 1856 interpret the signs of the times with the declaration that

> " The charity which springs up suddenly in the world and reflects credit on itself, the world will take care to requite, to honour by loud praise, to exalt by exclusive applause, to commemorate by lasting monuments "; but the charity which, " long nourished in the secret of the cloister, had been for years exercised amidst the infected and plague-stricken lanes of English and Irish cities, was denied even the passing tribute of one generous word from those whose mouths were open to praise charity."

In Dublin, Archbishop Cullen had a similar message to convey. The Crimean War, he said, while shedding lustre on the Catholic religion, had given the Catholic Church fresh claims on the affection and admiration of the world. Discipline, obedience, patience and resignation were the virtues inculcated by that religion; and these virtues had been gallantly displayed by the Catholic section of England's army as well as by England's Catholic allies. The zeal, devotedness and courage of the Catholic chaplains were next outlined by the Archbishop, who concluded his Pastoral by acknowledging the work of the Sisters of Mercy in the military hospitals:

> " And can we pass in silence those devoted spouses of Jesus Christ, the Sisters of Mercy and Charity? With unexampled heroism and devotedness, leaving their solitude, they determined to encounter all the dangers of contagion, of pestilential climates, and of war, in order to afford relief and consolation to the dying soldier. Their labours, their sufferings, their charity and zeal must excite the admiration of every true Christian. Human praises indeed, and the applause of power, are reserved for others engaged in the same great cause; but the merits of the good Sisters, though they are passed over and forgotten in silence by the world, are registered in Heaven, where they will receive an imperishable reward. Oh, what an answer they have given to the bigots and fanatics who, not long since, proclaimed war upon them and undertook to persecute them in their peaceful abodes."[21]

The publication of these Lenten Pastorals and the failure of the English authorities to bestow even a passing recognition on Mother Bridgeman and her Sisters was not lost on Emily Hutton, late Superintendent at Koulali. Rather than " the deep injustice of refusing all honour and thanks to the Roman Catholic Sisters of Mercy should be done in England's name," Miss Hutton decided to " break the silence most dear and fitting to a woman." A letter from her to Cardinal Wiseman contains the first of many complimentary reports on the worth of the Sisters which at this eleventh hour of the war, began to emanate from sources military and official both in England and at the seat of war.

> " Of the labours of the Sisters of Mercy in the Crimea it is not for me to speak," wrote Miss Hutton. " I knew them only by report of those who witnessed them, and thankfully bear testimony to their priceless value; but of the twelve nuns who worked at Balaclava, eight were under my direction at Koulali

from April 10 to October 1, 1855. I consider it a privilege to bear witness to their devotion and obedience, to the perfect truthfulness and exquisite tact with which they performed the duties of nursing during those weary months.

As an individual, my testimony is of little value; but the position which I then occupied gave me an opportunity which no other possessed, of watching—and I did so, narrowly—the spirit which guided them, and the manner in which their work was done. More might be said; but I know that neither Mother Francis nor her Sisters seek for praise here. Still, at the risk of exciting a smile at Protestant fondness for Scriptural allusion, I would add that they are surely blessed in not receiving their reward of men." [22]

The translation of the Nightingale Fund into actuality lies beyond the scope of the present work; nevertheless, a few explanatory observations may not be here amiss. By 1859 subscriptions for the Fund totalled £45,000, and in that same year Florence Nightingale began work to establish a Nightingale School of Nursing in connection with St. Thomas's Hospital, London. She was by then an ' invalid ', but her adventures in the Crimea had so focussed public attention on the problems of nursing that she was enabled to play from her sofa the major role in transforming the recruitment, training and practice of what was fast becoming the profession of the gentlewoman. Miss Nightingale was the greatest publicist of the new profession; yet on examination, the training which she instituted in St. Thomas's was far from being the first of its kind in England. Nurses, under the supervision of a clergyman, were trained in St. John's House as early as 1848, and from 1856 onwards, pupil nurses attended King's College Hospital. What Florence Nightingale really did was to build on the foundations laid by others. There was actually little originality in her venture. So closely did the scheme coincide with the spirit and practice of Catholic nursing institutions that *The Times*, in advocating the project, went to pains to make out a case for the Nightingale School, and to wriggle out of the suspicion of imitation by inventing a species of originality for Miss Nightingale's idea. The interesting article thus framed reads as follows:

" In neighbouring countries the Sisters of Charity are useful and honoured visitors in every hospital. It is not indeed desirable to have in this country any such servile mimicry of the usage of other lands or creeds. There is nothing so barren as imitation; for all true excellence must have an originality. We may therefore rejoice that the system of Miss Nightingale is a new one, requiring in its votaries no unnecessary promises, and only such an amount of duration of service as they may feel disposed to yield. Yet the same spirit which prompts the Sisters of Charity in other lands, must live in the hearts of Englishwomen, and will, when opportunity offers, urge them to similar works and a similar life."

The originality here suggested appears to consist in the absence of Vows and in the scope provided for allowing prospective probationers to withdraw from the work should they feel so inclined. In all things else, the Nightingale School was the secular equivalent of the nursing establishments run by Catholic Sisterhoods. Even the word " Sister " was retained, to signify those more experienced than the actual junior nurse or probationer. And this, whether intentional or otherwise, was undoubtedly a gesture to the Catholic Sisterhoods of Florence Nightingale's acquaintance: to the Sisters in the Trinita dei Monti and Santo Spirito in Rome; to the French Sisters of Charity in the Maison de la Providence in Paris, and to the Sisters of Mercy from whom she sought to obtain training at an earlier stage in her career. Imitation even went to the extent of imposing the conventual rule of companionship. Thus it was that no Nightingale probationer might leave the home unaccompanied: two must always go together. Reminiscing years afterwards on this piece of legislation, one of the earliest probationers enjoyed telling that " of course, we always parted as soon as we got to the corner."

In March 1856 a fresh outbreak of cholera was detected in the Hospital of the Land Transport Corps and called for extra nursing personnel. The war was practically over, there were nurses for the asking in Scutari, and as Doctor Hall had his future career to consider, expediency suggested that he might on this occasion apply to Miss Nightingale without prejudice. On March 10 he wrote her a letter asking that ten of her staff at Scutari be sent to the relief of the Land Transport Corps. It was the moment of triumph for Miss Nightingale; for though she was still excluded from the General Hospital at Balaclava, the invitation was the " Open Sesame " to the Crimea and to ultimate victory for her. But she had little faith in Doctor Hall's good-will; when she left Scutari on March 16 she brought with her a plentiful supply of food, stoves, cooking utensils and other amenities which she felt would be denied her in Balaclava. These private stores would suffice to feed her staff till official obstruction was finally removed.

Apologists of the Crimean War find little but censure for Doctor Hall when treating of his attitude towards Florence Nightingale. In retrospect it is easy to suggest remedies for the impasse which developed between them; but for Doctor Hall the whole difficulty revolved upon the fact that he found himself over-ridden in the discharge of his duties by an outsider who, however great her capacity for administrative work, never ceased to be regarded in an unfavourable light by the majority of the army medical officers. [23] The conferring of the K.C.B. on Doctor Hall in 1856 did little to vindicate the blot left by the Crimean War on his professional career, and he was human enough to resent it.

One effort to misrepresent Dr. Hall was fortunately out-witted by Mother Bridgeman. A certain Doctor Logan, on the eve of quitting the Crimea, wrote asking Reverend Mother if she had any suggestions to offer or any complaints to make relative to the management of the General Hospital at Balaclava. Doctor Logan was going to London and would lay her representations before Lord Panmure. Mother Bridgeman's reply was typical: complaints she had none, and any suggestions that occurred to her would be made to Doctor Hall under whose orders she was serving.

> " Now, my dear Smith," wrote Doctor Hall to the head of the Medical Department in London, " if we had been as honestly dealt with by others as by this pure and single-minded lady, we should have escaped much of the odium that has been laid upon us for self-laudation and newspaper stuff."[24]

That Doctor Hall had his supporters at the War Office cannot for a single moment be doubted; and in this respect a document* in the Museum Department of the Public Records Office, Chancery Lane, London, is worth studying. Like many of the Nightingale Papers it is a letter of criticism ; in this case, criticism of the Inspector General. The occasion cited was the posting of two nurses from Smyrna to Scutari† and the subsequent confusion in the matter of requisitions and wages. The changeover was effected by Doctor Hall in his capacity as Inspector-General of the Army ; it was objected to by Miss Nightingale in *her* capacity as " Superintendent-General " of the nurses, and because she considered it " inconvenient and perplexing to have others interfering or making arrangements " in *her* particular department. It never once occurred to Florence Nightingale that she herself, together with the entire male and female personnel of the army medical service, came within the sphere of Doctor Hall's jurisdiction and owed obedience to him. On the contrary, she demanded of Sir Benjamin Hawes, Under-Secretary at the War Office, that Doctor

---

*W.O.43/97/155656, No. 411.

†This complaint, it will be noticed, crops up occasionally in Miss Nightingale's correspondence.

Hall be notified that " all arrangements relative to the nurses for
the Crimea and Scutari should pass through her hands and hers
only ".

The most interesting feature of the Public Records document is
a marginal quotation. An eloquent pointer to a definite anti-
Nightingale attitude at the War Office, this reference deserves a
publicity other than that hitherto accorded to it. The writer, a
certain N. Prescott, says:

> " It really has come to this point: is every woman who
> can aid the sick and wounded to be forbidden to enter the
> Crimea, even at the request of the distinguished head of the
> Medical Department of the Army in the East, unless with
> the consent first obtained of Miss Nightingale?
>
> I trust this will not be decided to be the case. At any rate,
> Doctor Hall must, I conceive, be freed from any blame in
> the matter, as he has never—as far as I am aware—been
> officially informed that Miss Nightingale is supreme in his
> hospitals as far as regards the ' female element '. I confess I
> think it is time we curbed the pretensions of Miss Nightingale
> to unlimited and almost irresponsible command over the
> nurses attached to the Army in the East. When it suited her
> views, she threw over all those stationed at Koulali . . ."

Dangling thus in mid-sentence, the unfinished reference leaves
one surmising as to how deeply the actual truth concerning the
military hospitals had percolated through the ranks in Whitehall.
The answer must ever remain obscure. The remainder of the
Prescott quotation cannot be located, but the extant portion is
sufficient proof that officialdom, while throwing a blind eye on
many aspects of the Crimean War, was not altogether ignorant of
the undercurrent of intrigue and jealousy which that war had set
in motion.

It was against such an overcharged background that Sidney
Herbert arranged the framing of a document calculated at once
to gratify Florence Nightingale and to cut the ground from under
Mother Bridgeman. The document, enshrined in General Orders
for February 25, 1856, was announced to the Army on March 16.[25]
Nine days later Florence Nightingale set foot in Balaclava for the
third and last time. Her arrival precipitated a final conference
with Mother Bridgeman. But peace was in the offing, and whether
its declaration would be immediate or delayed, Mother Bridgeman
was already determined on her future course of action.

## CHAPTER 17

## GENERAL ORDERS

FLORENCE NIGHTINGALE was *en route* for the Crimea when news of a cease-fire pending the conclusion of an armistice was announced to the army. The announcement gave general satisfaction. " The Muscovites seem quite pleased at the prospect of peace," wrote a correspondent to *The Lamp* on March 16, " and ere many days I anticipate that the Russian bear will be hugging the British lion, with Gallic cock crowing in harmony."

Another winter had passed over the Crimea ; the bleak upland was already carpeted with flowers, and the vegetation of two successive springs had obliterated the last vestiges of Balaclava and Inkermann. Fighting was sporadic if not altogether at a standstill; the ranks were full ; the hospitals were emptying ; the camps were adequately comfortable, and the troops well-fed, well-clothed and well-hutted. In view of such auspicious circumstances one is not surprised to find the Irish regiments staging a special display for the feast of their National Apostle. Shamrocks were sported in many instances—shamrocks plucked in the fertile valley of the Tchernaya. A Russian ' shamrock ' may seem almost an anachronism; yet there they were all the same. Not indeed the " sweet-smelling crispy trefoils of old Ireland ", but for all that sufficiently resembling the original to pass muster on the occasion of ' St. Patrick's Day in the Morning ' in the Crimea. The Fourth Division honoured the day by organising a race meeting ; referring to which William Howard Russell reported to Delane of *The Times* that the cries of the applauding multitude had now and then a particular ' chique ' about them which showed that " the Hibernians who owned the voices had not forgotten the particular rites and ceremonies by which this once celebrated day was remembered in days gone by ".[1] Mother Bridgeman, in her *Diary*, adds that " not a drunken man was visible on the course ".

Meanwhile Lord Panmure's dispatch, which gave Florence Nightingale the full support for which she agitated, was going the rounds. The dispatch was not settled without stiff opposition from supporters of Doctor Hall and David Fitzgerald ; but Lord Panmure persisted in championing Miss Nightingale. Even when it was pointed out to him that this dispatch while supporting her would censure Doctor Hall, the Minister for War remained adamant. He wrote to General Codrington, Commander of the Forces, that Doctor Hall's attention should be directed to the irregularity of his proceedings in introducing nurses into a hospital without previous communication with Miss Nightingale, and that the following statement should be issued:

" It appears to me that the Medical Authorities of the Army do not correctly comprehend Miss Nightingale's position as it had been officially recognised by me. I therefore think it right to state to you briefly for their guidance, as well as for the information of the Army, what the position of that excellent lady is. Miss Nightingale is recognised by Her Majesty's Government as the General Superintendent of the Female Nursing Establishment of the Military Hospitals of the Army.

No lady, or sister, or nurse, is to be transferred into any hospital without consultation with her. Her instructions, however, require to have the approval of the Principal Medical Officer in the exercise of the responsibility thus vested in her.

The Principal Medical Officer will communicate with Miss Nightingale upon all subjects connected with the Female Nursing Establishment and will give all his directions through that lady."[2]

For Florence Nightingale this General Order was conclusive ; nevertheless, the delays of the ' Circumlocution Department ' robbed her victory of much of its flavour. The war was practically over, and she was sagacious enough to realise that this last-minute definition of her authority really meant little. The immediate problem facing her was how best to conciliate the discordant elements in the Crimea. But in March, 1856, time was at a premium for all concerned, and the methods by which the General Order was known to have been secured, did nothing to clear the atmosphere. The order was made ostensibly because of a complaint lodged by Florence Nightingale—the old complaint that Doctor Hall had introduced two female nurses into the Monastery Hospital without previous consultation with her.

Sir John, though he took umbrage at the allegations of Miss Nightingale, made a dignified reply to the General Order, dated March 12, and addressed to Sir Benjamin Hawes.

" Headquarters Camp, Crimea.

Sir,

I trust I may be permitted to state, for the information of the Secretary of State for War, that I never appointed any nurses to the Monastery Hospital, although I was advised to do so by Miss Nightingale's own letter of October 27, 1855, a copy of which, with my reply, is annexed ; and what is more to the purpose, every nurse that either now is, or ever has been employed there was sent up from Scutari by Miss Nightingale herself, as you will observe by the following documents which were given to me by Miss Weare, the Superintendent."

(Next follows a list of relevant notes and memoranda.)

" The position of Miss Nightingale will now be perfectly understood by the medical officers of the Army, but it is right that I should add that, until the present time, I have never received from the authorities at home any official instructions defining her exact powers and authority, as it was generally understood that her mission related solely to the hospitals at Scutari; and until the receipt of the present communication from the Secretary of State for War, I should not have thought that I was exceeding the authority of my situation, as head of the medical department of this Army, in appointing on an emergency two nurses to a military hospital ; but even that trifling act of authority, I beg distinctly to state, I have not exercised on the present occasion, and the only thing I can charge my memory with having done that could give even a colour to this accusation, is having, when Miss Weare was in tribulation about someone to accompany her to the Monastery, sanctioned the Purveyor writing down to Smyrna to inquire if two nurses could be maintained there. An answer from Mr. Fitzgerald in the negative was obtained. Subsequently I understood, when the Smyrna establishment was ordered to be reduced, that two nurses were sent up from there to Miss Nightingale at Scutari ; but I am not answerable for that.

Having been censured by the Secretary of State for information that is not correct, I request that you will do me the honour to submit this my explanation, which I trust will be satisfactory, to his Lordship."[3]

Sir John sent an equally dignified, if somewhat formal letter to Florence Nightingale. Though smarting at the manner in which she and Colonel Lefroy had compromised him, he acknowledged the arrival of ten Nightingale nurses to the Hospital of the Land Transport Corps, and gave Miss Nightingale the information she required on the requisition system then in practice in the Crimean hospitals. On arrival at Balaclava on March 25, Florence Nightingale intimated that the General Order had re-imposed upon her the supervision of the General Hospital: Doctor Hall's rejoinder on this cannot but have had a devastating effect upon her.

"With regard to the nurses at the General Hospital, Balaclava, the supervision of whom you state has been re-imposed on you by the War Department, I take leave to observe that all doubt has now been removed by the General Order as to your relative positions, and it is a question, not for me, but for Mrs. Bridgeman to decide; but in justice to her and the Sisters under her orders, I must state that they have given me the most perfect satisfaction by the quiet and efficient manner in which they have performed their duty since they have been employed here, and I should regret their departure."[4]

That the Sisters might resign had not entered Florence Nightingale's calculations, but the doubts raised by Doctor Hall's pronouncement cautioned prudence, tact and diplomacy as the only means of conciliating Mother Bridgeman. Negotiations were politely formal when in the early afternoon of March 25 Miss Nightingale visited the General Hospital. Business was discussed without preamble. Miss Nightingale having heard that the General Order had caused Mother Bridgeman " some uneasiness ", assured her that " things were but replaced on their original footing ", and that she would " not interfere or make any change so long as Doctor Hall was satisfied." In an interview with Doctor Beatson Miss Nightingale had learned how much gratitude " they all owed the Sisters and how much they would regret any change in the hospital ". Granted that the Lady Superintendent was conciliatory on this occasion, past experience confirmed Mother Bridgeman in her resolution of not again working under her. The connection severed by Florence Nightingale on Christmas Eve, 1854, was not to be renewed. To " admit an authority and submit to it " was one and the same thing to Mother Bridgeman. She refused to " place herself and the Sisters in such a false position as to admit Miss Nightingale's right of superintendence, and then restrict it or refuse to submit to it ".[5]

Miss Nightingale then referred to the document signed by Mother Bridgeman to the effect that the Sisters would work under herself as Lady Superintendent.

"I never attempted to deny that I *did* come out to work under you," was Mother Bridgeman's reply. "You yourself dissolved the connection. Were I at home now with my present experience, and the same emergency to be existing as when we came, I would *not* come under the same circumstances.

And now that I am disconnected with you as before I left my home, and no exigency at all existing now, since the war is over, I do not see the necessity of renewing our connection."

Miss Nightingale's only rejoinder to this was that Reverend Mother would have " a lame story " to go home with ; she failed to comprehend how such a story " could be propped on a crutch of conscience ". Mother Bridgeman decided to leave that to God. The interview over, Florence Nightingale refused to take Mother Bridgeman's answer as final. She would call again next evening.[6]

Reverend Mother's decision was endorsed by four army chaplains who called to the Sisters' quarters shortly after Florence Nightingale's departure. The whole bearing of the case was discussed, and it was unanimously agreed that Mother Brigdeman's wisest course was to remain severed from Miss Nightingale. Even were it judicious to take Miss Nightingale at her offer of non-interference, no one believed she would be faithful to it. Mother Bridgeman realised too that submission to Miss Nightingale would entail the loss of Doctor Hall and Mr. Fitzgerald and their many colleagues who had always befriended the Sisters. Neither Sir John nor any other friend of theirs in the Crimea would approve of the Sisters placing themselves under Florence Nightingale. Their doing so would give her an opportunity of placing them in some unpleasant or difficult situation where their resignation " should be either useless, or be made under more difficult or unseemly circumstances ". It might even afford her a further opportunity of misrepresenting them at the War Office or of eventually sending them home in disgrace like the Norwood Nuns. Mr. Fitzgerald took the same line as Doctor Hall. He advised that Mother Bridgeman's resignation be effected " before Miss Nightingale could humble or mortify her with the only alternative ".*[7]

The manner of Florence Nightingale's second visit to Mother Bridgeman was nothing if not unceremonious. She sought admittance to the Sisters' quarters by kicking at the door, and when admitted, advanced towards Mother Bridgeman saying, " I am bringing in General Codrington—walk in, General." The Commander-in-Chief did not prolong his visit ; on his withdrawal Miss Nightingale asked for Mother Bridgeman's decision. The latter referred her to Sir John Hall. The Sisters came to him " on certain specified conditions ", and should it happen that he was " no longer empowered to keep his arrangements with them ",

---

*It is interesting to see how this phrase of Mr. Fitzgerald's is misquoted in *Florence Nightingale*, p. 195 (Woodham-Smith), which says that Mother Bridgeman refused to be " humbled or . . . mortified."

Mother Bridgeman would submit her final decision " to him and to him alone ".[8] Apparently satisfied with this explanation, Miss Nightingale withdrew and wrote to Doctor Hall. Two days later, March 28, Mother Bridgeman received the following from Sir John:

" My dear Madam,

I beg to enclose a copy of a communication I have received from Miss Nightingale on the subject of the authority which the annexed General Order has given her over all the nurses with the Army in the East. You will see that she refers to me for a decision, well knowing that I have no power to alter that which has been issued by the authority of the Minister for War.

It must, therefore, rest entirely with you to decide whether you wish to remain subordinate to Miss Nightingale or not. The perfect satisfaction you have given me since you assumed charge of the Nursing Establishment at the General Hospital would induce me to wish no change, but unfortunately, no discretionary power is left to me on the subject.

I am, my dear Madam,
With much respect and esteem,
John Hall,
Inspector General of Hospitals.

Mother Bridgeman's reply was immediate. On this same March 28 she tendered her resignation to Doctor Hall, using the occasion to express her gratitude for the " uniform kindness, cordial cooperation, and generous appreciation " shown by him to herself and to the Sisters under her care.

" Dear Sir,

As I find it is no longer in your power to continue us here on the terms on which you accepted our services in the Crimea, I beg to resign my charge to you from whom I received it.

During the sixteen months of our mission in the East our difficulties and trials have been many, painful and perplexing; but it is due to the Medical Officers, as well as to those of the Purveying Department, to say that they did not arise from them. On the contrary, we have ever found them willing to work with us kindly, and cordially to accept our services.

The delicate and cautious respect and gratitude ever evinced by the patients, even those of different creeds and countries, has also been to us a source of thankfulness.

May I beg you will kindly take the necessary measures to arrange for our passage home as soon as is convenient ;
And believe me to be, dear Sir,
Yours faithfully in J.C.,
Sister Mary Francis Bridgeman."[9]

So terminated the mission which from the outset evoked bitter controversy in Protestant circles and merited but grudging approval from certain Catholic sources. Mother Bridgeman's resignation was not a desertion of duty, as might be inferred from the latest Nightingale biography which incorrectly gives April 29 as the date on which hostilities were finally suspended. The resignation actually coincided with the cessation of hostilities, for on March 28, 1856, was signed the Peace of Paris which gladdened the world with the news that the Crimean War was over.[10] It is not generally appreciated that Florence Nightingale assumed supreme command of the Female Nursing Establishment of the Army *only* when the war was over. But because she was so confirmed in authority by March 28, all the military hospitals fell under her jurisdiction, and the idea was fostered that she never resigned the superintendence of the General Hospital at Balaclava, but was excluded from that establishment by Dr. Hall. Thus it happened that she alone was given credit for the success of the nursing personnel. The heroism of her associates was left to fade into anonymous mediocrity.

Failure of Miss Nightingale's third attempt to woo Mother Bridgeman was conveyed to Sidney Herbert on March 28 : " Mrs. Bridgeman and her Irish Nuns have been instructed to resign and go home and make themselves martyrs, which they will do, I am afraid, on Saturday, though I have piped to her and done the Circe in vain."[11] Mother Bridgeman had but one reply to all Miss Nightingale's overtures : she had just tendered her resignation to Dr. Hall since it was no longer possible for either of them to keep their mutual engagements. It could be argued that Mother Bridgeman was somewhat unbending in face of Miss Nightingale's suggestions ; but it must be remembered that Reverend Mother could not possibly overlook the fact that co-operation between herself and Miss Nightingale had already failed hopelessly. Co-operation now could only lead to further misunderstandings. Not until then did Florence Nightingale believe that the Sisters would risk the public opinion which was so much in her own favour in England. She coaxed, she pleaded, she even begged of Mother Bridgeman to reconsider her decision ; and this because " she daily learned how valued were the services of the Sisters in the Crimea." She harangued Mother Bridgeman for turning her back on the work, but as Rev. Mother wrote in her *Diary,* " the declaration of peace had arrived, the army was very healthy, and all the soldiers then in hospital were convalescing, so there was little nursing for anyone to do."

Florence Nightingale finally asked that Mother Bridgeman would postpone her departure for nine days. Mother Bridgeman, " seeing no good reason for refusing," gave her consent, at the same time assuring Miss Nightingale that " the fixed resolve of months was not likely to change in a week." Nor did it; for at their next encounter Florence Nightingale learned that Mother Bridgeman had no intention of retracting her resignation. A promise of non-interference from Miss Nightingale was the only consideration on which Mother Bridgeman would consent to stay. Balaclava could then claim her for " as long as Dr. Hall considered the services of the Sisters necessary."[12]

Florence Nightingale demurred: the War Office, she said, would never allow such an arrangement ; but if Reverend Mother reconsidered her decision, there would be " no interference with the spiritual duties of the Sisters." For the last time Florence Nightingale and Mother Bridgeman failed to achieve the necessary balance between the spiritual and secular aspects of their respective positions. The next entry in the *Bridgeman Diary* is particularly relevant:

> " Miss Nightingale took notes of our manner of nursing which I explained to her, as I hoped someone might benefit by it. She was very excited at this interview. She laughed hysterically, used the most groundless and contradictory arguments, and said *I* was putting a stone of stumbling between the Churches which *she* was trying to remove. . . . I thought of her reports to the War Office, the several charges she had levelled at us, and the obstacles she had so constantly raised against us. She intimated that if I would leave because of peace, or because I did not think we had work equal to that which awaited us at home, she would not so much mind, and she assured me that I would ever look back on that day as the worst in my life and the one I would most regret. I made no reply to this prophecy. Miss Nightingale then requested I would let her know when all should be fixed for our leaving . . . When she finally took her leave I felt thoroughly exhausted."

Save for one brief encounter on the day of the Sisters' departure, this was the last interview between Mother Bridgeman and Florence Nightingale. The quarrel between them was never healed except in so far as they forbore to make their differences public.

The original *Life of Florence Nightingale* by Sir Edward Cook gives but a faint indication of her feelings at the time, and as already mentioned, Mother Bridgeman directed that her Crimean *Diary* should not pass outside the walls of her convent during the lifetime of those whose names she had had occasion to record. The quarrel was, perhaps, necessary, lest it be forgotten that these two extraordinary women were still only women, each excellent in her own way, each possessed of a forceful and energetic character, each somehow lacking in that spirit of forbearance which alone would have enabled them to complement and balance one another. Under more favourable circumstances, there are grounds for supposing that contacts between Mother Bridgeman and Florence Nightingale might have been as harmonious as those between Miss Nightingale and Mother M. Clare Moore. Unfortunately, they started off on the wrong foot, and from the beginning their relationship was complicated by a mutual inability to appreciate how the relative positions of Mother Superior and Lady Superintendent might best be accommodated.

Florence Nightingale did, from time to time, extend the olive branch to Mother Bridgeman ; she continued nonetheless in her private correspondence with Sidney Herbert to represent Mother Bridgeman as a constant storm-centre in the Crimea. And even though Miss Nightingale found Mother Bridgeman a somewhat difficult person to deal with, it still remains an incontrovertible fact that Miss Nightingale was the only person with whom Mother Bridgeman had any difference during the whole of her stay in the East. For Mother Bridgeman that difference was entirely a matter of principle. The quarrel-free character of her administration is all the more apparent when set against the tensions, the cross-purposes, the divisions and the rivalries which impeded so many philanthropic schemes prepared for the alleviation of the suffering troops in the base and field hospitals of the Crimea.

The wounds inflicted by the Nightingale-Bridgeman misunderstanding went deep, and continued to fester long after the Crimean War had passed into history. Mother Bridgeman could never think of Balaclava without sorrow. For Florence Nightingale it represented the most frustrating part of her mission. Perhaps, in retrospect, each in time saw matters in clearer perspective— saw too, how comparatively easy of solution were their mutual difficulties. One would also like to think that each at the end of a long and eventful life could remember the other without rancour.

After the war, Mother Bridgeman's apostolate was that of one whose "life was hidden with Christ in God." Florence Nightingale continued to pursue a more official career, beginning

with a scheme outlined in *Notes on Nursing* which she presented
to the War Office Committee in 1856. Published in 1859 this
pamphlet caused a sensation in the world of nursing, of medical
science and of hospital management. The most remarkable feature
of the pamphlet was its complete revision of Miss Nightingale's
earlier ideas on nursing—a revision which, in part, stems from
the notes taken at her last interview with Mother Bridgeman. In
admitting such a revision, Florence Nightingale did not acknowledge any similarity between her new system and that of Mother
Bridgeman: the long letters of criticism sent to Sidney Herbert
when Koulali was opened were enough to deter her from such
an admission. But while Miss Nightingale condemned, she also
copied, and she owed Mother Bridgeman far more than she ever
cared to acknowledge. Their otherwise turbulent relationship had
at least this one saving quality to recommend it.

As far as such a thing is possible, Florence Nightingale received
her canonization in this world . . . Her friends in the Church
never ceased to pray for her; and among Manning's papers there
is still to be seen an old soldier's request for a Mass to be said
"for the salvation of the soul of Florence Nightingale."

The dignified manner in which Mother Bridgeman resigned her
charge to Doctor Hall signified ultimate failure for the hopes of
Florence Nightingale. Although there was little to be done, and
all faces were turned homewards, the odium of being the occasion
of the resignation of a corps of most competent nurses, idolized
by the patients and trusted in the highest degree by the medical
staff, fell heavily upon the Lady Superintendent, and caused her
final sojourn in the Crimea to be not a little unpleasant. William
Howard Russell, taking the situation at its face value, reported
that there was " a secession among the Sisters of Mercy." This
information having duly found its way into the columns of
*The Times* was the final pronouncement of that journal on
Mother Bridgeman and her Sisters. Other newspapers were less
reticent. The correspondent for *The Lamp,* 12 April, 1856, left
no room for doubt in the minds of his readers by his announcement that

> " The Sisters leave the Crimea, the scene of their useful
> and hallowed labours, bearing with them the affectionate
> esteem and cordial good wishes of everyone who can appre-
> ciate the purity of their character, the disinterested piety of
> their lives, and their universally acknowledged usefulness in
> the sacred vocation of ministering to the sick and wounded
> soldier. Many will be the ardent prayer offered to Heaven

for the safe return of these excellent ladies to their native
land . . . Sir John Hall's sentiments respecting the perfect
manner in which the Sisters performed their duties in the
hospitals here are well known to be of the most favourable
nature. He is in every way completely satisfied with their
mode of nursing, and very much regrets their being obliged,
by the peculiar circumstances in which they were placed, to
quit thus prematurely the scene of their useful and charitable
labours."

At a later date—April 28—the leader writer of *The Cork
Examiner,* drawing upon information forwarded to the editor by
Father Augustine Maguire, made the Sisters the subject of his
column. The excerpt, though lengthy, is sufficiently important to
be quoted in full.

" If the reports which we receive be correct, the good nuns
have been badly treated by Miss Nightingale, whose greatest
glory consists in being their imitator. At present we cannot
publish all the facts, but we will do our best to aid towards
justice being rendered to the good nuns. This step, which I
regret to say has been made imperative owing to what has
occurred here, may be truly deemed a great casualty to the
poor soldiers of this army, whose prayers and blessings they
have well earned.

" The retirement from the scene of their useful and angelic
labours of these excellent ladies has caused quite a sensation
here amongst all classes and creeds, and the question
naturally arises: ' Why is it they leave a position where,
according to the unanimous concurrent testimony of all ranks
and persuasions, their usefulness was so distinguished?'
The circumstances connected with the whole affair are painful
(not as regards the nuns who are blameless), and will no
doubt come before the public at an early period. It is, I am
sure, superfluous to say that these inestimable ladies would
not have given up their sacred charge, had they not been
compelled to do so by a sense of what they owe to Religion,
to their Vows and to themselves. These nuns have only
consented to leave the Crimea because they have found their
remaining in it, under the circumstances, incompatible with
their profession as *Religieuses.*

" Willing and ready to obey the lawful order of the Medical
Officers here, these ladies cannot consistently consent to the
dictation of any lady, however she may be supported by
worldly authority, or however extolled by popular opinion

in England. The system of nursing, too, practised by the nuns, differs essentially (and for the better) from that of the lady placed by the Government at the head of the Nursing Department of the army, and the two systems clash. They have the warmest commendations of the medical officers of the army, and Sir John Hall's sentiments—favourable in the extreme to them—are well known.

" The nuns leave the Crimea, bearing with them the respect and admiration of officers of all ranks of the army, and with the affectionate regards and cordial blessings of the poor soldiers, both Catholic and Protestant. In the departure of Mrs. Bridgeman and her Sisters they have indeed sustained an irreparable loss."

In the six months during which the Sisters administered the General Hospital at Balaclava, a total of 1,358 patients passed through their hands.[13] News of the impending departure brought ' hordes ' of these ex-patients to the hospital, " just to have a last look at the Nuns," and to beg for souvenirs and keepsakes. Rosary beads, holy pictures and leaflets were greatly in demand, a book bearing the inscription, ' Given by a Sister of Mercy ' being by some regarded as more acceptable than even the Crimean Medal. Protestants also asked for books or pictures with " a bit of writing from the Sisters," and in later life many of these good fellows kept the Sisters posted with news of their varied fortunes, more particularly with accounts of their domestic and personal joys. " Sister, if it wouldn't be too bold, Ma'am," wrote one, " we'd like to call our baby after you." The respect and devotion of these genuinely grateful patients might well be deemed the richest reward the Sisters could receive outside of heaven ; and they thanked God for all as a grace that smoothed the difficulties of their path and made duties terrible in themselves, sweet and delightful.[14]

Only to his wife did Sir John Hall reveal the depth of feeling aroused in him by the General Order and the subsequent resignation of Mother Bridgeman. No rancour can be detected in his dealings with Florence Nightingale, but on April 1, ' a meet day for such a communication ', Lady Hall learned what her husband felt at the prospect of losing the Sisters.

" I am quite prostrate," he wrote, " as the General Order, procured by mendacity, has deprived me of the only real nurses we ever had ; for Mrs. Bridgeman, a very superior and conscientious person, the Mother Superior of the Sisters of Charity (Mercy),* has positively refused to acknowledge Miss Nightingale's authority, and I cannot blame her after what is past, and they all go home on Saturday next.† Thus, the Government loses the free services of these estimable women, and the soldiers the benefit of their ministrations, to gratify Miss Nightingale.

I was told, when I declined to interfere, that right or wrong, Miss Nightingale's friends were powerful enough to carry her through. My reply was ' So much the greater pity.' "[15]

Sir John's letter of April 5 to Mother Bridgeman, accompanied by an enclosure from General Codrington, testifies yet again to the Superiority of the Sisters of Mercy as military nurses in the Crimea.

" My dear Madam," wrote Doctor Hall,

" I cannot permit you and the Sisters under your direction to leave the Crimea without an expression of the high opinion I entertain of your ministrations, and of the very important aid you have rendered to the sick under your care. I can most conscientiously admit, as I have on other occasions stated, that you have given me the most perfect satisfaction ever since you assumed charge of the nursing department in the General Hospital at Balaclava, and I do most unfeignedly regret your departure ; but after what has occurred, I would not, even with this feeling uppermost in my mind, urge you to stay.

I enclose a letter from Sir William Codrington, Commander-in-Chief, expressive of the sense he entertains of your services and those of the Sisters under you, which I trust will be acceptable to your feelings ; and I feel assured you must leave us with an approving conscience, as I also know you do with the blessings of all those whom you have aided in their hour of need.

To Him who sees all our outward actions and knows our inward thoughts and wishes I commend you, and that He may have you and those under you in His holy keeping, is the prayer of

Yours faithfully,
John Hall,
Inspector General of Hospitals."[16]

General Codrington, for his part, regretted that circumstances

---

* The confusion between Sisters of Mercy and Charity was common to the time.
† Actually the Sisters did not go until the following Saturday week.

had induced Mrs. Bridgeman to quit the General Hospital and return to England with the " nurses who had so long been associated with her," and he requested that Doctor Hall would

> " assure that lady of the high estimation in which her services and those of her nurses are held by all, founded as that opinion is, upon the experience of yourself, the medical officers of the hospital, and of the many patients, both wounded and sick, who during the fourteen or fifteen months past, have benefited by their care . . . I am quite sure that their unfailing kindness will have the reward which Mrs. Bridgeman values, *viz.*, the remembrance and gratitude of those who have been the objects of such disinterested attention.
>
> Your obedient servant,
> William Codrington."[17]

From the War Office also came a message of appreciation, directed to Manning by Sir Benjamin Hawes, who wrote that

> " Lord Panmure, while regretting for the good of the hospitals in the Crimea that the services of Mrs. Bridgeman and the Sisters of Mercy should have ceased rather abruptly, desires to express his satisfaction at the work which they have performed with so much zeal and devotion ; and his Lordship requests that you will convey to these ladies expression of his thanks, and of his cordial approval of the services rendered by them to the sick and wounded of our Army in the East."[18]

The foregoing was, of course, a private communication. In public Lord Panmure, like Sidney Herbert, gave way to popular sentiment by upholding Florence Nightingale. His only reference to England's indebtedness to nurses other than the Lady with the Lamp is to be found in the concluding paragraph of a letter written to Miss Nightingale on the closing of the war hospitals of the east.

> " I am bound to express our heartfelt acknowledgement of those ladies—Protestant and Roman Catholic—who were associated with you in your labours, and have not shrunk from encountering privations, disease, and, unhappily in some instances, death itself, in ministering to the relief and consolation of those who have fought in the late war."[19]

Doctor Hall secured comfortable accommodation for the Sisters on the steam transport *Cleopatra*, due to leave for England on April 11. Such concern for their welfare stands in marked contrast to the indifference of officialdom in their regard on the outward journey. So insistent was Sir John in securing privacy for the Sisters, that several officials of rank, even on the plea of pressing business affairs awaiting them at home, found it exceedingly difficult to get any accommodation on board. One of them, Major Charles Pakenham, had to give his word of honour as a gentleman not to keep late hours and " to abstain from dancing so as not to annoy the nuns!" On the homeward journey Major Pakenham spoke often to Mother Bridgeman of his cousin and namesake, the Honourable Charles Reginald Pakenham, who embraced Catholicism, sold his commission in the army and entered the Congregation of the Passionist Fathers with the words of Wellington ringing in his ears: " Charles, my boy, you have been a good soldier ; now be a good monk." The subsequent career of Paul Mary Pakenham C.P., more than fulfilled the Iron Duke's command.

Having promised to inform Florence Nightingale as to the actual date of departure, Mother Bridgeman did so officially through Doctor Hall on April 10. All arrangements were by that time concluded and the Sisters were due on board the *Cleopatra* on the following afternoon. One farewell visit to the twin graves above the General Hospital marked their final outing in Balaclava. Next evening amid goodbyes from priests, doctors and soldiers and with a blessing from the Reverend Mr. Cooney, they embarked, each preoccupied with her own thoughts, and all deeply grateful that a difficult mission had been faithfully accomplished. There were no histrionics, no bugles, no trumpets. As Sir Shane Leslie puts it :

> " Unexpectedly the Sisters had come upon the scene, and suddenly they disappeared. Without noise or hurry they exchanged the calm of medieval convents, where orders were given in whispers, and the hours spent in prayer and meditation, for what were then the ghastliest horrors known of modern warfare."

In his farewell address Manning had bidden them to " make the hospital a cloister and their own heart a choir," and they had done so. Amid the grim surroundings of the military hospitals they kept their Religious Rule intact, fulfilling at the same time their twin vocation to humanity and to religion. Softly and without flurry or excitement, they carried out the nursing duties assigned to them ; and when the war was over, they packed their slight belongings and were gone as quietly as they had come. Not a single historian recorded their names. Indeed, few historians realise that the Irish Sisters of Mercy laboured for over sixteen months in two of the busiest military hospitals of the East. This was a record surpassed only by Miss Nightingale and some of the first group of Bermondsey Nuns who accompanied her.

Once on board the *Cleopatra* Mother Bridgeman, though exhausted, was not without a certain sense of deliverance.

> " We were really going home," runs an entry in her *Diary,* " and well might we say that at last ' the snare has been broken and we are delivered '. It was really true ; but for my part, I felt so worn out, wearied and stultified after all we had gone through, I could not yet fully realise the joy of our deliverance. I felt as if I could neither think nor feel again. I could just thank God, for what, I hardly knew ; but it was just as if He had snatched me from a precipice, on the verge of which I had long been walking."

Florence Nightingale's final encounter with Mother Bridgeman was every bit as tempestuous as their first meeting. She boarded the *Cleopatra* and demanded the keys of the store-room attached to the General Hospital. Reverend Mother, acting on instructions from Doctor Hall (who intended to exclude Miss Nightingale from the hospital as long as he could do so with impunity), had sent the keys to Mr. Fitzgerald. Miss Nightingale next enquired about the bad cases then in hospital: there were but six, all civilians, one a case of frost-bite, and disposed in the hospital huts. " I wondered she was not ashamed to make such a rout now about providing nurses for these few," wrote Mother Bridgeman, " when she left this same hospital for months full of serious cases, with only Miss Weare to nurse and Mrs. Davis to cook." Upon this observation she stood up, wished Miss Nightingale good-bye, and they parted.

Florence Nightingale however was determined upon two points: she would get control of the General Hospital at Balaclava, and she would instal some of the Bermondsey Sisters there as nurses. In pursuance of the former objective, she intercepted the orderly to whom Mr. Fitzgerald had entrusted the keys and introduced herself and her nurses into the General Hospital without Doctor Hall's consent. Her action was " a direct violation of the General Order on the authority of which she had already made such commotion ".[20]

In the second instance, she chartered a special transport to convey four Bermondsey Sisters and some extra nurses from Scutari to the Crimea. But the war was over, and there was no need for any such implementation of the nursing personnel in Balaclava,

By April 11, preparations for the speedy evacuation of the Crimea were being pressed on with rapidity and energy. The Army Works Corps was on the move homewards, several hundreds of them having already embarked, for the navvies' work in the Crimea was over forever. At this particular date there were only two men of a regiment 700 strong on the sick list.[21] Slowly but surely the soldiers were beginning their last march down the road to the harbour, the road of a hundred thousand dreadful memories, the road upon which Russell in January, 1855, saw ' one of the ghastliest processions ever imaginable ' the road which for so many ended, not in the harbour of Balaclava but on the shores of Eternity. Yet in spite of the evacuation and despite all protests to the contrary, Florence Nightingale concentrated the bulk of her nurses in the Crimea rather than at Scutari where they were more urgently needed. By this unnecessary move she put the public to unnecessary expense ; nor could any adequate advantage be seen to have accrued from the arrangement.

The incident did not help to mollify Doctor Hall, who was further incensed by Miss Nightingale's assumption of authority relative to the Purveying Department. Her contention on this head was that

> " I have personally exercised the right of requisition without approval from any Medical Officer ever since I received my instructions in October, 1854. I am in the habit of doing so in Scutari, and have always hitherto done so in the Crimea . . . and the definite position which I now occupy with regard to the Hospitals in the Crimea cannot be considered to have deprived me of the above-mentioned right, and I should therefore feel obliged by your giving the necessary instructions."[22]

Doctor Hall's reply to these demands of Miss Nightingale is an exposition of those qualities which, in his mind, constituted the ideal nurse—the nurse as personified by Mother Bridgeman and her Sisters:

> " My dear Madam,
>
> Anything you require for your own personal use or the personal use of the nurses under your superintendence, I have given instructions to the Purveyor to comply with without question. But all supplies for the sick in hospital, and their distribution, I think, ought to be under the direction of the Medical Officer in charge, who is held responsible for them by the regulations of the service.

I am not aware that any power or privilege you are entrusted with is infringed by this rule—certainly none that has ever been communicated to me ; and until the Queen's Regulations for the Management of Army Hospitals are altered, I must, without wishing or intending any discourtesy to you, request that they may be observed.

You must, however, allow me to observe, my dear Madam, that the custom in the hospital at Scutari is no guide to me, nor can I permit it to supersede the Queen's Regulations ... Suggestions of yours will, I am quite sure, meet with that attention which they merit.

My opinion of the duty of a nurse in a military or any other hospital is that she should implicitly obey the instructions of the medical attendant in the charge of any case or cases placed under her immediate care ; prepare and administer the nourishment ordered and attend to the personal wants of the patients, giving them medicine or nourishment at stated periods if required to do so, but initiating nothing of her own accord.

Under this impression, I see no occasion for two sets of demands on the Purveyor's Stores for the same patients in the same hospital, as it is fair to assume that the medical officer in charge is the best judge of what is necessary for the sick under his care. Besides, it would be unfair to tax you with the administrative duties of the hospital and Medical Department in addition to those of Superintendent of Nurses."[23]

Thus rebuffed, Florence Nightingale compiled a document for the War Office files which was nothing less than " a libel on the humanity of the doctors attached to the Balaclava hospital ",* and not least on the Sisters of Mercy, whose greatest offence was their refusal to remain in the Crimea after the cessation of hostilities. The hospital, said Miss Nightingale, was indescribably filthy. Quantities of extra bedding, clothes, carpenters' tools, boots, shoes and slippers cumbered the wards. One patient suffering from frostbite had not been moved for a week and was in a state " indescribably horrible." An " excellent second-class surgeon " who came on duty simultaneously with Miss Nightingale, set about introducing " real order and cleanliness " but was severely censured by Doctor Hall for his efforts. The members of the Medical Staff Corps were never sober, concluded Miss Nightingale, and it was customary for men of the Irish Regiments to talk and drink in the kitchen.[24]

_____

*Vide, Appendix p. 312.

The foregoing report, though disproved on all counts, was in 1858 published by the War Office Committee, with the result that the participation of the Irish Sisters of Mercy in the English military hospitals of the Crimea was given a negative, derogatory and prejudicial slant. The following unpublished memorandum was the refutation of the charges prepared for Sidney Herbert by Doctor Murray, one-time staff-surgeon at Balaclava:

" Sir, I beg to state,

1. That in April, 1856, I held the local rank of second-class staff-surgeon attached to the General Hospital, and had ample opportunities for making myself acquainted with all the details of that establishment.
2. That no men belonging to the Irish or other regiments, except those told off for the purpose of orderlies, were in the habit of frequenting the extra-diet kitchen.
3. That is was *not* customary to have extra bedding and clothes cumbering the wards, and that the statement of ' large boxes, carpenters' tools ', etc., is in my opinion, a gross exaggeration.
4. That the patient referred to as suffering from frostbite, although not under my immediate charge, was visited at least daily by me in company with Doctor Huish. That the dressings were generally changed in our presence. That we did not consider it advisable that he should be put to the amount of suffering caused by having his bed changed daily; and that in this case, as in all others requiring great attention, we found Mrs. Bridgeman and her Irish nurses quite equal to Miss Nightingale and *her* nurses, and much more willing to be guided by the wishes of the medical officer. That the charge of neglect is utterly false and unfounded.
5. That although I had, on occasion, to complain of want of sobriety among some of the orderlies, I consider the charge brought forward by Miss Nightingale as far too sweeping and not in accordance with facts.
6. I may be permitted to express my astonishment that the Commissioners should have allowed such uncontradicted statements to go before the public, when an examination of Sir John Hall, Mr. Deputy-Purveyor-in-Chief Fitzgerald, and other officers connected with the hospital would have shown how much such statements were exaggerated and biassed." [25]

Doctor Hall, in his turn, censured Sidney Herbert for allowing a statement such as Miss Nightingale's to go forth to the world "without either contradiction or comment," and he pointed out the utter impossibility of any patient being neglected for a whole week, as stated in her evidence.

> "From the kind and efficient manner in which the Sisters of Mercy performed their nursing duties during the whole of the period they were employed at Balaclava," he wrote, "I do not believe these good women could have neglected for one single day, much less a whole week, any human being placed under their care; and I think Miss Nightingale must have been misinformed regarding the case to which she has referred." [26]

Reflecting on Miss Nightingale's accusation that he himself had censured the surgeon in charge in Balaclava for introducing "real order and cleanliness," Doctor Hall pointed to a personal experience of hospital economy "which was surely long enough and extensive enough to enable him to distinguish between dirt and cleanliness." The General Hospital at Balaclava was a model of cleanliness and efficiency for many months before Florence Nightingale ever joined it, continued Doctor Hall. Its condition was the theme of praise amongst army and medical officers both British and foreign. It was a general hospital in the broadest sense of the term, and all who were suffering from disease were admitted into its wards irrespective of caste or creed. Everything connected with the hospital was conducted in strict conformity to the established rules of the service, one of which was that "the pack, arms and clothing of every soldier admitted into hospital shall be taken from him, lodged in the store, and a correct list of articles entered in the store register." This regulation was strictly enforced by the Purveyor; and though on one occasion a carpenter admitted from a transport brought a box of tools with him and placed it under his bed, "this trifling, unimportant, and almost unavoidable deviation from hospital regulations" did not merit the severe and unjust castigation pronounced by Florence Nightingale.

> "So far as I am individually concerned, these comments of Miss Nightingale are of little consequence, and I am persuaded they will be viewed, if not with like indifference, at least with Christian charity, by Mrs. Bridgeman and the Sisters of Mercy," concluded Doctor Hall. "But I have called on you to trouble you, the President of the Royal Commission, with this communication, in vindication not only of the

professional character . . . but of the humanity of the whole Medical Department of the Army which is so seriously impugned by the charge of culpable neglect thus brought against it by Miss Nightingale; and I appeal to your sense of justice to make public this explanation which I trust will, in some measure, remove the unfavourable impression that has been created."

The only return Doctor Hall received for his trouble was a curt reply from Sidney Herbert to the effect that " Miss Nightingale could have attached no blame to the Sisters of Mercy, or else she would not have invited them to remain in office under her." [27] Much to Dr. Hall's disappointment, his explanation was never published.

The unworthy aim with which Florence Nightingale's statement was written excited more pity than anger in the mind of Sir John Hall; but while he was convinced that " she obtained supreme authority over the whole nursing department by representations which did her no credit," he was genuinely puzzled as to why she was so rabidly angry against himself, seeing that " he never did anything willingly to offend her." His first and gravest offence against the Lady with the Lamp was his disinclination to ride round the regimental hospitals in her entourage when she first visited the Crimea in the summer of 1855. She had notified him of her arrival; but Dr. Hall whose time was then somewhat occupied, had asked Doctor Hadley to accompany her.

" Miss Nightingale was then at the zenith of her popularity," wrote Doctor Hall to Mother Bridgeman, " and no wonder she was offended after the abject homage that had been paid to her in Scutari."[28]

Neither in April 1856 nor at any later date did Mother Bridgeman vouchsafe any public reply to the charges adduced by Florence Nightingale. It was enough that these charges were dealt with by Dr. Hall and others more competent than she; and though in 1858 she wrote a lengthy explanation of certain matters at Dr. Hall's request, she insisted on its being kept confidential and only made use of should circumstances demand. Her letter (despite its length), deserves to be quoted in full.

Convent of Mercy,
Kinsale,
April 15, 1858.

My dear Sir,

The frost-bitten patient McDonald was not able to leave his bed from the time he entered hospital, a period of some months I think. It is not true that the bed sores on his back had remained undiscovered. They were well known and daily dressed. The doctors and dressers knew of them, the Sister of the ward knew of them, so did I. Even his poor head was becoming sore.

A number of down pillows (given me by the Church of England Chaplain, Mr. Crosier) were principally devoted to McDonald's use. One was usually under his head, one under his hip. These were changed as was found necessary. He cried and complained even for the disturbance caused by removing them. The least move seemed to torture him.

For a considerable time after McDonald's admission his wounds were dressed twice each day. After he had become so diseased and so miserably irritable, Dr. Murray considered any advantage that might result from the second daily dressing should be more than counterbalanced by the irritation and torture that always resulted; so latterly he was dressed but once a day. The daily dressing used to be regularly done, generally under the superintendence of the Medical Officer.

Probably it is not necessary for me to tell you that it was not by any of us that McDonald's wounds were dressed.

While I was in Scutari under Miss Nightingale in January '55, an order was issued forbidding any nurse to dress wounds, as this duty was considered to belong entirely to the surgeons and their appointed dressers. From that time on we never opened or dressed any wound without the express permission of the surgeon in charge. The Medical Officers never deputed to us the charge of McDonald's dressings; therefore we never did attempt them. They always superintended them themselves, and not only did those surgeons who were in regular charge of the ward do this, but those also who supplied the place of the regular surgeon in his absence. Drs. Huish and Murray together usually examined this poor sufferer's wounds, and it is our conviction that he received the kindest and most considerate care and attention. His every wish and even fancy used to be complied with if at all possible.

It may be well to remark that though the Sister did not herself dress these wounds, she is just as sure of their having been regularly dressed, as if she did them herself. She usually cut the linen to the sizes required for each wound. She saw the poultices prepared. The dressings, usually five in number —two for the back, two for the feet and one for the hip—she saw these going on and heard the piteous complaints of the sufferer.

The Medical Officers sometimes asked did we usually attend operations. I replied that that entirely depended on them, that we never intruded ourselves, and that our services were at their disposal. The Medical Officers seemed to consider our care more needed after than during operations, to guard against bleeding etc. Our work consisted principally in receiving the directions of the M.O.s, and seeing them punctually fulfilled; to inform them of any important changes we might observe in their absence; to receive the extra diets and see them properly prepared and individually distributed in the proper time and portions; to take charge of the stimulants; to endeavour to influence the orderlies to discharge their duty faithfully, and to preserve the needful tranquillity and order in the wards. In short, to add by every means in our power to the comfort of the patients, but always in conformity with the obedience we owed the doctors.

It is quite true that McDonald's *bed* had not been changed for a week (and this is one of the many cases in which a truth may be forced to do the work of a falsehood). The Sister who nursed him says she believes it was nearly a fortnight before we left since his *bed* had been dressed, and that the intervals between the changes before that had often been longer, but the inference those unacquainted with nursing should naturally draw from this does not really follow.

Every nurse knows that there are means which prevent the necessity of frequent changes of the *beds* of helpless patients, which are used when those changes are productive of great suffering or exhaustion. These means had long been in use in McDonald's case: i.e., a waterproof cover over his mattress, and over this the sheets so folded and placed that they could be removed with the least possible amount of suffering to the patient. This, with as many soft pillows as he pleased, was and had been the usual manner in which poor McDonald was arranged.

The last time Sister M. Clare found it necessary to change his bed, she enquired of Dr. Murray if it might be done. He replied that the patient was not then in a state to admit of it, that it should be done as soon as it could be safely undertaken. Some days passed, then Dr. Murray expressed to her his hope that McDonald might be able to bear the change next day. All was ready for it, but at his morning visit the doctor found it necessary to defer the change still, and so it was deferred for two or three successive mornings. At length it was effected under Miss Nightingale's own superintendence. This was the last time, and was about ten or twelve days before we left Balaclava on 12 April.

I can well believe that between the doctor's visits on two successive days, a patient in poor McDonald's state might be neglected by the orderlies and get into a condition which could not bear description; but I did not know before that any nurse however clever, might put a patient through the ordeal described by Mrs. Roberts without the express consent of the surgeon in whose charge he was.

Late in the afternoon of the day we embarked Miss Nightingale came on board to enquire for the kitchen keys etc. I then mentioned to her that there were at that time but nine soldier patients in hospital, none of them seriously ill ; that amongst the other patients who were principally in the huts, there were three dangerously ill. I particularly mentioned as one of these this fatal case of frostbite and I gave her the number of his hut.

Before leaving I also accompanied Mr. Fitzgerald into the extra kitchen. We had in this kitchen three soldier orderlies. I never met three domestics more sober or satisfactory. We did not allow these orderlies inside the kitchen door and I never saw any but one enter the extra kitchen who had the least appearance of intemperance. I directly sent one of the orderlies to conduct him to his bed, and in the morning forbade him in my name to enter the kitchen again or present himself before us. I told him also that I wished to spare him the disgrace and punishment he so well deserved, and which I knew would follow if I complained him; therefore he must ask permission to return to his regiment. He did so, and seemed more touched and corrected by the mercy shown him than if the most condign punishment had been inflicted. The orderlies were strictly forbidden to allow anyone into the extra-kitchen without our permission, and we found them obedient.

I believe the neatness and order of the General Hospital was for many months matter of notoriety. Under the beds used to receive special attention from Mr. Fitzgerald. I confess I often thought the wards might be kept with equal neatness without so much scrubbing and moving. It seems to me impossible that any disorder could accumulate there.

In applying the rules of military order to the Huts, one should, I think, know the peculiar circumstances and construction of them before any just opinion could be formed. In some of them you may remember there was no spot in which to put brooms, dusters, etc., but *under the orderlies' beds.* Then with regard to the clothes, what could those do in whose ward there was no press or other place to put their clothes? Everything put in the stores at Balaclava was likely to be rendered useless by the rats. I never knew of extra bedding being left in the wards—except the unoccupied beds ready for patients could be considered extra: these were usually in the wards.

All had to deplore the spirit of intemperance among the Medical Staff orderlies, but there were many exceptions. I can state this with the more certainty, as some days before we left, I thought it well to give some token of approval to those whose sobriety and fidelity in the wards had merited it. When I found that these gifts, though of little value, were likely to be much prized—before distributing any of them, I not only required the recommendation of the Sisters of the different wards, but got the book in which their committals to the Guard Room were entered, and I found about thirty (it may have been more) irreproachable.

The reports you allude to *did* reach me in various forms while we were yet in London on our return from Balaclava in May '56, but I too heartily disregarded them to notice them. Some friends informed me that discreditable reports had been sent to the War Office. I was told of various reports that were being industriously circulated. I was urged to take measures to contradict all, but I perseveringly declined doing so. I could not see that these reports were of any real importance to us, now that our work was done, and they were much less than I had reason to expect, for during the entire time we were in the East I knew we were being constantly misrepresented. The shafts aimed at us are, thanks be to God, blunted by our happy enclosure, and either may never reach us or fall harmlessly at our feet.

Then I felt to win public opinion had no share in inducing us to undertake that mission, why then should we concern ourselves about it? If we really laboured for God as best we could, I felt we could well afford to suffer reproach if we did not labour for Him as He deserved. Then above all, the thought that we shall be soon summoned before the just, the *only* Just Judge, who cannot deceive nor be deceived. Oh! how clearly shall we then see the little importance we should attach to what is said or thought by our poor fellow-creatures. We shall then be convinced that all the favours of all creatures would be too dearly bought by one even venial violation of that Christian charity we all owe to each other.

I regret these charges exceedingly inasmuch as they may be painful or injurious to those Medical Officers who I so well know did not merit censure. My reply to those who urged me to take measures to contradict these reports was : " I shall not do it. I have, thank God, finished the work to the satisfaction of those who were the legitimate judges of how it should be done. I shall give no explanations unless called on to do so by the proper authority. Vindication will come in God's own time, be that sooner or later."

I feel you, my dear Sir, have a perfect right to any information I can give. I only fear it is not in my power to write what can really help you; but at least this long letter will serve to assure you of my good-will to aid in removing any unfavourable impression created against those Medical Officers whose humanity and kindness won our most sincere esteem and who deserved different treatment.

Gratefully yours in J.C.,

Sister M. Francis Bridgeman.

P.S. But two of those Sisters who were with me in the East belong to this Community; all the rest belong to different houses. One died since (she never recovered the mission); two others are gone to the foreign missions—" to the ends of the earth"—one to Buenos Aires, and one to New Zealand.

Do you know how long McDonald survived Mrs. Roberts' dressings? Clever indeed must she be if she could make him comfortable. I believe the Rev. Mr. Parker, perhaps Mr. Crosier too, must remember the case. Both were Church of England Chaplains, and they seemed much pleased with the state of the hospital.

Have you ever in England cases of frostbite like those of the Crimea, with all its attendant miseries? If you have not, one may safely state, that such a case as McDonald's could not occur at St. Thomas's!

Sister M. Francis Bridgeman.

In the six months during which Mother Bridgeman and her Sisters worked at Balaclava, the 1,358 patients who had passed through their hands, not to mention those other thousands in Koulali, added up to a harvest of which any person might justly be proud. All of this was placed by Mother Bridgeman in the Divine Treasury and directed solely to God's greater glory. For this end alone she had undertaken the mission, and with this ever in view, she and her Sisters had cheerfully accepted the labours and fatigues attendant on the nursing duties assigned to them in the British Military Hospitals of the Crimea.

It mattered not to them that others were entering into their labours, and perhaps, stealing their honours. What really mattered was that their mission proved that a group of Irish Sisters of Mercy could pull as much weight in the army of England as the Sisters of Charity were doing in that of France. Florence Nightingale, in a letter to Mother M. Clare Moore, assured the Bermondsey Superioress that " the gratitude of the army is yours." The gratitude of the army meant, in the last analysis, recognition by the nation, and by implication, future possibilities for religious as military nurses. Subsequent events were to prove how premature and illusory were such hopes.

## CHAPTER 18

## HOMEWARD BOUND

AT five o'clock on the evening of Saturday, April 12, 1856,* the *Cleopatra* steamed out of Balaclava harbour "amid the blessings and good wishes of all and the prayers of many."[1] Conspicuous among the grief-stricken throng at the wharf were three orderlies protesting their unwillingness to serve under any other superintendent now that "Lady Bridgeman" was gone. As the boat left her moorings the Sisters, with eyes focussed on the distant hill, raised their hands in last farewell to the two white crosses silhouetted against the eastern sky. Visible for many miles across the Black Sea, these monuments had become a beacon for all approaching vessels. Few ships anchored at Balaclava without dipping flag in deference to the holy dead; a custom which was observed on the present occasion by Captain Paton of the *Cleopatra*.

Arriving at Constantinople on Tuesday, a forty-eight hour anchorage in the Bay of the Golden Horn provided opportunity for new contacts with old friends. First among the arrivals on board were Mr. Robertson, the Purveyor-in-Chief, and Miss Emily Hutton, late superintendent at Koulali. She had come out from England to marry Mr. Robertson to whom she had become engaged before resigning her charge at the Barracks Hospital, and they were honeymooning in and around the Dardanelles. Mother Bridgeman noted with satisfaction in her *Diary* that each of the three lady volunteers with whom she worked in the base hospitals found the air on the Bosphorus conducive to the making of momentous decisions! Unlike Mary Stanley and Fanny Taylor, Emily Hutton did not become a Catholic, but divergence of creed did nothing to weaken the bonds of friendship and attachment between her and Mother Bridgeman, with whom she maintained a steady correspondence for many years after the Crimean War.[2]

Notwithstanding the pressing invitation of the newly-weds, the Sisters declined going ashore, preferring to admire from the deck

---

*The date of the Sisters' departure is incorrectly given as March 28 in *Florence Nightingale*, p. 195, Woodham-Smith.

of the *Cleopatra* the architectural beauty of Santa Sophia. Mirrored in the waters of the Bosphorus, its massive grandeur was so breathtaking that Sister M. Joseph Croke expressed the sentiments of all in her regret that " its ancient glory should have vanished, and that the once venerable fane where preached Chrysostom, Nazianzen and Basil should be now a Turkish Mosque."

From Constantinople the Sisters sailed for the last time, past Therapia, Koulali and Scutari—names which were to be forever graven in the memories of all. Scutari hospital was again crowded; there was the same dearth of nurses as in the early days of the war. But with a difference. In 1854 the number of nurses was inadequate. In 1856 there were more than enough to cope with the situation, were it not that they were stationed in Balaclava— unwanted and unemployed.[3]

After safely navigating the Dardanelles, the *Cleopatra* skirted the island of Abydos, giving her passengers a glimpse of the house where Byron had once lived; after which she set her course for Malta, arriving there on April 21. On the following morning two Jesuit Fathers came to convey the Sisters and Father Woollett, S.J., to the island. The crew of the Maltese tug chartered for the occasion wore their scapulars *outside* their shirts the better to give the travellers practical proof of their religious persuasion! It was fitting that at Malta the Sisters should attend Mass and communicate in the Church of the Knights of St. John. The Knights were a military order of hospitallers: the Sisters of Mercy were the first religious to blaze a similar trail with the British Army in the Crimea.

Re-embarking at 10 a.m., the Sisters reached Gibraltar on April 30. Because of their inability to go ashore at this port, they were visited by Most Reverend Bishop Hughes, who came on board with some of his priests to bless and congratulate them. Here was a man who was thoroughly Irish and enthusiastically proud of his nationality. Sister M. Aloysius records that he was dressed in a heavy black coat and sported a large broad-brimmed hat with a band of green ribbon around it.

The foregoing almost casual reference occurring in most of the sources to hand recalls the story of one of the most illustrious figures in Irish Franciscan history during the last century, and suggests a short biographical deviation here. Born in Wexford in June 1788, Henry Hughes was ordained in the Franciscan College of Andalusia, Spain, in 1811, after which he returned to Ireland and between 1815 and 1824 discharged the office of Guardian in Ross, Wexford and in the old Friary of St. Francis,

Cork. In 1832 he was appointed Guardian in Dublin where, in a small house in Cook Street, he guided the Friars through the last rigours of the penal days. He was elected Provincial on July 19, 1837. It was during his guardianship in Dublin that the foundation stone of the beautiful Church of Adam and Eve's, Merchants' Quay, was laid, on April 16, 1834 ; and twelve years later it was Father Hughes who solemnly dedicated the small altars of this Church.

On March 15, 1839, Father Hughes was appointed titular Bishop of Hierapolis and Vicar-General of Gibraltar. The first outsider to fill this post, his appointment aroused the hostility of the so-called *Catholic Junta,* or *Board of Elders,* who organised a systematic persecution against him, refusing him possession of his Church, attempting to assassinate him, and finally imprisoning him. But Dr. Hughes was more than a match for his persecutors. From his prison cell he ordered that all Church services in Gibraltar be performed *gratis* during his absence, and in this way he deprived the Junta of the profits it sought to make out of religion. Public opinion in Ireland, England and Scotland was soon aroused, more especially when it became known that the maltreatment of the Bishop was due to the connivance of the British authorities in Gibraltar. A sum of £500 was raised which enabled Dr. Hughes to defend his case and eventually to win his release. Some months after his meeting with the Irish Sisters Dr. Hughes resigned from the See of Gibraltar. The last years of his life were spent in Ireland, mostly in Wexford ; and in Wexford he died in October 1860 in the 73rd year of his age.[4]

On Ascension Thursday (May 1), Cape St. Vincent introduced the *Cleopatra* to a rough and squally passage over the Bay of Biscay. Spithead was sighted on the 7th. On the following afternoon the travellers disembarked at Portsmouth, and a wire was sent to London announcing that " the Sisters and the cannons have landed!" And then occurred the unforeseen. The officer commanding the regiment which returned to England on the *Cleopatra* asked the Sisters to share their triumph by walking at the head of the regiment from the ship to the railway station, a short distance away. Their compliance with the officer's request shows how little the events of the Crimean War had helped to water down the anti-Catholic prejudices of England, for with woeful lack of chivalry and appreciation the crowd began to hoot and pelt the Sisters until the soldiers lifted their rifles to the rescue.[5]

Arriving at London at 10 p.m., on May 8, the Sisters were once again accommodated at the Convents of Mercy in Blandford

Square and Chelsea. Since October 1854 their expedition had entailed some ten thousand miles of travel, not a single mile of which was undertaken save at the call of duty. " And we had more reasons than one to rejoice in this," explained Mother Bridgeman. " Our spirit of enclosure served to distinguish us entirely from our secular colleagues, and to give much edification to non-Catholics, who seemed not a little surprised that when nuns got out of their prisons they did not take every opportunity of seeing and being seen." Some there were who considered it a great boon for the Sisters to be emancipated from conventual restrictions under any conditions.[6]

While at Blandford Square Mother Bridgeman was visited by Cardinal Wiseman and Dr. Manning; the latter was negotiating with Lord Panmure on the matter of supplying travelling expenses for the Sisters. The money was eventually issued to Manning by Sir John Kirkhead, 80 Pall Mall. There was neither question nor expectation of remuneration on any side. The War Office recorded not the Sisters' names, sent them no decorations, offered them no eulogy. The only royal benefaction which the sisters were given opportunity either to reject or accept was a gift of £230 donated by Abdul Medged, the Turkish Sultan, who saw and appreciated their ministrations among his subjects.[7] The unexpectedness of the donation, and the fear of offending the Sultan by a refusal, caused the Sisters to lay the matter before authority. On the combined advice of Cardinal Wiseman, Archbishop Cullen and Bishop Grant of Southwark, it was decided to accept the money for distribution among the poor. Bishop Grant, acting as intermediary for the Irish communities, informed Archbishop Cullen that " the War Office had taken great pains to arrange the Sultan's gift in the way least likely to make it difficult for the nuns to receive it. They told me to write the accompanying letter, which was to express that the Sisters received it for distribution among the poor and in no way for themselves."

The ' accompanying letter ' was a copy of one written by Bishop Grant to Sir Benjamin Hawes stating that

" the revised lists of the Sisters of Mercy who attended the hospitals in the East are now in your hands, and in the name of their respective communities, I beg leave to express their gratitude to the government for having allowed them to assist their fellow-countrymen during the war.

It is pleasing to them to reflect that their desire to undertake the duties assigned to them solely from motives of charity, and without any personal remuneration, has been admitted

and recognised, and that therefore, in being permitted to distribute the gift of his Imperial Majesty, the Sultan, amongst
the poor and the infirm, they will not lose the honour which
they so highly prized, of having been allowed devote their
services without hope of any earthly reward, to the alleviation
of the sufferings and the care of the sick and dying soldiers
of the Eastern Expeditionary Army."[8]

The Sultan's gift was duly issued, each of the Convents of
Mercy, Bermondsey not excluded, receiving its *pro rata* share of
the money according to the numbers sent out from each
establishment.

Another distinguished caller at Blandford Square was Dr.
Andrew Smith, head of the Medical Department, who sent his
servant ahead with "lamb, fresh eggs, fruit and confectionery."
Doctor Smith conferred with Mother Bridgeman for "about two
hours" on the happenings of the preceding sixteen months, and
urged her to preserve carefully any documents which she had relative thereto.[9] They would be required some day. He spoke of a
forthcoming investigation which he hoped would establish the
truth by the exposure of the grave misrepresentations then current.
On this head Sir Andrew was disappointed. The public enquiry
was never called: Sidney Herbert vetoed its introduction in the
House of Commons, even though Florence Nightingale ranged
herself on the side of those who agitated for it. Mr. Herbert in a
private communication, pointed out to her that such an enquiry
would suggest that there was "great doubt" in the minds of the
medical officers of the army as to the value of nurses in the military hospitals. Doctor Hall's testimony to the superiority of the
nuns . . . "would to all times, be claimed as conclusive by the
Roman Catholics. A controversy would be engendered. All who
have been . . . offended or slighted by you, would take up the one
side and your friends the other . . . and the public . . . would
settle that it was a pack of women quarrelling among themselves,
that it was six of one and half-dozen of another, and that everybody is to blame all round."[10] Sidney Herbert's efforts at shielding
Florence Nightingale against criticism are, to a certain extent,
understandable. After all, Miss Nightingale was the epitome of
the scheme for female nurses of which he was himself the chief
exponent.

When questioned as to charges of proselytism and to the number of conversions which highlighted the mission of the Sisters
of Mercy to the military hospitals, Mother Bridgeman had but one
reply. She simply quoted a relevant passage from her Holy Rule

—a sentence which, taken as the creed of service for all Sisters of Mercy, places Catherine McAuley among the great predecessors of, and pathfinders for, Florence Nightingale:

> " They (the Sisters) should act with great tenderness, and when there is no immediate danger of death, it will be well, first, to relieve distress and to endeavour in every practical way to promote the ease, comfort and cleanliness of the sick person ; since we are always better disposed to receive advice and instruction from those who show compassion for us."
> [Rule ; Ch. III]

While aware of the fact that a great deal of good could be done for the sick by way of advice and admonition, Catherine McAuley at the same time appreciated very well the minimum of regard the sick have for the counsel of those who offer them much advice but little practical help. Her golden rule was never ask questions : do things for people, and if they want to confide in you, well and good. It was by faithful adherence to such wise counsels that Mother Bridgeman could pronounce her final verdict on the expedition of the Irish Sisters of Mercy to the Crimea :

> " I believe there is no second opinion but that the amount of good that has arisen from the mission is far beyond human calculation, in numberless sinners reconciled to God, souls saved, prejudices removed, the true Catholic spirit enlivened or enkindled in the soldiers' hearts. They became proud of being Catholics instead of being ashamed of it. It was thrilling to see them parade for Mass on Sundays. A spirit of enquiry was excited among the Protestants—and this, notwithstanding all the mismanagement of those who organised the mission, or, I should say, who sent it out unorganised. What might have been the happy results had it been well organised, only God alone can tell."[11]

Before resuming her journey to Ireland, Mother Bridgeman decided to visit her foundation in Derby. Her decision precipitated the dissolution of her little community and the inevitable parting of the ways.

> " That parting left a blank in our lives which can never be filled," wrote Sister M. Stanislaus, " for we all loved and revered Mother Francis. She was a very remarkable woman, endowed with rare qualities of mind, besides being the possessor of many external attractions which rendered her pleasing to us all."[12]

Mother Bridgeman, on her own part, felt no regret at relinquishing the responsibility which, at the bidding of her Ecclesiastical Superiors, she had reluctantly assumed some seventeen months previously. There was in her none of that urge to power which characterised her great protagonist in the military hospitals. Her one desire was to return to her convent in Kinsale, there to place all documents relative to the Crimean Mission in the hands of her superiors, and to rededicate her remaining years to ' the service of the poor, the sick and the ignorant.' She was never known to have regretted going to the Crimea: she merely protested against the peculiar circumstances in which she and her Sisters became involved.

" With my present experience," she said, shortly after her return, " I would consider it little less than sinful presumption to co-operate again in such a work."

Thus in a single meaningful sentence did Mother Bridgeman summarise her conclusions on the mission to the Crimea.

Her objection was fourfold : the placing of Sisters under a secular Superintendent, especially a Protestant; the absence of security; the want of an Ecclesiastical Superior; the formation of a community recruited from different convents where there must, of necessity, be divergence of views and training. " It seems to me," she wrote, " that since our Rule and Constitutions do not provide for such a mission, it would be rash to attempt it again." All such observations to the contrary, Mother Bridgeman was visibly moved when on May 15, 1856, she said good-bye to the little company who with her had weathered the climate, the miseries and the misunderstandings of an historic and ill-fated Crimean campaign.

Travelling *via* Liverpool, the Sisters from Dublin, Carlow, Charleville and Cork reached St. Catherine's, Baggot Street, on the morning of Corpus Christi, May 22, 1856. They were received by Reverend Mother M. Vincent Whitty who within five years was to leave her native land to establish the first Convent of Mercy in Brisbane, Australia. The ecclesiastic who enlisted Mother M. Vincent for the Australian mission was the same Dr. James Quinn who, in 1854, travelled overnight by coach from Dublin to Kinsale recruiting volunteers for the Crimea.

The return of the Sisters was celebrated by a *Te Deum* and first-class recreation day. Next morning, the southern Sisters, hoping to get home unnoticed, made an early start for their respective convents. But good news travels fast, and the countryside was ablaze with bonfires and tar barrels, which had been posted at special vantage points the better to give a truly Irish *Céad Míle Fáilte* to the Russian Nuns! It was a long step from Ireland to the Crimea, but the ' Walking Nuns ', as they were once called, accomplished it, and were in consequence loved and revered as " our own Sisters of Mercy " by soldiers who continued to visit them for many a year after the events recorded in these pages. Those unable to put in a personal appearance sent letters, touching in their sincerity, and genuinely expressive of grateful regard for their beloved nuns, two of whom had served them unto death.

" I thank you kindly for all your goodness to me," runs one letter. " I hope your reward is in store in Heaven for you and the remainder of your dear Sisters that served God, and with His help saved many a poor soldier's life. When far from a friend, in a distant land, our meek Sisters brought the heavenly smile and the spirit of God into the wards among the broken-hearted soldiers. I can never forget your kindness. May the Lord reward you for all your goodness and kindness to me. No more for the present, but I remain,

Your faithful servant,<br>Corporal James Brazil."

There are also extant some letters written by the Sisters during the post-war years, the military phraseology of which is an indication of how apt even nuns can be in acquiring a vocabulary not quite in keeping with accepted conventual parlance. One such letter written to Father William Ronan, S.J., by a Sister who had been informed that her recovery from tuberculosis was impossible, concludes with the following appeal:

" Another of your volunteers has been summoned to the last campaign, and, conscious of a deficiency of supplies, is sending to all the friendly fortresses for aid. I am going to die, and am asking prayers of all my charitable friends that I may fulfil God's holy will in all things unto the end. There is no one to whom I can apply with more confidence than our kind drill-master. I will pray for you in Heaven, please God."[13]

On arrival in Liverpool, Mother Bridgeman was distressed at news of a circular issued from Baggot Street announcing the formation of an influential committee for the setting up of a general fund, the proceeds of which were to remunerate the several communities who had sent Sisters to the Crimea. Here was the very thing which Mother Bridgeman wanted most to avoid. Any suggestion of payment, even one emanating from the Mother House in Dublin, was so repugnant to her that in her determination to oppose it, she addressed herself, on June 10, 1856, with not a little energy and with pardonable bluntness, to Archbishop Paul Cullen of Dublin.

> " Convent of Our Lady of Mercy,
>                         Liverpool.
>
> " My Lord,
>
> Here, on my way to Ireland, I have just accidentally learned, with real dismay and concern, that our friends intend to acknowledge their sense of our services in the east by a subscription, the proceeds of which are to be divided between the communities which sent Sisters on the Mission, to be applied by them to whatever charities they please.
>
> " Will Your Grace forgive me if I offer a remonstrance? It seems to me that such a thing will quite tend to mar the future good results of our mission. Let the soldiers be able to reflect when all is over that the Sisters who served them, did so without honour or profit. Let them feel that while England piled her honours and her riches on the Lady or Ladies whom the emergency sent forth, the Sisters of Mercy served them and received neither. And I do hope and believe this conviction will bring forth fruits of salvation in many.
>
> " My Lord, what have we done that should be marked as extraordinary for Sisters of Mercy to do? Are we not the vowed and consecrated servants of ' the poor, sick and ignorant '? Is not serving them and ministering to them, in health and in sickness, our daily bread, the work of life for us? It is true we have been discharging these duties in the East under particularly difficult circumstances. Still, we have been but discharging *our duties,* though in no ordinary manner.
>
> " Will it not then, tend to secularise us to regard our part in this mission as such a wonderfully heroic work that subscription should be instituted to commemorate it? I cannot but view it in this light, my Lord. My experience of the mission convinces me that this subscription will tend more than any other step that could be taken, to lessen its good effects, both with Protestants and with Catholics.
>
> " I have earnestly invoked our Blessed Mother to stop it in honour of her Immaculate Conception, to which the mission was devoted from the start.
>
> " Pardon me, my Lord, for so freely intruding my opinion on your Grace, and believe me to be, with greatest esteem,
>                         Yours most respectfully in J.C.,
>                         Sister Mary Francis Bridgeman."[14]

Archbishop Cullen had the circular withdrawn; the proposed subscription was dropped and nothing more was heard of the influential committee.

On Wednesday, June 25, 1856, Mother Bridgeman, accompanied by Sister M. Joseph Lynch, and escorted by the Parish Priest of Kinsale, re-entered her convent home after an absence of one year and eight months. Her return home was commemorated by a Solemn Mass of Thanksgiving, at which the townspeople gathered in their hundreds to welcome her once more into their midst, and to show that her absence had tended rather to increase than to diminish their affection for their beloved " Mrs. Francis."

Once home, Mother Bridgeman again declined taking measures towards contradicting the many reports that continued to be " industriously circulated " against her.[15] The desire of winning public applause had had " no share in inducing her to undertake the mission," and she believed that " all the favours of all creatures would be too dearly purchased by even one violation of that Christian charity we all owe to each other." Silence, then, was her motto; hard experience her treasure. Her work in the Crimea had given satisfaction to those who were best competent to judge its merits: here she wished the matter to rest. Only in later life did she unbend, when as an old nun, ' full of years and wisdom ', she would recount for the younger members of her community the saga of fifteen Sisters of Mercy employed in the military hospitals of the British Army. A similar reticence was observed by her companions until 1897 when Sister M. Aloysius Doyle was prevailed upon to write her memoirs. The result is a charming volume entitled *Memories of the Crimea,* to which the present writer is indebted for several details omitted in other sources to hand.

After the departure of the Irish Sisters from Balaclava, Florence Nightingale's attempts at under-rating their system proved unavailing. In details of nursing, her arguments held no weight with Doctor Hall. The Purveyor gave her to understand that " she should not question for an instant anything done by Mrs. Bridgeman." In matters of hospital administration, she discovered that by order of the Inspector General, the Queen's Regulations " as followed heretofore in Balaclava " were not to be contravened.[16] It was on this note of conflict that the final curtain was destined to fall in Balaclava; for though Florence Nightingale might be applauded by the War Office and the Cabinet, it still remains an indisputable fact that her differences with the medical staff in the military hospitals were never satisfactorily healed.

By late April, 1856, the number of patients in Balaclava had reduced itself to ninety-eight, and as none of these were serious cases, Dr. Hall despatched them with all speed to Scutari. Their departure, and the steady evacuation of the Crimea, were a further argument against Florence Nightingale's remaining in Balaclava. But she determined to stay on ; she even retained the Bermondsey Sisters there also, apparently regardless of the discomfort which her decision entailed for them. On their first night in Balaclava their only shelter was a canvas tent, which by morning was completely snowbound. They were subsequently accommodated in the hospital of the Land Transport Corps where, in the words of an eye-witness, " they were badly provided for, being at times without even the necessaries of life."[17] Having no chaplain, they were obliged to walk two miles to Mass on Sundays. The army chaplains, save alone Father Michael Cuffe, regretted the arrival of the Bermondsey Sisters at Balaclava. " Their coming here," wrote Father Michael Gleeson, C.M., " implies that they tacitly approve of all that Miss Nightingale does—which certainly does not appear to be for the good of religion."

There were four Sisters in Balaclava with Miss Nightingale in March, 1856. She expected Mother M. Clare Moore to come up later from Scutari, and she contemplated summoning others out from England. But Mother M. Clare did not go to Balaclava: ill-health necessitated her return to Bermondsey on April 25. From Balaclava Florence Nightingale wrote her a long letter of farewell which many years later found its way into the Press, though not in its complete context. The biography of Miss Nightingale by Mrs. Woodham-Smith cites only a few disjointed phrases of this letter, full of affection and gratitude, but otherwise insignificant. The really revealing passage of the letter was that in which Miss Nightingale assured Mother M. Clare that

" you were far above me in fitness for the General Superintendency, both in worldly talent of administration, and far more in the spiritual qualifications which God values in a superior. My being placed over you in our unenviable reign in the East was my misfortune and not my fault. I will ask you to forgive me for everything and anything which I may, unintentionally have done, which can ever have given you pain, remembering only that I have always felt what I have just expressed—and that it has given me more pain to reign over you than to you to serve under me. Believe me, whether I return to see you again in this world or not, my dearest Reverend Mother's gratefully, lovingly, overflowingly— Florence Nightingale."[18]

Florence Nightingale's declared affection for Mother M. Clare Moore is somehow inconsistent with her disregard of the circumstances surrounding the remaining Bermondsey Sisters in Balaclava. That they were ill-provided with spiritual facilities meant little to her ; and while she professed gratitude to the Sisters of Mercy as such, she still sought opportunity to discredit Mother Bridgeman and her community. She got this opportunity in the disinclination of Father M. Gleeson, C.M., and in the ' refusal ' of Father M. Duffy, S.J., to attend to the spiritual wants of the Sisters in the hospital of the Land Transport Corps. " The Reverend Mr. Duffy, Jesuit, has been instructed to refuse Confession, and therefore Holy Communion to, or even to visit those Bermondsey Sisters whom I brought up from Scutari," she wrote to Sidney Herbert ; " and he calls them . . . a disgrace to their Church."[19]

Father Gleeson had been chaplain to the Irish Sisters in Balaclava. Father Duffy had been for some time extraordinary Confessor. Neither priest approved of the Bermondsey Sisters' coming to Balaclava. Father Michael Cuffe's intervention did not help. He also refused to assume charge of the Bermondsey Sisters, but his insistence that the other two chaplains should do so,[20] complicated an already difficult situation and furnished Miss Nightingale with an excuse for transmitting to Sidney Herbert the information that " the R.C.s were divided against themselves, the seculars against the regulars and the regulars against the seculars ; one set of priests and nuns *with* the government, and one set against it."

Recurring Nightingale biographies have so over-played this complaint that a few words of explanation from the two priests involved will best serve to get the incident into proper perspective.

Father Duffy's attitude was inflexible, though perhaps not altogether indefensible. For him it was entirely a question of faculties.

" I *disapprove totally* of your visit to the Crimea under existing circumstances, and I cannot consent to connect myself with the transaction in any way whatever. In my opinion, your Superioress has committed a grave error in consenting to your coming here in the manner you have come. Such a proceeding tends to the disgrace rather than to the honour of religion. You cannot wonder then, that it is my motive to have nothing to do with the matter, directly or indirecly. Besides, in my case, I could not undertake the charge of you in spirituals without authorisation from home. I assure you, it is with deep pain that I have written the foregoing. Were I to listen to personal feeling, there is nothing I would not do to serve you. But you know that for a religious the way between personal feeling and duty is plain."[21]

Father Michael Gleeson, C.M., took a more liberal stand. He too objected to the arrival of the Bermondsey Sisters at Balaclava, and he declared his unwillingness to form any connection with them which might bring him into unnecessary contact with Miss Nightingale. A letter of his to Sister M. Joseph of Kinsale on April 21 is particularly relevant:

"Mother M. Clare has gone home, hence the responsibility of superior necessarily devolves upon Miss Nightingale. This is the first time I ever heard of a religious Community being governed by a Protestant Superior; but then it is only a natural consequence, for since these ladies came up here under the guidance of a Protestant Minister, without even consulting a Catholic chaplain beforehand, they have not, I am sure, any difficulty in placing themselves under a Protestant Superior.

I never came in contact with any of them except on Saturday last when they presented themselves for Confession. Although I do not approve of their manner of acting, yet I cannot refuse hearing their confessions as long as I am here, when they present themselves in that way. But I have taken the resolution that as long as I am here I will never visit the Sisters in the Land Transport . . . .

I cannot express to you the feeling of sorrow which was manifested by the congregation on the Sunday morning after you left. It was with difficulty I could say Mass, listening to the sobbing and weeping of many of those present. You are not forgotten by these poor fellows, and the good that you have done amongst them will remain deeply engraved in their hearts all the days of their lives.

Ever yours sincerely,
M. Gleeson, C.M."[22]

Another letter, May 2, 1856, speaks of sixty-three patients in the Balaclava hospitals with "no less than ninety-five nurses and orderlies to take care of them." Every vessel leaving the harbour carried its complement of sick either to Scutari or to England. By early June, two thousand patients, caught in the evacuation draft, were in Scutari; yet Miss Nightingale held on at Balaclava. By mid-June the last of the regiments were on the way out. They were shortly followed by the first detachment of nurses. The Bermondsey Sisters sailed for home early in July. Florence

Nightingale, one of the last to leave, followed them incognito from Constantinople on the 28th. Arriving in London, she presented herself, at eight in the morning, at the Convent of Mercy, Bermondsey, and having spent the day in recollection with Mother M. Clare Moore, she travelled on the afternoon train to her home at Lea Hurst. Nothing could have been more unpretentious; nothing more unobtrusive; but as Florence Nightingale was an unpredictable woman, the strangeness of her arrival was a fitting prelude to the unusual role she was to assume for the remainder of her long life.

In marked contrast to Miss Nightingale's unobtrusive arrival was the return of what Russell called ' the remnant of the army.' England was *en fête*, though the fighting had settled nothing permanently and had cost the country over twenty thousand lives. Of this number only an estimated twenty-five per cent died of wounds sustained in battle. Cholera, typhus, gangrene, exposure and malnutrition claimed the rest. Few campaigns in history reveal more confusion of purpose, more incompetence in command, more costly casualties, more negative results than the Crimean War. In a very real sense, it shattered the peace which Europe had enjoyed for over forty years, and it ushered in a succession of conflicts which have transformed the world into an armed camp by making war and conquest the summit of human ambitions and the goal of human endeavour. The Peace of Paris, signed on March 28, 1856, was only another ' scrap of paper ', destined to be conveniently forgotten in the early post-war years. Presidency of the Congress of Paris was a personal triumph for Napoleon III. It enabled him to pose in the eyes of the nation as the arbiter of the destinies of Europe, more particularly since French victories in the Crimea had helped to erase the ignominy of the ill-fated campaigns of 1815 and 1840. But the triumph was ephemeral. In less than two decades the spectre of Prussian militarism and the events of 1870 sounded the death-knell of Napoleonic ambitions.

England, likewise, had other lessons to learn. The South African War found her with an army organisation only slightly improved upon that with which she entered the Crimean War. Matters indeed were such that years later Hitler could think of no greater insult to offer England than to refer contemptuously to the improvised condition of the English camps, the consequent prevalence of fever and disease and the inhuman methods eventually adopted to overcome the stolid resistance of the Boers. But in the summer of 1856 English horizons were bright, the future was fortunately veiled, and every effort was directed towards effacing the ignominy of the Crimean campaign. Banquets, parties, civil and political functions all over the country toasted the Lady of the Lamp, and suggestions were invited as to the manner in which the achievements of ' this illustrious English lady' might best be commemorated.

The return of the Irish regiments evoked similar celebrations in the home country. And though the Crimean War had been a costly and disappointing campaign, with high casualties and little dramatic reward, the Crimean Medal and the battle-honour of ' Sevastopol' would always serve as a token of Ireland's participation therein. A national banquet was accordingly held on October 22, 1856, in the bonded stores at the Custom House, Dublin, for " the victorious soldiers returned from the Crimean War and stationed in the Irish garrisons ". There must have been numerous regiments stationed in Ireland at the period ; thirty-one companies were represented at the national banquet. The committee charged with the organisation of the function included, among others, such notables as Fergus Farrell, Lord Mayor of Dublin, Lord Gough, Isaac Butt, M.P., and Lord Talbot de Malahide. Subscriptions were so generous that the residue— amounting to one thousand pounds—was put by " for the advancement of one or more of the most worthy pupils of the Royal Hibernian School ". Henry Brennan, a Dublin vintner, supplied " a pint of port or sherry for each of the four thousand guests "; Messrs. Guinness and Company were paid forty pounds for porter supplied ; Todd Burns and Company provided linen, flags and banners, and the Railway Company gave free transport to the troops. An interesting feature of the banquet was the arrival of the potatoes " in four vans, one of them a pantechnicon, all steaming hot ". In the course of the afternoon the usual toasts were proposed, and special honour was accorded to Florence Nightingale and her associate ladies".[23]

But Florence Nightingale did not want publicity. She had other ideals for which to work. Her experiences in the Crimea fired her with the notion that her mission in life was only beginning. Any suggestion of rest was entirely out of the question. She plunged at once into a scheme for the reform of the Army Medical Services and worked at such a pitch that in August, 1857, she collapsed and was forced to take a water-cure at Malvern. From that date until her death more than half a century later, she lived on a couch or in a wheel chair. Not that she was paralysed, or that she suffered from any known organic disease. It has now been corroborated that her collapse developed in her a certain neurosis or disordered action of the heart, recovery from which, in the case of an ordinary individual, would normally have followed rest. But Florence Nightingale, it has been said, was not an ordinary person, nor did she wish to live the life of an ordinary person. She discovered, almost unconsciously it would seem, that her invalidism enabled her to withdraw from family and society to enjoy that seclusion which she considered essential to the accomplishment of her mission. By pleading the helpless invalid, she could dismiss her visitors at will (she never saw more than one at a time and only three or four a day), she could exclude all undesirables, and she could more effectively impose her opinions on those with whom she chose to confer. Sensitive and highly-strung by nature, frustrated to the point of persecution by her family, her rejection of marriage developed a certain repression in her, for there is a strain of self-pity in her character and a lack of love in her life. In a certain sense, therefore, her invalidism was an escape from that conventional and Victorian outlook on life which had always annoyed her and which, after her experiences in the Crimea, she found intolerable.

The years of Miss Nightingale's invalidism were years of voluminous correspondence. Her letters during this period reveal her primarily as a statistician, an authority on hospital construction, sanitation and drainage, a woman who was dogmatic in her views and who had no inhibitions when it came to airing those views even against the most illustrious medical authorities of her day. Her attitude to bacterial causation, infection and contagion was unique: " I only modestly and humbly say that I never saw a fact adduced in favour of contagion which would bear scientific enquiry." She believed that " facts are everything, doctrines nothing ", and she wrote off the doctrine of contagion as " a great thing for weak minds ".[24] The publication in 1867 of Lister's famous paper on sepsis left her unconvinced. To the end of her life she adhered unwaveringly to her own sanitary gospel from which she refused to deviate even when an outbreak of pyaemia in St. Thomas's Hospital in 1873 must have convinced many of her colleagues that medicine does not swivel on sanitation alone.

Miss Nightingale's almost fanatical belief in the righteousness of her own cause enabled her to over-rule all promptings of opposition, to impose her fads and fancies on her medical friends, and even to convince them that no matter who was right, Florence Nightingale was seldom wrong. In a very real sense she *was* right in many ways. Her long life of seclusion gave her ample scope for the development of her scheme of reform, and from this angle medicine owes much to her endeavours.

In the domain of nursing, on the other hand, Miss Nightingale's position is not so easily justified. Here, her long life was not paralleled by any widening of practical experience. She had no scientific training, and at most could only boast of five years actual contact with hospitals during which time she concentrated on administration rather than on practical nursing. Her idea of a nurse was almost as unique as her attitude towards contagion. " The less knowledge of medicine a hospital matron has, the better," she wrote ; because " (i) it does not improve her sanitary practice ; (ii) because it would make her miserable and intolerable to the doctors."

Her opposition to the certification and registration of nurses was so violent that the scheme had to be abandoned until after her death. Doctors attained legal status by the Medical Act of 1858, but owing to the objections posed by Florence Nightingale the nursing profession remained the Cinderella of the medical world until 1919* when the State Register for nurses was set up.

> " Nursing," said Miss Nightingale, " does not come within the category of those arts (or sciences) which may be usefully ' examined ' or ' certified ' . . . Nursing is not only an art but a character, and how can that be arrived at by examination?"[25]

Another of her tenets was that as midwifery stood on a different plane from nursing, a qualifying certificate for midwives was permissible, even desirable.

The training provided by Florence Nightingale at St. Thomas's Hospital, therefore, had not in view that efficiency which to-day attaches to the qualified nurse. Why then, was Miss Nightingale accorded so exalted a place in the nursing world? The Crimean War, as we have seen, was her opportunity. It afforded her a launching site from which she could project her ideas on a grateful nation. Her Crimean adventure was, in fact, the fulcrum with which she hoped to move the world; it was but a stepping-stone in her career, for the extraordinary thing about Florence Nightingale was that her real life began at the very moment when, in the popular imagination, it had ended. Her exposure of the inefficiency of the army medical services focussed attention on a situation which clamoured for reform. In suggesting the necessary changes for this reform Florence Nightingale worked from the top, from the élite to the people; and it is now almost generally admitted that had she not enjoyed the backing of the aristocracy, success might never have come her way. Her ideas were in many ways too narrow, too

---

* Miss Nightingale died in 1910.

pragmatic, and many of her theories were discarded after her death.[26]

Her efforts for the reform of the army medical department were, in time, productive of good in her own country. But such re-organisations are of their nature, slow; and so it was that the reformed organisation of England did nothing to avert the tragedy of Solferino. It required the genius of Henri Dunant and the co-operation of a Geneva Convention to arrange for a voluntary system of nursing and purveying, which showed that the founder of the International Red Cross was more enlightened than was Florence Nightingale. " I need hardly say I think its views most absurd," wrote Miss Nightingale of the Convention; " just such as would originate in a little state like Geneva, which never can see war." The big difference between her and Dunant was that *she* sought only to benefit the English soldier; *he* wanted to help suffering mankind everywhere.

" What I want," he cried, " is a general mobilisation of all the charities of the world. I want an organisation which will be confined neither to England nor to any other country, but which will automatically go into action in every conflict—anywhere."[27]

Nursing histories in general, and the Nightingale biographies in particular, argue that the impetus towards modern nursing move-ments dates from the opening of the Nightingale Training School attached to St. Thomas's Hospital. This may very well be true as regards English civil hospitals, where nurses were till then recruited from the flotsam and jetsam of the Sairey Gamp category. Otherwise it is not so. Side by side with, and antecedent to, the Nightingale Reform, stood the Catholic Church with her eternal message of faith and hope and healing; and within the frame-work of this universal Church the Sisters of Mercy, while their Congregation was still in its infancy, early attained proficiency as nurses. It will be remembered too, that it was to the Sisters of Mercy that Florence Nightingale turned when she first decided on nursing as her career.

" For what training is there compared with that of the Catholic nun?" she wrote to Manning in July, 1852. " Those ladies who are not Sisters have not the chastened temper, the Christian grace, the accomplished loveliness and energy of the regular nun. I have seen something of different kinds of nuns, and am no longer young, and do not speak from enthusiasm but experience." [28]

Training schools under the aegis of the Sisters of Mercy were an early development in this country; and here the community of St. Maries of the Isle, Cork, led the way by opening Ireland's first Mercy Hospital on March 17, 1857. Three years later the Mater Misericordiae was established in Dublin; while on their return from the Crimea in 1856, the Sisters from Bermondsey opened a small hospital in Great Ormond Street, Bloomsbury, London, which in 1891 was transferred to its present site in St. John's Wood, to be thereafter known as the Hospital of St. John and St. Elizabeth.

Mindful of such expansion, the failure of England to acknowledge the services of the Sisters of Mercy in the Crimea, and the exclusion of the Sisters from further military service, can only be explained in terms of the prejudice created by Florence Nightingale against them. The rejection of the Sisters was to the detriment of the English soldier, since by comparison with the armies of France, it was realised in the later wars of the century that Catholic Nursing Sisterhoods had in them the stimulus of devotion, heroism and self-sacrifice which enabled them to accomplish more than what their secular colleagues were as yet prepared for. In France, despite the rapid growth of Socialism, the Sisters of Charity were retained in a military capacity, occupying two military hospitals and serving in Ambulance Brigades, until 1945. In America, the Nuns of the Battlefield have gone down in history as

" gentle and womanly, yet with the courage of soldiers . . . veritable angels of mercy . . . exorcising pain by their very presence or their words."

And among the letters of official appreciation preserved in the records of the American Civil War is a blank cheque made out by Abraham Lincoln decreeing that

" on application of the Sisters of Mercy to the Military Hospital in Washington, furnish such provisions as they desire, and charge same to the War Department."[29]

In England, the Sisters of Mercy, though sponsored and applauded by the medical officers and army authorities, were ignored by the government and people. The complications caused by their quarrel with Florence Nightingale was doubtless responsible for this coldness. It is beyond question, too, that the picture of nursing which England wished to communicate to the public was entirely secular, and found expression in the achievements of

Florence Nightingale. Finally, it is doubtful, if a Protestant government, such as England's was, would be likely to allow nuns form a permanent part of their military organisation.

" All honour to Miss Nightingale," ran an article in *The Lamp* on March 22, 1856. " All honour to the Sisters of Mercy. May they secure immortal crowns and have the record of their deeds inscribed in the Book of Life. And had England given them the ' passing tribute of one generous word ', I would say all honour to her too. But I will say, may she soon see with the eye of true faith, work in hope, and reap the golden harvest which springs from charity."[30]

The writer's hopes were not at once realised. Most of the Sisters died undecorated. It was not until the Victorian Jubilee, more than forty years later, that the survivors of the Bermondsey group received the Royal Red Cross from their sovereign, and that the last of the Irish Sisters was recommended for a similar decoration.

## CHAPTER 19

## RECOGNITION

THE post-Crimean War period saw a far-flung dispersal of Mother Bridgeman's ' Mercy Brigade '. Death early claimed three of the volunteers. On May 25, 1857, Sister M. Magdalen Alcock died in Liverpool, a week later Sister M. Paula Rice died in St. Maries of the Isle, Cork, and in the following year Sister M. Clare Lalor died in Charleville.

Sister M. Aloysia Hurley worked in the Mercy Hospital, Cork, until shortly before her death in 1871. Sister M. Clare Keane, who died in the same year, spent the post-war period of her life in the Workhouse Hospital, Kinsale. In Carlow, Sister M. Stanislaus Heyfron was assigned a post in the convent pension school which she retained until her death in 1887. Her companion, Sister M. Aloysius Doyle, went in November, 1857, as foundress to Gort, County Galway. Educational projects to the credit of this Kildare-born nun include the establishment, in 1887, of a new primary school in Gort to replace the wooden shed which till then had served as a classroom. In 1878 Sister M. Aloysius had already opened another primary school in Kinvara. A foundation of hers at Ennistymon in 1872 though at first successful, had to be abandoned owing to transport difficulties ; the project was later carried to completion by the Sisters of Mercy, Ennis. When in 1872 Sister M. Aloysius was given charge of the Workhouse Hospital, Gort, the efficiency acquired by her experiences in the Crimea and her apprenticeship with Mother Bridgeman, was of no mean significance when it came to tackling the herculean task of reform. In the words of the community annalist in the Convent of Mercy, Gort, the progress of the Workhouse Hospital owes not a little to the courage and initiative of Mother M. Aloysius Doyle.

In 1859 we find Sister M. Joseph Lynch[1] in the Brooklyn Convent of Mercy (founded that year from New York), where she lived to enjoy the official recognition accorded by America's government to the Sisters of Mercy and others who served behind the lines during the Civil and Spanish-American Wars. In 1873 Sister M. Joseph founded the Grand Rapids Convent in Michigan. At the time of her death, 1898, the Sisters of Mercy had flourishing hospitals in most of America's greatest cities—in New York, San Francisco, Pittsburgh, Philadelphia, Chicago, to mention but a few—and all over the States the extension of their activities was such that today their multi-storeyed hospitals and clinics are monuments to a steady pace maintained with the onward, ever-varied and constant march of time.

Of the two Sisters from Baggot Street, Sister M. Agnes Whitty was sent in 1859 to Buenos Aires ; but the South American climate played such havoc with a constitution already undermined by the extremities of two Crimean winters, that Sister M. Agnes was obliged to return to Dublin where she died on October 14, 1876. Sister M. Elizabeth Hersey in 1865 joined the recently established community in All Hallows Convent, Brisbane. She died there on February 17, 1901. Also to go to the Antipodes was Sister Mary Bernard Dixon of Chelsea, who worked among the Maori tribes in Wellington, New Zealand, until 1882.

As superioress in Charleville, Mother M. Joseph Croke governed her community intermittently for nearly eighteen years. Her achievements during this period prove her a worthy sister to the illustrious and patriotic Archbishop of Cashel. In 1886 Mother M. Joseph sent a group of Sisters to establish a Convent of Mercy in Bathurst, Australia. Among those selected to go on this distant mission was her only sister, Margaret, in religion—Sister M. Ignatius. Previous to this—in 1879—Mother M. Joseph opened a branch-house in Buttevant; in the same year she set up a foundation at New Inn, County Tipperary; and in 1881, at the request of the Board of Guardians, she assumed charge of the Workhouse Hospital, Kilmallock. Her death in 1888 was " deeply regretted by her mourning community, to whom she had been in her early religious life a kind, bright and cheerful Sister, and in after years ever a large-minded, generous and warm-hearted Mother."

Her lively and mischievous sense of humour is apparent in every page of her Diary, and is seen to best advantage in its supplementary rhymed version. Father Woollett, S.J. emerges from her pen as

> " a Jesuit of the first class; one you might venture to throw from a tower and be sure he would come up on his feet. If thrown into an Irish bog-hole, the same man would be certain to get out, if not *dry,* at least unhurt."

His fellow-Jesuit, Father William Ronan, the Sisters' first chaplain, is described as

> " A comfort to our dearest Mother,
> When sorrow's cup o'erflowed with gall;
> To each ' good Sister ' he was brother,
> And a priest he was to all."

Her own experiences include an interview with an excited orderly who stopped her on the day of the cease fire, asking, " Please, *Miss,* did you see the Reverend Mother knocking around anywhere?" She mentions " two rats in my bed last night, or one rat twice—which comes to the same thing." And she sums up the ridiculous situation in the Convent Hut at Balaclava as follows:

" We lacked a table, so our fare
Was on the floor, it's worth revealing ;
While on *that* too, the Sisters were
All squatting, sitting, crouching, kneeling." [2]

Mother M. Joseph Croke was, by many standards, an outstanding woman, with rare qualities of mind, an attractive personality, and a heart as light as her purse.

By comparison with the spectacular expedition to the Crimea, the post-war years of Mother Bridgeman's life were spent in the doldrums ; but they were doldrums rather of tranquillity than of inactivity, for a Sister of Mercy can never be idle as long as there are human bodies to heal and immortal souls to save. Shortly after her return from the Crimea, Mother Bridgeman was appointed Mistress of Novices, an exacting office which requires that she upon whom it is conferred shall be " discreet, meek and pious, of great prudence, and experienced in all the duties of the Congregation ; judicious in directing the dispositions of those under her care, and endowed with talents to form their minds to the practice of every virtue ". The choice of Mother Bridgeman was a fortunate one for the Novices of Kinsale, who soon learned from the example of their Mistress that the Rule and Constitutions of the Congregation of Our Lady of Mercy were to be for them, as they were for her, the surest design for holy living.

In 1858 Mother Bridgeman was reinstated as Mother Superior on the departure to Cincinnati of the reigning Superioress, Mother M. Teresa Maher. Until her death, three decades later, Mother Bridgeman was successively re-elected to this office every alternate six years. A less humble religious would have shirked a responsibility so exacting, so time-absorbing, and in this case, so prolonged ; not so Mother Bridgeman. The motto, " I can do all things in Him who strengtheneth me ", was for her, as for St. Paul, the expression of a love so great and a confidence so sure that, forgetting all else, she gave of herself wholeheartedly to God and to her community.

For that community the years of her government were years of progress and expansion. She sent out many filiations endowed with her own spirit: San Francisco, Derby, Skibbereen, Doon and Ballyshannon were founded by Sisters from Kinsale, whom she commissioned to promulgate the gospel of Mercy in its spiritual and corporal aspects. And from her convent in Kinsale she continued to advise and regulate the affairs of these new offshoots until, as flourishing and self-supporting institutions, they became, in time, prolific themselves.

At home, nothing was too trifling for Mother Bridgeman's attention. It was part of the versatility of her character that she could be equally at her ease in the schools, the hospital, the orphanage or the lace-room. Even to-day, certain aspects of these departments bear the impress of her hand and testify to the accuracy of her administrative ability.

The apostolate of the sick poor had ever a special appeal for her. Like Catherine McAuley, she would willingly suffer want herself rather than see God's poor neglected. Hence the importance of the visitation in her programme of charity. In the homes of the poor Mother Bridgeman found her natural element. There she might be seen—cheerful and light-hearted—going from hovel to hovel, tending the sick and dying; making comfortable the last moments of many an unhappy and lonely creature long bereft of friends and family; rescuing still others from the snares of the proselytisers, who tried to exploit the miseries of the people in an endeavour to wean them from Catholicism. Among these unfortunates " Mrs. Francis " was held in veneration by old and young and her name resounded in the very cobblestones of Kinsale.

The convent of Kinsale is similarly full of tributes to the memory of this great nun. She is remembered primarily as a woman of prayer, one who in the spirit of her Holy Rule, " by frequent visits every day paid assiduous court to her Heavenly Spouse on the Throne of His Love." The Eucharist was the wellspring whence she drew the courage, the confidence and the initiative that were hers. To it she ever turned like a homing bird. Before it, she placed her troubles and her perplexities, there to be ironed out in the sunshine of God's smile. In it, she laid her heart, to be immolated unreservedly to the Master who was the joy of her youth and the consolation of her advancing years. For her, as for the great Saint of Avila, the Tabernacle was the fulcrum of her thinking and her acting, and her absorbing devotion to the Most Holy Sacrament expressed itself in a Holy Hour booklet which she compiled and edited for private circulation in her own community.

The marked restraint in certain passages of her Diary, the obvious gaps, and the oft-repeated reference to " many other

things better left untold ", reveal in Mother Bridgeman that spirit
of charity which Catherine McAuley most cherished in her
spiritual daughters, and which she bequeathed to them as her
greatest legacy. For Mother Bridgeman, this virtue of charity was
something very positive. It urged her to overlook and forgive the
many embarrassments she endured at the hands of Florence
Nightingale. She could even make excuses for Miss Nightingale,
attributing the inconsistencies in her character to the fact that she
had not that broadness of outlook, that gift of sympathy and
understanding, that regard for the rights and claims of others
which are the marks of true leadership. Authority for Florence
Nightingale meant power; for Mother Bridgeman it meant service.
Herein lay the essential difference between them. Hence arose in
Miss Nightingale that attitude of hostility and criticism towards
any and every one who might even remotely compromise that
position of supreme authority which she claimed for herself.[3]
From the moment of their first encounter, she refused to recognise
Mother Bridgeman as anything but a dangerous rival: hence their
protracted quarrel and the bitterness which it engendered.

Still, it would be incorrect to infer that Miss Nightingale and
Mother Bridgeman were constantly at daggers drawn. There were
times of comparatively peaceful relations between them. One has
but to recall the circumstances of Sister M. Winifred's death and
Miss Nightingale's offer to erect a headstone to her memory. There
is also a letter to Sidney Herbert in which Miss Nightingale is
known to have declared that " the Reverend Brickbat and I are
the best of friends". On this point, however, the discrepancy
between her private notes and her official correspondence shows
that she cannot have been really sincere in her protestations.
Insincerity is not the stuff of which the coping-stone of reconcilia-
tion is quarried; therefore negotiations between Reverend Mother
and Lady Superintendent were bound to fail.

Early experiences in Scutari discouraged any further overtures
on Mother Bridgeman's part. Her attitude, through force of
circumstances, became defensive. Yet she cannot be said to have
proved inflexible, since it was when the quarrel was bitterest that
she imparted those valuable hints and suggestions on nursing
which Miss Nightingale accepted and subsequently published in
her revised *Notes on Nursing*.

Gentleness, kindness and affability were natural corollaries to
Mother Bridgeman's charity. References to the " kind and gentle
Mother Bridgeman " run like a golden thread through the official
records preserved in the Convent of Mercy, Kinsale. Sir John
Hall, aloof, impersonal, even officious, referred to her as " a

noble upright lady ". To Mr. David Fitzgerald, the Deputy
Purveyor-in-Chief, she was " Reverend and Beloved Mother ".
Mary Stanley, Fanny Taylor and Emily Hutton found her ever
sympathetic and gracious. To the non-Catholic patients in Koulali
and Balaclava she was " Respected Lady ", and to the Irish
Catholic soldiers she was " our very own ". Added to the foregoing testimonials are countless references from medical officers
as to her implicit obedience; all of which are an eloquent refutation of the charge that she was " an Irish nun of ardent and
rebellious temperament, assertive, loud-voiced, voluble ".[4]

Assertive she undoubtedly was in the sense of maintaining the
independence of her community against what she considered the
encroachments of Miss Nightingale. Assertiveness in this sense was
a virtue, made all the more imperative when it is remembered that
the Irish Sisters of Mercy went to the Crimea " not as individuals
with the nurses, but as a community under their own Superior ".
Manning summarised the situation for Archbishop Cullen with
the remark that " the mission of the Sisters is not from the
Government, but from their own Ecclesiastical Superiors ",[5] in so
far as the Government had acquiesced in the demands he
(Manning) had made in his capacity as intermediary between the
Archbishop, the War Office and the Sisters. Encroachments on
such ecclesiastical preserves could not for one moment be tolerated.

Mother Bridgeman was equally assertive, even aggressive, in her
insistence on the right to console dying Catholics. Her agreement with the War Office stated specifically that the Sisters
" should refrain from introducing religious topics with Protestant
patients "; with Catholics they were to be " absolutely free ". Miss
Nightingale's efforts at restricting such liberty of intercourse were
" an unpardonable intrusion " in matters touching so closely the
essential characteristic of the vocation of a Sister of Mercy. In
resisting the interference of Miss Nightingale on this point, assertiveness became a matter of principle; and on such matters Mother
Bridgeman could be inflexible. The integrity of her community
and the right to minister in a spiritual way to the Catholics was,
at the outset, officially confirmed by Sidney Herbert. One can
scarcely condemn Mother Bridgeman, therefore, for endeavouring
to maintain that integrity with all the ardour of her Irish nature.
It was unfortunate, if not disastrous, that assertiveness at
times outweighed Mother Bridgeman's more admirable characteristics; it was little less than catastrophic that the same was also
true of Florence Nightingale. Under the circumstances, a clash
of personalities was inevitable sooner or later. That it came so
early in their relationship is regrettable: a proper handling of

the situation could have produced some excellent team-work between the Sisters, Miss Nightingale and the medical officers. In time, such co-operation might have led to that harmonious interdependence between the medical and nursing personnel in the military hospitals which was the principal aim of Sidney Herbert, the Bishop of Southwark and Manning in organising the nursing expedition in 1854.

Not unnaturally, Kinsale and its environs offered Mother Bridgeman safe anchorage after the squally cross-currents of the Crimea. Here she found security and solitude which provided opportunity for the development in her of that motherliness which was her most lovable trait, more especially in later life when advancing years mellowed and smoothed away the rough edges which are part and parcel of every human character, and which at times lent a suggestion of dictatorialism and imperiousness to Mother Bridgeman's. Yet for all that she had a certain magnetism of personality, an adaptability of temperament and an overall sincerity which could not but impress those with whom she came in contact.

For children she had a special attraction: one never knew what treasures might issue from those magic pockets of hers! The lozenge solicited by the convalescent soldier in Koulali was found to be equally in demand among the toddlers of Kinsale. It was a touching sight to see her, in the evening of her life, surrounded by these youngsters, some on her knees, others at her feet, others again hanging on to her shawl, all listening wide-eyed to the stories with which she simplified the catechism for them. To be so engaged with the young was the greatest joy of Mother Bridgeman's declining years. Time came when she was able for little else. A malignant growth began slowly but surely to gnaw its insidious way through her system, undermining by degrees, but relentlessly, that hardy constitution which had so generously borne the burdens of the day and the heat. Weeks and months of excruciating agony saw her practising those virtues of patience and resignation which all her life she had encouraged in others: in the cholera victims of Limerick in 1832; in the famine victims of Kinsale, and in the wounded, gangrened and neglected soldiers of the Crimea. With these and countless other good works invoiced to her credit over a period of seventy-five years by the Recording Angel, Mother Bridgeman could, and did, face her Maker with a smile. The end came peacefully on February 11, 1888, when she passed to her reward " with an eye full of gentle salutations and soft responses, whispering soft like the last low accents of an expiring saint," as one reads in *Tristram Shandy*.

It was the feast of Our Lady of Lourdes, to whose Immaculate Conception she had dedicated her great mission to the Crimea in October 1854.

News of her death brought letters of condolence from many quarters to Kinsale. It would be a tedious task to recount them all; yet for obvious reasons those selected require neither explanation nor comment.*

Father William Ronan, S.J., wrote,

> " I thank God that our dear Mother is gone to her eternal rest. Of course we shall do all that grateful hearts will inspire to follow her with our prayers, though we believe that she has finished her purgatory with her mortal life. She will be a great power for us all in Heaven, so cheer up. It would be mere selfishness to wish her back again . . ."

> " I will pray of course for dear Mother M. Francis," wrote Father Michael Duffy, S.J., " and if for no other reason I will pray for her in memory of days long since gone by in the far-off Crimean land! We were fellow-soldiers there, under the same flag—Christ's—and it belongs to fellow-soldiers to help each other in the hour of need. Not that *she* has any great need, after her long service in the ' King's ' cause. Therefore it is not a *De Profundis* that I shall sing for her, but rather a *Te Deum Laudamus*!"

From Father Michael Gleeson, C.M., came the following:

> " I feel most grateful for your kind letter giving me the details of the happy end of the good and saintly Mother Bridgeman. I said Mass for her yesterday. Her holy death has been in accordance with her well-spent life, verifying to the letter the words of the Holy Ghost, 'As we live, so shall we die.' I have no doubt whatever but she has received an immense reward for all her labours. She certainly did not spare herself during life but laboured unceasingly for the glory of God and the sanctification of souls; and since God is never outdone in generosity, we may hope that her reward is exceeding great in Heaven.

> I have always had the greatest esteem for her, and well she deserved it all. I shall never forget all that she and her companions had to endure in the Crimea. The sufferings

---

*For letter of condolence from Most Reverend Thomas Alphonsus O'Callaghan, Bishop of Cork, cf. Appendix p. 314.

she went through, and all the annoyances she had to put up with during her time there were more than enough for her to win for her a crown of surpassing beauty.

Candidly speaking, I do not think she stands in need of prayers. In one sense you all have suffered a great loss in her removal from amongst you, for she was the soul of good example. She loved ardently the holy life she embraced, and practised with fidelity the virtues of a good Sister of Mercy. May her blessed soul rest in peace. I am sure she will not forget to pray for me, for we were fast friends, and bore the burden and the heat of the day together."[6]

Within a fortnight of Mother Bridgeman's death, *The Tablet* —20 February, 1888—in an article entitled "The Nun in the Crimea," published the following account of her achievements:

"On the 11th February, one of the most remarkable women of recent times, Sister Mary Francis Bridgeman, was called from us. She died in the Convent of Mercy, Kinsale, Ireland.

"Thirty-four years ago it was she who organised the band of Ladies (Sisters) who went from Ireland and England to the Crimea, to nurse the sick and wounded in that terrible war. Here, the kind hands and words of sympathy of the Sisters gave consolation to many a wounded soldier. And here, the gentleness and saintly presence of these good nuns, their unremitting care and tender watchfulness, made happy the death-bed of hundreds of men of all creeds who received their death wounds in the battles of the campaign.

"When the war was over, Mother Bridgeman returned to her convent in Kinsale, Ireland, and there continued her life of sanctity and charity. Her life was one long errand of Mercy and Charity. Her works at Kinsale, and in the many convents of her Order which she was instrumental in founding, will endure. And though her great labours in the Crimea were never fully recognised by the British Government, they are gratefully remembered to-day by many a man whose life she saved amid the carnage of the Crimean battlefields."

Nine years after Mother Bridgeman's death London metaphorically went ablaze to mark the Diamond Jubilee of Queen Victoria. Outstanding episodes of the past six decades were recalled; among them, the Crimean War. Florence Nightingale and the survivors of the nursing personnel were to be honoured by receiving from their sovereign the decoration of the Royal Red Cross in token of their services in that war.[7] Three Bermondsey Sisters were included in the Honours List. Many long years had indeed elapsed since Florence Nightingale wrote her eulogy on Mother M. Clare Moore. In all that time, the English Sisters were ignored by the countless organs of public opinion which so applauded Miss Nightingale "and her associates." But alas, recognition came too late for Mother M. Clare Moore. She died in December 1874, recognising as did Mother Bridgeman, that Florence Nightingale continued to reap where the Sisters of Mercy had helped to sow.

The decoration offered in 1897, though tardy, was welcomed by the Bermondsey Sisters. Preparations for a Palace garden party were almost completed when *The Times* carried a significant article announcing that there still lived in the Convent of Mercy, Gort, County Galway, the last-surviving member of Mother Bridgeman's party. So, almost as an afterthought, and as a gesture of grace, the name of Sister Mary Aloysius Doyle was appended to the Honours List. On February 15, Mother M. Aloysius, a jubilarian herself, received the following communication from the Government Offices, Pall Mall, London:

" Madam,

The Queen having been pleased to bestow upon you the decoration of the Royal Red Cross, I have to inform you that in the case of such honours as this, it is the custom of her Majesty to bestow the decoration upon the recipient, when such a course is convenient to all concerned; and I have, therefore, to request that you will be so good as to inform me whether it would be convenient to you to attend at Windsor some time within the next few weeks. Should any circumstances prevent your receiving the Royal Red Cross from the hands of her Majesty, it could be transmitted to your present address.

I am, Madam,
Your obedient servant,
George M. Farquharson."[8]

All unconscious was the irony in Mother M. Aloysius' reply of thanks for a decoration which she had never coveted. Forty-three years had passed since she went to the Crimea as a nursing Sister, and as Sir Shane Leslie puts it, she was now in need of nursing herself. The journey to London was out of the question, but she availed herself of the alternative offered, and conveyed her decision as follows on February 17:

" Sir,

I received your letter of the 15th, intimating to me that Her Most Gracious Majesty, the Queen, is pleased to bestow on me the Order of the Royal Red Cross, in recognition of the services of my Sisters and my own in caring for the wounded soldiers in the Crimea during the war. My words cannot express my gratitude for the great honour which Her Majesty is pleased to confer upon me. The favour is, if possible, enhanced by the permission to receive this public mark of favour at Her Majesty's own hands. The weight of seventy-six years, and the infirmities of age will, I trust, dispense me from a journey to the Palace. I will, therefore, with sentiments of deepest gratitude, ask to be permitted to receive this mark of the Sovereign's favour in the less public and formal manner you have kindly indicated.

I am, Sir,

Faithfully yours in J.C.,

Sister Mary Aloysius." [9]

The decoration was forwarded in due course to the Convent of Mercy, Gort.

At the time of her death, October 3, 1908, Mother M. Aloysius was in her eighty-seventh year. Two years later, on August 13, 1910, Florence Nightingale died at the age of ninety. They both exemplified the truth of the dictum that hardship and hard work are not hindrances to reaching a mellow and calm old age.

The participation of the Irish Sisters of Mercy in the Crimean War is a brief but glorious epoch in the history of the Catholic Church as well as in the annals of their own Congregation. It is a point too often lost sight of that before going to the Crimea the Sisters were an effective spearhead in the reaction against those appalling social abuses rampant at the beginning of the nineteenth century, which made hospitals and other institutions for the sick poor such satires on humanity. Another point similarly jettisoned is that the work of Florence Nightingale at Scutari did not at all represent the only successful nursing done in the military hospitals. The medical officers, as a body, showed a decided preference for the methods introduced by the Sisters of Mercy in Koulali and Balaclava; and that preference is still noticeable in the fact that the practice obtaining in the military hospitals of our modern age resembles more closely the organisation evolved by

Mother Bridgeman than it does that attempted by Florence Nightingale.

The essential difference between Florence Nightingale and the Sisters lay in an entirely different concept of nursing. Miss Nightingale, were she alive to-day, would hardly recognise the profession of which she was the greatest publicist and the reputed originator. Schools of Nursing still render lip-service to her memory, but the adaptation of nurse-training to the advances of modern science and technology has gone far towards exploding the Nightingale Legend. Lister has long since come into his own. Hospital matrons today are required to possess something more than " a little medical knowledge ". Even the least initiated in the art of healing will question Miss Nightingale's theory that the only patients requiring medical attention are those suffering from wounds. This, it will be recalled, was her main objection to Mother Bridgeman's offer of service in December 1854. She was at that time quite forthright in declaring that there was no work just then for the Sisters, because the majority of the patients in Scutari were " not wounded; they were only suffering from disease, and therefore needed no nursing "![10]

So much for the Nightingale Legend. The Crimean chapter of that Legend—in so far as the explicit duties of nursing are concerned—is obviously an exaggeration, altogether unwarranted when measured against hitherto untapped sources of contemporary documentation. The Irish Sisters of Mercy, therefore, deserve more credit for their work in the British military hospitals than has been hitherto accorded to them.

In the century and more that has elapsed since the Crimean War, the expansion of the Sisters of Mercy (they number at present anything up to 30,000) and the extension of their labours has brought them into closest contact with modern progressive movements in the realms of medicine, education, science and social service. To-day, as in the days of Catherine McAuley, the Sisters teach, nurse and catechise among the poor, the sick, and the ignorant. All over the world they conduct orphan asylums, hostels for working girls and homes for the aged. They have night refuges and convalescent homes in some of the world's biggest cities.

The Sisters still visit the sick in their homes and prisoners in their cells, where

" they never argue, discuss, or theorise about religion, but help the convicts in the only practical, useful and efficient ways . . . They furnish money to needy relatives and to the men themselves when they come out of prison. They never inquire into a man's crimes: all they ask is to be told of his troubles and worries, and to be allowed do what they can to relieve them."[11]

Secretarial and catechetical schools, and social service centres are another facet of their work. And in recent years, when religion in education has come to be recognised as such an important desideratum, the Sisters by organising colleges, high-schools and academies for women, have helped enormously to stem the tide of modern paganism. In America, this development is widespread; in other countries less so. In Ireland, the only Training Colleges for Catholic women teachers are in the hands of the Sisters of Mercy in Dublin and Limerick. Three of the most recent educational endeavours of the Sisterhood are as far afield as the Philippines—the Holy Infant Academy, Tacloban City, Leyte; Assumption Academy, Tanauan, Leyte, and Fatima College, Misamis Oriental, all staffed by Sisters from St. Maries of the Isle, Cork.

The number of Mercy Hospitals functioning throughout the world to-day runs into hundreds. The total is considerably augmented if one considers as well the countless general, regional, orthopaedic and fever hospitals where Sisters of Mercy continue to be staffed. Mercy Hospitals, properly so-called, are self-supporting voluntary establishments, in receipt of neither emolument nor grant from Government or Board of Health. The world's newest Mercy Hospital is the Mater Misericordiae, opened in 1962 in Nairobi, Kenya, East Africa. The establishment of this new hospital is indicative of the rapid growth of a mission to Africa undertaken in 1956 by four Sisters of Mercy from the Motherhouse in Dublin.

The Sisters of Mercy also conduct maternity hospitals and clinics in many lands; while in Mahaica, British Guiana, Guam, New Guinea and India they have added the care of lepers to an already over-laden schedule. In short, the Sisters of Mercy are ever ready to embark upon any scheme of charity which has for its aim the spiritual and temporal improvement of the poor. This, the hallmark of Catherine McAuley's particular spirituality, continues to be the distinguishing characteristic of her daughters.

It is the glory of the Sisters of Mercy to-day that they are, perhaps, the most adaptable unit in the forces of the militant Catholic Church. Few orders of either men or women have the same breadth of apostolate. Fewer still can boast of the multifarious activities which stem from the word " service " and which in the design of Mercy is given the widest possible interpretation, to embrace mankind of every description irrespective of caste, creed or colour. Of the Sisters of Mercy it has been truly said that

> " They move ever with a certain stately calm and precision, great-hearted, clear-eyed, and fully conscious of their aims to execute them. Their annals reflect a holy monotony of service, unbroken by romantic individualism or the assertion of self or of selfish interests."[12]

Military nursing has, of course, long since passed out of the hands of Religious Orders. To-day, the responsibility for the health of the world's armies rests with Ambulance Brigades, Emergency Field Units, an International Red Cross and the medical services supplied by the United Nations Organisation. And it is one of the paradoxes of history that of the 30,000 Sisters of Mercy at present dispersed throughout the five continents, few know with any degree of accuracy the details of Mother Bridgeman's expedition to the Crimean Military hospitals in 1854. Yet the Crimean War, for all its blundering and ineptitude, has a perennial fascination, and the participation of the Sisters of Mercy therein has an undeniable historical significance; more especially since documentary evidence, by shedding light on much that till now has been incorrectly interpreted, goes far towards rewarding the confidence expressed by Mother Bridgeman in her letter to Sir John Hall written in April 1858. Her conviction as then stated was that " sooner or later vindication would come—*In God's own time."*

# APPENDIX

1. (Bishop William Delany to Mother Bridgeman.)

Cork,
January 25, 1855.

Dear Reverend Mother,

I received your two letters. Notwithstanding the unpleasant circumstances attendant on the opening of your Mission, it afforded me the truest happiness to hear of the safe arrival of yourself and all the Sisters at your place of destination. I would instantly have replied, but your first letter was so discouraging, that I thought better to wait a little and ascertain what remedy could be provided by the authorities at home, to whom Manning undertook to represent the circumstances. In the meantime, I am happy to find that although matters are not as we would wish them, there is however an improvement, which to me, at this distance, seems likely to progress. You have done great service I hope, by placing yourself even temporarily in connexion with the Bermondsey Nuns. It is thereby rendered manifest to all parties concerned in the business that you are not influenced by any kind of selfish feeling whatever. Should any new emergency arise that would not permit a convenient reference home, you have my full consent to act according to your own prudence on which I fully rely. Even at present, I would much rather that you did for the best whatever you find within your power, as you can readily conceive how difficult it is for those who cannot view all the circumstances, to arrive at a satisfactory conclusion. As it may afford you some gratification however, I give a brief general statement of my views on the subject.

I consider your mission, in addition to the blessings it contains intrinsically for the objects of your zeal and charity, to be of the utmost importance to the interests of Religion in general, at least in these countries; and should its failure, which I cannot anticipate, be ascribable to any precipitancy or imperfection on our part, I would consider it nothing short of a calamity. Whilst therefore, the personal comforts of the holy Sisters are sufficiently secured, and their Religious Observance reasonably provided for, I would be quite content to submit to modification in whatever is only of secondary importance. Even this much cannot be expected all at once.

There must of necessity be such a vast complication of affairs and incalculable varieties of detail to engage the attention of the authorities, that it is only reasonable to make considerable allowances for some confusion at starting in each department. We must therefore exercise some patience and trust to the efficacy of a just remonstrance wherever it may be necessary. Friends would then be ashamed not to sustain you. Opponents would scarcely venture to put themselves in a wrong position; and you will accordingly retain your post until it is manifest to all reasonable men that you abandon it only through necessity.

I recommend therefore that you continue to give the services of such Sisters as may be required and wait still longer to ascertain, if all may not be in requisition. Should this take place as I hope, the only remaining difficulty would be as to the distribution of the Religious. I would not hesitate, in such a case, to adopt the necessity of the service in which you are engaged as the rule for your guidance, always provided however that the Religious form a Community under their own Superior. And although the Sisters who went with you as Superior would feel a disappointment as a serious trial if some had to unite themselves with a distinct community, yet, as the whole undertaking is of a temporary nature, and as they could not fail to find a Mother and Sisters wherever placed, it would not be right that an inconvenience of this sort should be allowed to render the mission abortive.

I assume it as a matter of course, manifestly understood, even if it were not explicitly stated, that no portion of the Flock sent under your guidance should be obliged to return home without your sanction and protection. Indeed, it is superfluous to allude to the possibility of such an idea being entertained.

A variety of minor difficulties may possibly arise in working out the objects of your mission. Such as I might contemplate may be found to be only imaginary: any that are real you will use your own discretion in remedying. I will expect to hear frequently from you, especially as to any inconveniences worth noting which you may have to endure. I feel confident in God's Providence that with the counsel and good offices of our excellent friends in England, that all will be made to go right.

I congratulate you on your happiness in having enjoyed the acquaintance and secured the friendship of so admirable a lady as Miss Stanley; and from all I can learn, Miss Nightingale also is likely to afford you the benefit of her support.

Had the issue of your dangers and voyages proved so unfavourable as to necessitate an abrupt return, I would have suggested an offer of your services in Malta for some period, rather than exhibit to the world such zeal and devotion of the Sisters without an adequate result. But I cannot yet divest myself of the hope that with the bright example of France before them, our rulers will still order such arrangements as must insure the efficient and happy discharge of the duties of the Sisters of Mercy.

You will have the goodness to convey to the Sisters my kindest regards, and assure them of my earnest prayers for their own happiness and the success of the glorious work in which they engaged; and believe me,

> Dear Reverend Mother,
> Yours very faithfully,
> ✠William Delany.

2. Letters of Archbishop Paul Cullen.

## A.

(Undated fragment from the Archives, Convent of Mercy, Kinsale.)

I have just heard that several Sisters of Mercy are about to start for the East. I am glad of it, and confidently hope that they will do a great deal of good. Will you be so good as to see how things are arranged before they start. Here it is reported that they are placed under a Protestant, Miss Nightingale. I hope this is not true, as it would be unseemly and perhaps very inconvenient to have nuns under such jurisdiction. The Pope thinks that such a thing ought not to be agreed to. However, it may be that at this distance we do not understand things properly.

I have not heard what promise is made for a Chaplain, or whether the Sisters are to have a Chaplain. Our nuns would require someone to guide them: they are not accustomed to live among soldiers like the French Sisters, and they would certainly be much in need of the assistance and protection of a prudent Priest. I dare say there will be great difficulties and dangers to be encountered in a Protestant camp, if it be true that Miss Nightingale is such a Protestant. I am persuaded that great experience and prudence would be required to prevent the evils which might spring up under such trying circumstances. . . .

## B.

Irish College, Rome,
April 18, 1855.

My dear Mrs. Bridgeman,

I have had the happiness of receiving your long and interesting letter, and I immediately sent it to the Pope by Dr. Kirby who happened to be going to him at the moment. His Holiness sends you and all your Sisters his warmest good wishes and blessing.

I am sorry to hear you have so many trials to meet. Bear everything patiently. Do not let your enemies frighten you away. Hold your ground until you shall be sent away by force, or recalled by your spiritual Superiors. I think you are quite right in not putting your little community under any authority except your own.

Your devoted servant,
Paul Cullen.

3. (Correspondence of Rev. William Ronan, S.J., and the Rev. Mr. Hobson, Protestant chaplain at Koulali and Scutari.)

## A.

Koulali, April /55.

Reverend Sir,

I am informed on the report of Miss Emily Anderson that you accuse the Sisters of Mercy in the General Hospital of violating a solemn promise. Amongst other engagements, these Sisters have pledged themselves not to interfere in the religious concerns of Protestants in our British Hospitals, and I, their guardian and protector, consider myself bound, if needful, to enforce the strict observance of all such promises. Hitherto none that I know of, has been broken. May I then ask you when and in what instance have these Sisters interfered in the religious affairs of Protestants.

The charge of violating a solemn engagement is too serious to be lightly passed over.

I remain, Reverend Sir,
Your obedient servant,
William Ronan, S.J.,
R.C. Chaplain.

### B.

Scutari, May 1, 1855.

Reverend Sir,

I have such confidence in Miss Emily Anderson that I feel quite sure that the report which you mention was not received from her personally. A mere general report without an author, I cannot, of course, notice. I may add that I should not deem it right in charging any fault against the Roman Catholic ladies, to forward any such charge through yourself, but only through Miss Nightingale, under whose control immediately all the ladies and nurses, not only of the Established Church of England, but of the Roman Catholic Church, are placed by the Queen's Government.

I beg to thank you for your voluntary declaration respecting the propriety of confining the Roman Catholic ladies and nurses to their proper duties as nurses only.

I am, Reverend Sir,
Your faithful Servant,
A. Hobson, Chaplain,
General Hospital.

### C.

Koulali,
British Hospital,
May 4, 1855.

Reverend Sir,

In reply to your note of the 1st inst., I beg to say that Miss Stanley received from Miss Emily Anderson personally the accusations to which I referred in my last.

No one is more ready to acknowledge and respect the authority vested in Miss Nightingale by the Government than I am. But surely it is no interference with this lady's rights, in the accused to inquire into the charges brought against them—charges which in justice they ought to get notice of, that they may prepare their defence.

Now, I am recognised by the Government the guardian and protector of the Sisters of Mercy in the General Hospital. I have therefore a right to know what are the accusations made.

In fine, there is no part of my note from which it can be lawfully inferred that I acknowledge the Roman Catholic Ladies under my direction should be employed " as nurses only ", since they came out with the right to instruct Roman Catholics when this does not interfere with their duty as nurses.

> I remain, Reverend Sir,
> Your humble servant,
> William Ronan, R.C. Chaplain.

### D.

> Scutari,
> 9 May, 1855.

Reverend Sir,

I beg to thank you for the candour with which you acknowledge the authorship of the report received by you.

If Miss Stanley made use of my name at all, in reference to the Roman Catholic Ladies at the General Hospital, she did wrong, having no authority in any way from me, to do so.

I beg to refer you to my previous note for the rule of my conduct in regard to any charge of fault against the Ladies referred to.

Be assured that I wish to be the last to do injustice to anyone, whether the ladies or yourself.

> I remain, Reverend Sir,
> Your very obedient servant,
> A. Hobson.

4. (Mother Bridgeman to Doctor John Hall.)

> Balaclava,
> General Hospital,
> March 21, 1856.

Dear Sir,

I have heard from our friends at home that misrepresentations have been made in England regarding us.

May I ask you to ascertain for me if Miss Nightingale stated in any report of hers to the War Office that we had withdrawn from her authority. If so, this is false, as only five of us were under her, since she refused the rest on our arrival in the East, disclaimed all control over us, all responsibility in our regard. She had resigned the General Hospital in Balaclava on the 1st October: we did not arrive until the 10th.

If Miss Nightingale stated that we felt it our duty to convert Protestant patients—if this, or any statement implying it, has been made, it is most untrue. I repeatedly assured Miss Nightingale that we should consider it a sin against God and a disgrace before man to violate the contract we had distinctly and deliberately made with the authorities on this subject.

It seems to me that Miss Nightingale, holding the position she does, could not be justified in making or implying such a serious charge at the War Office without having first incontestably *proved* some facts of religious interference against us, which during so many months' service, she could not fail to do if they existed.

Again, I have heard that Miss Nightingale has formally charged us with extravagance. This also is false. I have never confounded requisitions for the Sisters with those for the patients. My requisitions marked 'for the Sisters' therefore, stand as a testimony of what I have received. I have kept the counterparts. Our housekeeping has ever been distinct: I have ordered nothing from the stores which I would not have felt it my duty to buy for the Sisters under the same circumstances if our Community were supplying them.

Miss Nightingale could have had no means of *really* knowing what we did or did not order. Therefore, it seems to me such a statement on her part should be most unwarrantable.

I have also heard that Miss Nightingale complained of the number of Sisters here as being too large for the number of patients. Perhaps she did not bear in mind that all the extras, food as well as stimulants, pass, not through the orderlies' hands, but through those of the Sisters to the patients; that the food is prepared under the *constant* direction of the Sisters; that we have had much night watching by the express desire of the Medical Officers, who require the constant attendance of the Sisters for those patients who need frequent doses of medicine or stimulants, and in this hospital such cases are of frequent occurrence. Then we have here neither servant, nurse, nor laundress, and our domestic arrangements, simple though they be, must have hands to do them.

I feel assured you will agree with me that it is but *mere justice* to our friends to enquire into this report, and that you will kindly take for me the necessary means to do so.

> Believe me to be, dear Sir,
> Yours very sincerely in J.C.,
> Sister Mary Francis Bridgeman,
> Mother Superior,
> Sisters of Mercy, Balaclava.

*No. of patients admitted.*

| | |
|---|---|
| October | 230 |
| November | 301 |
| December | 349 |
| January | 268 |
| February | 210 |
| Total | 1,358 |

5. (Father M. Gleeson, C.M., to Mother Bridgeman.)

St. Peter's Church,
Phibsboro, Dublin,
April 14, 1858.

My dear Mrs. Bridgeman,

I am aware that Mr. Fitzgerald sent to the War Office a report contradicting the statements made there by Miss Nightingale, but what the particulars were I have not the smallest recollection now. Never has there been made by anyone such false, malicious and unworthy statements.

As regards the 'horrible neglect of the patients', I have no hesitation in saying that this is wholly unfounded; for whether this charge be brought against the Sisters or against the medical men who were in charge of the hospital, it is entirely false.

You are aware that from the time I came to Balaclava until the time you left, I had been attached to the General Hospital and did duty there. During that period of time I do not think a single day passed without my visiting the hospital. On that account I had an opportunity of judging of the attention paid to the patients both by the Sisters and by the medical men in attendance. Now, as regards your attendance on the sick, I would merely suggest to have a fair enquiry made, and to let those who have been attended by you be consulted. They will speak for themselves and tell the truth. It grieves me to the very heart and soul that your zealous labours towards the sick should be so calumniated, and that jealousy should now so misrepresent things as to try and conceal all the good you have done. God, who is a just God, will not always allow the truth to be thus misrepresented, nor light to be turned into darkness. The day of final retribution will come, and that ere long, when those who now shine so brilliantly in the estimation of men will fall low in the scale of the judgment of God.

My dear Mrs. Bridgeman, your sleepless nights—which I can testify to—and those of your Sisters, spent in watching beside the sick patients' bed, whilst those who now make those false and unwarrantable statements were at rest in their easy beds, loudly speak your praise.

As regards the statements of the hospital being dirty and disorderly, I can bear ample testimony to the contrary. I can certify that I have never seen any hospital better kept than the General Hospital of Balaclava. I have gone frequently through many of the other hospitals in the Crimea, and nowhere did I see the same order, the same cleanliness and regularity as in the General Hospital. It was the Model Hospital for all the others. Another thing too I can certify is that from the time of Miss Nightingale's coming to Balaclava after your departure, until the breaking-up of the whole establishment, the hospital did not, nor could not, undergo any essential change as to cleanliness, order and regularity.

Hoping these general remarks will prove of some use.

I remain,
Ever yours sincerely,
Michael Gleeson, C.M.

6. (Letter of Sir John Hall to Sidney Herbert.)

27 Clifton Villas,
Maida Hill,
20 March, 1858.

Sir,

My attention has been drawn to the written answer given by Miss Nightingale to question 10,020 of the Royal Commission appointed to enquire into the Regulations affecting the Sanitary Conditions of the Army, and as this statement has gone forth to the world without either contradiction or comment, and has obtained extensive circulation through the report of the Commission I feel called on, in justice to those who were in charge and doing duty in the General Hospital, Balaclava, prior to Miss Nightingale's arrival there on 11 April, 1856, to enter my protest against her thus taking exception as to the general rule of management of the Balaclava Hospital, and to record my convictions, which I am enabled to do from my own observation and from the written statements of others, of the utter impossibility of any patient having been neglected for a whole week, as stated in her evidence. This accusation, after the explanations that have been forwarded to me, I can view in no other light than that of a libel on the humanity of the medical officers attached to the Balaclava Hospital; and more especially on the humane and attentive Sisters of Mercy who acted as nurses there until Miss Nightingale's arrival, when they declined serving under her orders and returned to England.

From the kind and efficient manner in which the Sisters of Mercy performed their nursing duties during the whole period they were employed at Balaclava, I do not believe these good women would have neglected for one single day any human being placed under their care, much less for a whole week, and I think Miss Nightingale must have been misinformed regarding the case to which she has referred; and in confirmation of this I beg to annex a letter from Dr. Murray who was doing duty in the Hospital at the time. I select his letter in preference to that of any other person because he is totally unconnected with the public services, and therefore can in no way be either benefited or injured by the report, and is in the most favourable position for giving unprejudiced testimony on all matters that came under his own observation in the General Hospital at Balaclava.

The General Hospital was a model of neatness and cleanliness for many months before Miss Nightingale joined it, and its condition was the theme of praise amongst both British and Foreign Officers. It was a general hospital in the broadest acceptation of the term, and all who were suffering from disease, no matter of what caste or persuasion, were admitted into its wards. It is possible therefore, that articles of clothing belonging to these patients may occasionally have been left in the hut wards, and on one occasion I believe a carpenter who was admitted from a transport, brought a box of tools with him and placed it under his bed. But this trifling, unimportant and almost unavoidable deviation from the hospital regulations had no reference whatever to the military part of the establishment, which was conducted in strict conformity to the established rules of the service, one of which is that the pack, arms and clothing of every soldier admitted into Hospital shall be taken from him, lodged in the store, and a correct list of the articles entered in the Store Register; and this I know was strictly enforced by the Purveyor.

The duty of looking after the cleanliness and order of the whole establishment was also imposed on him by me, and as he was a remarkably intelligent and energetic young man, it was performed both willingly and efficiently. When therefore I paid my visit to the General Hospital at Balaclava on 14 April, 1856, and found it in a state so different from what it had been only a few days before, it was for him and not the Medical Officer who was merely in temporary charge of the hospital during Dr. Huish's absence that I sent, to explain the cause of the change. He informed me that he had been prohibited from interfering with the wards of the hospital by Dr. Beatson, P.M.O., of Balaclava, who had found one of the orderlies occupied by his order removing some dirt from the floor of a ward on the Sabbath Day, and he hoped I would not hold him responsible any longer for the cleanliness of the interior of the hospital. Miss Nightingale says I censured the surgeon in charge for introducing ' real order and cleanliness '. Now I hope it is scarcely necessary to say I should never have been so unreasonable as to do that, and my experience of hospital economy is long and extensive enough to enable me to distinguish between order and regularity and between dirt and cleanliness. And had the process of change been merely going on at the time of my visit, the M.O. would have obtained credit for it, and there would have been no occasion for my department memorandum of the 15th. With regard to the surgeon himself, there could have been no previous prejudice on my part against him, as I had just appointed him to an important charge, though I am sorry to say his subsequent conduct proved that my confidence had been misplaced.

So far as I am immediately concerned, these comments of Miss Nightingale are of little consequence, and I am persuaded they will be viewed, if not with like indifference, at least with Christian charity, by Mrs. Bridgeman and the Sisters of Mercy. But as they are calculated to injure the prospects of Dr. Huish who is a very zealous and deserving officer, I have called on you to trouble *you*, the President of the Royal Commission with this communication, in vindication, not only of his professional character but of the humanity of the whole Medical Department of the Army which is so seriously impugned by the charge of culpable neglect thus brought against it by Miss Nightingale ; and I appeal to your sense of justice to make public this explanation which I trust will, in some measure, remove the unfavourable impression that has been created.

I have the honour to be, Sir,

Your most obedient and humble servant,

John Hall.

7. (Letter of Bishop of Cork)

San Clemente,
Roma,
Feb. 17, 1888.

Dear Reverend Mother,

The news of Mother M. Francis' death came to me by surprise. I had not the least suspicion that so great a trial was in store for you and the Community, and I must add, for myself; for I venerated her as a holy and great Religious. I cannot realise at the moment her great loss, as I did not expect it. I had counted on her for years to come, that her example and her presence in the Community would be the source of many spiritual blessings.

I have known her great zeal for religious discipline, her religious spirit, and her full-heartedness for the cause of Almighty God. You and the Sisters have known them by experience, and I would wish that you all should consider the good she effected in the Community left to you as an inheritance, which you will preserve always intact, and that you should receive it with a responsibility to hand it down to those who come after you.

She already, I trust, has been rewarded as the good and faithful servant. God could not despise the life so thoroughly devoted to Him, and could not delay to receive her into His presence. We should still pray for her in gratitude, that we may merit her prayers, and that her spirit may continue to dwell among us.

I am very anxious to be back in Cork, but I am detained here longer than I expected. We had an audience with the Holy Father on Sunday last which lasted an hour and a half ; and there is to be another, the date of which is not fixed, so that I am left in uncertainty. I shall not delay an hour when I am at liberty to take my departure. Pray for me.

Yours very faithfully in Christ,

✠Thomas Alphonsus O'Callaghan.

# NOTES

### Introduction

1. Stanmore: *Memoir of Sidney Herbert, Lord Herbert of Lea*, i, 412.
2. *Selection of Parochial Examinations relative to the Destitute Classes in Ireland,* pp. 165-192.
3. Carroll: *Leaves from the Annals of the Sisters of Mercy*, ii, 19.
4. Walsh: *These Splendid Sisters*, p. 120 ff.
5. Fink: *Catholic Influences in the Life of Florence Nightingale*, p. 10.
6. Editorial: *The Freeman's Journal*, August 17, 1855.

### Chapter 1

1. During the Crimean War there was no medical corps properly so-called: the *Royal Army Medical Corps* was not established until 1896.
2. Cook: *The Life of Florence Nightingale*, i, 321.
3. Russell: *The British Expedition to the Crimea*, pp. 285, 286.
4. Steevens: *The Crimean Campaign with the Connaught Rangers,* 1854-1856, p. 172
5. Russell: *op. cit.,* p. 288.
6. As quoted in *The Freeman's Journal,* October 22, 1854.
7. Steevens: *The Crimean Campaign with the Connaught Rangers,* p. 156.
8. Clifford: *Henry Clifford, V.C., his Letters and Sketches from the Crimea*, p. 110.
9. Fink: *Catholic Influences in the Life of Florence Nightingale,* p. 22.
10. Published in *The Freeman's Journal*, October 17, 1854.
11. Cook: *The Life of Florence Nightingale*, i, 242.
12. Osborne: *Scutari and its Hospitals*, p. 43 ff.
13. Cook: *op. cit.,* p. 146.
14. Cook: *op. cit.,* p. 147.

### Chapter 2

1. Carroll: *Leaves from the Annals of the Sisters of Mercy*, ii, 134.
2. Fink: *Catholic Influences in the Life of Florence Nightingale*, p. 3; Murphy: *They Did Not Pass By*, p. 187.
3. Fink: *op. cit.,* p. 5.
4. Major: *War and Disease*, p. 81.
5. Cook: *The Life of Florence Nightingale*, i, 158. Stanmore: *Memoir of Sidney Herbert, Lord Herbert of Lea*, i, 342.
6. Davis: *Autobiography of Elizabeth Davis, a Balaclava Nurse*, ii, 93.
7. Stanmore: *op. cit.,* i, 404, 406 ff.
8. Ramsay: *Thomas Grant, First Bishop of Southwark*, pp. 110, 128.
9. W.-Smith: *Florence Nightingale*, p. 106.

10. Leslie: " Forgotten Passages in the Life of Florence Nightingale," *The Dublin Review*, 161, October 1917, p. 179 ff.

11. *The Tablet*, January 27, 1855.

12. " J.H.G.": Letter to *The Tablet*, January 20, 1855.

13. The Archives, Convent of Mercy, Kinsale; undated letter.

14. Cook: *loc. cit.*, i, 216.

15. Bridgeman: *The Bridgeman Diary*, p. 5.

16. *The Nightingale Papers, MS. 43,402*, British Museum.

17. Letter written from Scutari on December 3, 1854; published in *The Freeman's Journal*, January 12, 1855.

18. Carroll: *op. cit.*, ii, 140.

19. Stanmore: *loc. cit.*, i, 347.

20. Stanmore: *Memoir of Sidney Herbert, Lord Herbert of Lea*, i, 355.

CHAPTER 3

1. Gavan Duffy: *The League of North and South*, p. 11.

2. *The Manning-Stanley Correspondence*, October 24, 1854.

3. *The Cullen Papers*, Dublin Archiepiscopal Archives; uncatalogued.

4. Doyle: *Memories of the Crimea*, p. 6.

5. *The Archives*, Convent of Mercy, Kinsale; undated letter.

6. Carroll: *Leaves from the Annals of the Sisters of Mercy*, ii, 146-147.

7. Walpole: *The Life of Lord John Russell*, ii, 177.

8. *The British Army List*, The War Office; and Fortescue: *A History of the British Army, 1852-1870*, xiii, Index pp. 592 et. seq.

9. Cunliffe: *The Royal Irish Fusiliers*, 1793-1950, p. 210.

10. Jourdain: *The Connaught Rangers*, iii, 153-155.

11. Extract from a letter written from Sebastopol towards the end of 1854, and published in *The Cork Constitution* on January 4, 1855.

12. Letters published in *The Freeman's Journal*, October 17, 1854.

13. Croke: *The Croke Diary*, p. 1.

14. The Archives, Convent of Mercy, Kinsale. Bridgeman: *The Bridgeman Diary*, p. 6.

15. *The Archives*, Convent of Mercy, Kinsale.

CHAPTER 4

1. The exact date of Joanna Bridgeman's birth cannot be ascertained. The Annals of St. Mary's, Limerick, give St. Tola's Church, Ruan, Ennis, as her place of Baptism; but as the Parish Register of St. Tola's does not date beyond 1845, more precise data on the matter are not available.

2. She was descended from " Maurice O'Connell of Dunmaniheen (1680-1720), whose descendants took over the Clare property. This Maurice was younger brother to John O'Connell, the first permanently to settle on the Derrynane property; which John was the great grandfather of the Liberator." [From *The Genealogical Office*, Dublin Castle, by kind permission of Basil O'Connell.]

3. Words spoken by Right Reverend Dean O'Brien of Limerick.

4. Burke-Savage: *Catherine McAuley*, p. 241.

5. Carroll: *Leaves from the Annals of the Sisters of Mercy*, i, 452.
6. Carroll: *op. cit.*, i, 463.
7. Wiseman: Extract from Lenten Pastoral, 1856; as published in *The Lamp*.


CHAPTER 5

1. The Archives, Convent of Mercy, Kinsale.
2. *The Freeman's Journal;* Letter from a War Correspondent, March 5, 1855.
3. Bridgeman: *The Bridgeman Diary*, p. 7.
4. *The Manning-Stanley Correspondence*, November 5, 1854.
5. Cullen: *The Cullen Papers;* Letter dated November 18, 1854.
6. Major: *War and Disease*, p. 87.
7. W-Smith: *op. cit.*, pp. 139, 140.
8. *The Manning-Stanley Correspondence;* December 1854; otherwise un-dated.
9. Bridgeman: *The Bridgeman Diary*, p. 7.
10. *The Manning-Stanley Correspondence*, November 27, 1854.
11. Ward: *The Life of John Henry Cardinal Newman*, i, 79.
12. Bridgeman: *The Bridgeman Diary*, p. 8.
13. Doyle: *Memories of the Crimea*, p. 18.
14. Bridgeman: *The Bridgeman Diary*, p. 8.
15. Volunteer: *Eastern Hospitals and English Nurses*, i, 16.
16. *The Manning-Stanley Correspondence*, November 29, 1854.
17. *The Manning-Stanley Correspondence*, November 25, 1854.
18. Leslie: 'Forgotten Passages in the Life of Florence Nightingale,' *The Dublin Review*, 161, October, 1917, 179 ff.
19. Volunteer: *op. cit.*, i, 12, 13.
20. Devas: *Mother Magdalen Taylor*, pp. 17-24.
21. *The Tablet*, January 26, 1855.


CHAPTER 6

1. W-Smith: *Florence Nightingale*, p. 108.
2. Archives: Convent of Mercy, Kinsale.
3. Doyle: *Memories of the Crimea*, p. 21.
4. Bridgeman: *The Bridgeman Diary*, p. 9.
5. Carroll: *Leaves from the Annals of the Sisters of Mercy*. ii, 159.
6. Volunteer: *loc. cit.*, i, 23.
7. Bridgeman: *The Bridgeman Diary*, p. 9.
8. Doyle: *Memories of the Crimea*, pp. 22, 26.
9. Croke: *The Croke Diary*, p. 3.
10. Volunteer: *Eastern Hospitals and English Nurses*, 31 ff.
     Bridgeman: *The Bridgeman Diary*, p. 9.
     Croke : *The Croke Diary*, p. 4.
     Doyle: *Memories of the Crimea*, p. 27.
11. Bridgeman: *The Bridgeman Diary*, p. 10.
12. Carroll: *Leaves from the Annals of the Sisters of Mercy*, ii, 160.
13. Lane-Poole: *The Life of Sir Stratford de Redcliffe, Viscount Canning*, p. 380 ff.

14. Concannon: *The Irish Sisters of Mercy in the Crimean War*, p. 13.

15. Volunteer: *Eastern Hospitals and English Nurses*, i, 37, 38.

16. *The Nightingale Papers*, MSS. 43,402; 43,393 passim.

17. Doyle: *Memories of the Crimea*, p. 30.

18. Bridgeman: *The Bridgeman Diary*, p. 10.

19. *The Cork Examiner*, February 8, 1855: post-war review.

20. Jackson: *The Inniskilling Dragoons, The Records of an Old Heavy Cavalry Regiment*, pp. 169-171.

CHAPTER 7.

1. Strachey: *Eminent Victorians*, p. 115.

2. W-Smith: *Florence Nightingale*, p. 94.

3. Cope: *Florence Nightingale and the Doctors*, p. 26.

4. Cook: *The Life of Florence Nightingale*, ii, 424.

5. Croke: *The Croke Diary*, p. 7.
   W-Smith: *Florence Nightingale*, p. 170.

6. Cope: *op. cit.*, p. 72.

7. *The Nightingale Papers*.

8. Cook: *op. cit.*, i, 424, 426 et seq.

9. Cook: *op. cit.*, i, 155, quoting from War Office Document, October 17, 1854.

10. Cope: *op. cit.*, pp. 16, 44, 45.

11. Lammond: *Florence Nightingale*, pp. 84-85.

12. Mitra: *The Life and Letters of Sir John Hall, M.D., K.C.B., F.R.C.S.*, pp. 377, 379.

13. Stanmore: *Memoir of Sidney Herbert, Lord Herbert of Lea*, i, 381.

14. Pavey: *The Story of the Growth of Nursing as an Art, a Profession and a Vocation*, p. 284.

15. *Report upon the State of the Hospitals of the British Army in the Crimea and Scutari, together with an Appendix.* Presented to both Houses of Parliament by command of Her Majesty, 1855. (The Hospitals Commission).

16. Cope: *Florence Nightingale and the Doctors*, p. 46.

17. Cook: *The Life of Florence Nightingale*, i, 238.

18. Volunteer: *Eastern Hospitals and English Nurses*, i, 70.

19. *The Nightingale Papers*, MSS. 43,402; 43,393; 43,395, passim.

20. *Ibid.*

21. Cope: *op. cit.*, p. 23.

22. The Woodham-Smith biography makes the writing of this letter coincide with the actual arrival of the *Egyptus*, possibly with a view to minimising the impulsiveness of Miss Nightingale's reaction.

23. Stanmore: *op. cit.*, i, 371.

24. Archives, Convent of Mercy, Kinsale. Letter dated December 22, 1854.

25. *The Nightingale Papers*, p. 46, MS. 43,393. Letter dated Christmas Day, 1854. The disparity between this letter and that of Mary Stanley to Mother Bridgeman is too obvious to demand special treatment.

26. *The Nightingale Papers*.

27. W-Smith: *Florence Nightingale*, p. 142.

28. Bridgeman: *The Bridgeman Diary*, p. 8.

29. Cook: *The Life of Florence Nightingale*, i. 246.

30. Stanmore: *Memoir of Sidney Herbert*, i, 375.
31. Cook: *op. cit.*, i, 252.
32. Davis: *Autobiography of Elizabeth Davis, a Balaclava Nurse*, ii, 110.
33. Archives, Convent of Mercy, Kinsale.
34. Cook: *loc. cit.*, i, 189. Letter dated December 27, 1854.
35. *The Manning-Stanley Correspondence*, January 1, 1855.

CHAPTER 8.

1. Archives: Convent of Mercy, Kinsale.
2. Bridgeman: *The Bridgeman Diary*, p. 10.
3. *The Manning-Stanley Corespondence*, letter dated February 8, 1855.
4. Bridgeman: *The Bridgeman Diary*, p. 10.
5. Bridgeman: *The Bridgeman Diary*, p. 10.
6. *The Nightingale Papers*, MS. 43,402, passim.
7. *The Cullen Papers: Religiosae*. Letter dated, Scutari, June 8, 1855.
8. Archives: Convent of Mercy, Liverpool; letter dated, Therapia, January 3, 1855.
9. Letter from ' An English Priest '; *The Tablet*, January 20, 1855. Letter from ' J.H.G.'; *The Tablet*, January 6, 1855.
10. *The Cork Constitution*, January 16, 1855.
11. *The Cullen Papers:* Letter dated, Scutari, February 12, 1855.
12. Archives: Convent of Mercy, Kinsale. *Bridgeman Diary*, p. 11.
13. Cook: *The Life of Florence Nightingale*, i, 249.
14. W-Smith: *Florence Nightingale*, p. 144.
15. *The Cullen Papers; Religiosae;* letter dated March 20, 1855, from Bishop Grant of Southwark to Archbishop Cullen, in which there is mention of Mother M. Clare's return at the request of Father Michael Cuffe.
16. Archives: Convent of Mercy, Kinsale; letter dated, " Scutari Barracks Hospital, Christmas Eve /54."
17. Bridgeman: *The Bridgeman Diary*, p. 11.
18. Archives: Convent of Mercy, Kinsale.
19. *The Nightingale Papers*, MS. 43,393, p. 200.
20. Archives: Convent of Mercy, Kinsale.
21. Bridgeman: *The Bridgeman Diary*, p. 12.
22. *The Nightingale Papers*, Vol. 1, MS. 43,393, p. 65 versa.
23. Bridgeman: *The Bridgeman Diary*, p. 13.
24. Bridgeman: *Ibid.*
25. Bridgeman: *Ibid.*, p. 15.
26. Bridgeman: *Ibid.*, p. 16.
27. Volunteer: *Eastern Hospitals and English Nurses*, i, 72.
28. *The Nightingale Papers.*
29. Carroll: *Leaves from the Annals of the Sisters of Mercy*, ii, 172.
30. Bridgeman: *The Bridgeman Diary*, pp. 17-18.
31. Volunteer: *op cit.*, i, 72.
32. Davis: *Autobiography of Elizabeth Davis, a Balaclava Nurse*, ii, 128. There is also a statement from Dr. John Hall to the same effect.
33. *The Cullen Papers.* Letter dated, June 28, 1855.
34. Doyle: *op. cit.*, pp. 35-37.
35. Doyle: *op. cit.*, p. 36.
36. Volunteer; *op. cit.*, i, 120; 273. Carroll: *op. cit.* ii, 169, 170.

37. Cook: *The Life of Florence Nightingale,* i, 251.
38. Archives: Convent of Mercy, Bermondsey, London.
39. Bridgeman: *The Bridgeman Diary,* p. 17.
40. W-Smith: *Florence Nightingale,* p. 140.
41. Stanmore: *Memoir of Sidney Herbert, Lord Herbert of Lea,* i, 370 ff.
42. Archives: Kinsale. Letter dated January 12, 1855.
43. *The Nightingale Papers,* MS. 43,402.
44. *The Cullen Papers; Religiosae;* Letter from Father Michael Cuffe to Archbishop Cullen, dated June 28, 1855.
45. Bridgeman: *The Bridgeman Diary,* p. 18. (The Archives in Liverpool, Carlow, Charleville mention Miss Nightingale's concurrence).
46. Bridgeman: *The Bridgeman Diary,* p. 19.

CHAPTER 9.

1. Jackson: *The Inniskilling Dragoons,* p. 171.
2. Gretton: *The Campaigns and History of the Royal Irish Regiment, 1684-1902,* i, p. 168.
3. Russell: *The British Expedition to the Crimea,* p. 182.
4. Kinglake: *The Invasion of the Crimea,* vii, 281.
5. Kinglake: *Ibid.,* vii, 234.
6. Kinglake: *Ibid.,* vii, 134.
7. Doyle: *Memories of the Crimea,* p. 43.
   Volunteer: *Eastern Hospitals and English Nurses,* i, 93.
8. Bridgeman: *The Bridgeman Diary,* p. 24.
9. Burton: *The Loveliest Flower,* p. 118.
10. Volunteer: *loc. cit.,* i, 82-83.
11. Kinglake: *The Invasion of the Crimea,* vii, 189.
12. Cook: *The Life of Florence Nightingale,* i, 214.
13. *The Lamp;* an Illustrated Catholic Magazine; March 1856.
14. Letter written in March 1855, and published in *The Freeman's Journal,* July 16.
15. Bridgeman: *Diary,* p. 38.
16. Carroll: *Leaves from the Annals of the Sisters of Mercy,* ii, 202 ff.
17. Bridgeman: *Diary,* pp. 40, 58.
18. Archives: Convent of Mercy, Kinsale; letter dated January 25, 1855.
19. *The Nightingale Papers,* MS. 43,402.
20. *The Nightingale Papers.*
21. Pincoffs: *Experiences of a Civilian in Eastern Military Hospitals,* p. 70 ff.
22. Osborne : *Scutari and its Hospitals,* p. 48 ff.
23. Archives: Convent of Mercy, Kinsale.
24. Carroll: *Leaves from the Annals of the Sisters of Mercy,* ii, 174, 175.
25. Stanmore: *Memoir of Sidney Herbert,* i, 412.
26. Bridgeman: *Diary,* p. 62.
27. Bridgeman: *Ibid.,* pp. 62, 63, 64.
28. Volunteer: *Eastern Hospitals and English Nurses,* i, 273.

CHAPTER 10.

1. Volunteer: *Eastern Hospitals and English Nurses,* i, 112.
2. Stanley: *Memoirs of Edward and Catherine Stanley,* pp. 344-345.

3. Volunteer: *Eastern Hospitals and English Nurses*, i, 116.

\* The position was otherwise in France as is evident from the following extract from the *Annales de la Compaignie des Filles de la Charité de St. Vincent de Paul*, 140 Rue du Bac, Paris:

"Pendant longtemps notre Communauté a desservi en France un certain nombre d'Hôpitaux Militaires. C'est lors des laicisations, en 1904, que nos Soeurs ont été forcées d'en abandonner le service.

Lors de la guerre de 1914-1918 nous n'avions plus d'Hôpitaux Militaires proprement dits, mais les Filles de la Charité se sont devouées auprès des blessés dans les Ambulances organisées un peu partout. La guere terminée ces Ambulances se sont fermées par le fait même.

En 1919 la Communauté prit en charge l'Hôpital Militaire de Strasbourg, lequel fût transféré en 1939 à Obernai (bas Rhin), puis complétement evacué en 1940 avec toute de la population de cette region. Il na fut pas possible d'y redonner des Soeurs après la derniére guerre.

Les Soeurs de la Charité été demandées à Chalons-sur-Marne en 1907 et y sont restées jusqu'en 1940, lors l'évacuation. Après la guerre elles y sont retournées quelques mois, fin 1944, debut 1945, puis l'hôpital fut réquisitionné par les Americains et elles laissèrent la place."

4. Bridgeman: *Diary*, p. 38.

5. *The Cullen Papers;* Religiosae; Letters dated March 23, 1855, and May 2, 1855.

6. *The Nightingale Papers.*

7. *The Manning-Stanley Correspondence.*

8. Bridgeman: *Diary*, p. 21.

9. Volunteer: *Eastern Hospitals and English Nurses*, i, 131.

10. *The Nightingale Papers*, MS. 43,402.

11. A letter in *The Dublin Archiepiscopal Archives* written in June, 1855 confirms this.

12. Lane-Poole: *The Life of Sir Stratford de Redcliffe, Viscount Canning*, p. 385 ff. The extravagance imputed to the Koulali administration on pages 149 and 177 of the Woodham-Smith biography is incorrect in view of this statement of General Storks.

13. Bridgeman: *Diary*, p, 56.

14. Volunteer: *loc, cit.,* i, 178.

15. Volunteer: *Eastern Hospitals and English Nurses*, i, 105. Kinglake: *The Invasion of the Crimea*, vii, 366-367.

16. Carroll: *Leaves from the Annals*, ii, 178.

17. Volunteer: *op. cit.,* i, 273.

18. Stanmore: *Memoir of Sidney Herbert*, i, 377.

19. *The Nightingale Papers.*

20. W-Smith: *Florence Nightingale*, p. 146.

21. Bridgeman: *Diary*, p. 31.

22. *The Manning-Stanley Correspondence.*

23. Archives: Convent of Mercy, Kinsale. Letter dated 'March 1855'.

24. Carroll: *op. cit.,* ii, 183.

25. Stanley: *Memoirs of Edward and Catherine Stanley*, pp. 342, 352.

26. Lane-Poole: *The Life of Sir Stratford de Redcliffe, Viscount Canning*, p. 388.

27. *The Nightingale Papers*, MS. 43,402.
28. Volunteer: *Eastern Hospitals and English Nurses*, i, 145.
29. Bridgeman: *Diary*, p. 23.
30. Bridgeman: *Diary*, p. 42.
31. Volunteer: *Eastern Hospitals and English Nurses*, i, 262; ii, passim.


CHAPTER 11.

1. Doyle: *Memories of the Crimea*, p. 52.
2. Doyle: *Ibid.*, p. 53.
3. Volunteer: *Eastern Hospitals and English Nurses*, i, 186, 273.
Carroll: *Leaves from the Annals of the Sisters of Mercy*, ii, 177.
Doyle: *op. cit.*, p. 44.
4. Volunteer: *op. cit.*, i, 143.
5. Osborne: *Scutari and its Hospitals*, p. 36 ff.
6. Russell : *The War in the Crimea*, i, 374.
7. Volunteer: *op. cit.*, i, 176.
8. Stanmore: *Memoir of Sidney Herbert*, i, 414.
9. Bridgeman: *Diary*, p. 50.
10. Bridgeman: *Ibid.*, p. 53.
11. Carroll: *op. cit.*, ii, 173.
12. Leslie: ' Forgotten Passages in the Life of Florence Nightingale.'
*The Dublin Review*, 161, October, 1917, p. 179 ff.
13. Bridgeman: *Diary*, pp. 40, 52, 61.
14. Bridgeman: *Ibid.*, p. 53.
15. Archives: Convent of Mercy, Kinsale.
16. Archives: Convent of Mercy, Liverpool, letter from Sister M. Elizabeth Butler.
17. Bridgeman: *Diary*, p. 59.
18. Croke: *Diary*, p. 5.
19. Croke: *Ibid.*
20. Article published in *The Tablet*, March 24, 1855.
21. Archives: Kinsale, Convent of Mercy.
Davis: *Autobiography of Elizabeth Davis*, ii, 251. Published also in several other works on this period, but omitted in the Woodham-Smith biography.
22. Bridgeman: *Diary*, p. 53.
23. Archives: Convent of Mercy, Kinsale.
24. Bridgeman: *Diary*, p. 54.
25. Archives: Convent of Mercy, Bermondsey.
26. *The Manning-Stanley Correspondence;* letters dated May 6, 1855, June 8, 1855, June 13, 1855, June 23, 1855.
27. Bridgeman: *Diary*, p. 56.
28. Leslie: ' *Forgotten Passages in the Life of Florence Nightingale.*'
*The Dublin Review*, 161, October, 1917, p. 179 ff.
29. Bridgeman: *Diary*, p. 58.
Volunteer: *Eastern Hospitals and English Nurses*, i, 260.
30. Volunteer: *op. cit.*, i, 265.
31. *Joyce: Red Cross International and the Strategy of Peace*, p. 95.
32. W-Smith: *Florence Nightingale*, p. 169.

## CHAPTER 12.

1. Wood: *The Crimea in 1854 and 1894*, p. 232.
2. Russell: *The War in the Crimea*, i, 435.
3. Atkins: *The Life of Sir W. H. Russell, C.V.O., LL.D.*, i, 181.
4. Archives: Convent of Mercy, Kinsale.
5. Bridgeman: *Diary*, pp. 56-58.
6. Bridgeman: *Ibid.*, pp. 57-59.
7. Archives: Convent of Mercy, Kinsale.
8. Bridgeman: *Diary*, passim.
9. Bridgeman: *Diary*, pp. 60-61.
10. Bridgeman: *Diary*, p. 64.
11. Cook: *The Life of Florence Nightingale*, i, 288.
    W-Smith: *op. cit.*, pp. 164-165.
12. Clifford: *Letters and sketches from the Crimea*, p. 209.
13. Wood: *The Crimea in 1854 and 1894*, p. 285.
14. Gretton: *The Campaigns and History of the Royal Irish Regiment, 18th Foot, 1684-1902*, p. 197.
15. Jourdain: *The Connaught Rangers*, iii, 179.
16. Davis: *Autobiography of Elizabeth Davis, a Balaclava Nurse*, ii, 162, 164, 221.
17. Volunteer: *Eastern Hospitals and English Nurses*, i, 260.
18. Carroll: *Leaves from the Annals of the Sisters of Mercy*, ii, 212 et seq.
19. Bridgeman: *Diary*, pp. 67, 68.
20. Mitra: *The Life and Letters of Sir John Hall*, pp. 435-436.
    Volunteer: *Eastern Hospitals and English Nurses*, ii, 164.
    Bridgeman: *Diary*, p. 64.
    Doyle: *Memories of the Crimea*, p. 59.
    The Woodham-Smith Biography makes no reference to Miss Nightingale's resignation; Sir E. Cook also ignores it.
21. Bridgeman: *Diary*, p. 65.
22. Archives: Convent of Mercy, Kinsale.
23. Bridgeman:*Diary*, p. 66.
24. Bridgeman: *Ibid.*, p. 67.

## CHAPTER 13.

1: Simpson: ' Henry Press Wright, First Archdeacon of Columbia '; from *The British Columbia Historical Quarterly*, July-October, 1955, pp. 127-134.
2. *The Freeman's Journal*, July 27, 1854.
3. *The Freeman's Journal*, July 20, 1854; August 18, 1854
4. *The Freeman's Journal*, August 18, 1854.
5. *The Journal of the Royal Army Chaplains' Department*, v., July, 1935; No. 40.
6. Clifford : *Letters and Sketches from the Crimea*, p. 106.
7. *The Freeman's Journal*, August 18, 1854.
8. *The Tablet*, April 7, 1855.
9. Clifford: *op. cit.*, pp. 147, 160.
10. Clifford: *Ibid.*, p. 154.
11. Bridgeman: *Diary*, p. 93 ff.

12. Simpson: *op. cit.*, p. 137.
13. *Ex Archivis Dubliniensis; Religiosae;* Non-catalogued. Letter dated June 1, 1855.
14. *Ex Archivis Dubliniensis;* letter dated March 23, 1855.
15. *The Freeman's Journal,* September 15, 1855.
16. Russell: *The War in the Crimea,* ii, 47.
17. Simpson: *loc. cit.,* pp. 136-137.
18. *The Freeman's Journal,* March 18, 1855. Article re-printed from *The Morning Herald,* March 11.
19. *The Tablet,* April 7, 1855. Letter from a Catholic officer.
20. Bridgeman: *Diary,* passim.
21. *The Freeman's Journal,* December 21, 1854.
22. *Ibid.,* May 31, 1855.
23. *The British Army List,* 1857.
24. Ramsay: *Thomas Grant, First Bishop of Southwark,* p. 139.
25. *The Journal of the Royal Army Chaplains' Department,* v., July, 1935, No. 40, pp. 88-102.
26. *The Journal of the Royal Army Chaplains' Department;* Army List, February, 1859, p. 116.

CHAPTER 14.

1. Cook: *The Life of F. Nightingale,* i. 214.
2. Mitra: *The Life and Letters of Sir John Hall,* p. 435 ff.
3. Mitra: *Ibid.*
4. Archives: Convent of Mercy, Kinsale. Miss Nightingale denied ever receiving any such communication from Dr. Hall. *Vide:* W-Smith, *Florence Nightingale,* pp. 186-190.
5. Bridgeman: *Diary,* p. 71.
6. Archives: Convent of Mercy, Kinsale.
7. Archives: Kinsale. Letter dated October 2, 1855.
8. Archives: Convent of Mercy, Kinsale.
9. *The Nightingale Papers.*
10. Archives: Convent of Mercy, Kinsale.
11. Bridgeman: *Diary,* p. 71.
12. Mitra: *The Life and Letters of Sir John Hall,* p. 418.
13. Archives: Convent of Mercy, Kinsale.
14. Archives: Kinsale.
15. *The Bridgeman Diary* pp. 76-78.
16. Bridgeman: *Diary,* p. 79.
17. Volunteer: *Eastern Hospitals and English Nurses,* ii, passim.
18. Bridgeman: *Diary,* p. 81.
19. Bridgeman: *Ibid.,* pp. 81-82.
20. Bridgeman: *Diary,* p. 84.
21. Bridgeman: *Ibid.,* pp. 85-86.
22. Bridgeman: *Diary,* p. 90.
23. Bridgeman: *Diary,* pp. 92-94.
24. Cook: *The Life of Florence Nightingale,* i, 213.
25. Archives: Convent of Mercy, Kinsale.
26. Mitra: *The Life and Letters of Sir John Hall,* p. 442.
27. Mitra: *Ibid.,* p. 443.

### Chapter 15.

1. Gretton: *The Campaigns and History of the Royal Irish Regiment, 1684-1902*, i, 184.
2. Russell: *The War in the Crimea*, ii, 239.
3. Bridgeman: *Diary*, p. 87.
4. Bridgeman: *Diary*, p. 86.
5. Ramsay: *Thomas Grant, First Bishop of Southwark*, p. 132. This book states incorrectly that Sister M. Winifred was one of the Bermondsey Sisters.
6. Volunteer: *Eastern Hospitals and English Nurses*, ii, 219.
7. Bridgeman: *Diary*, p. 88.
8. *The Cullen Papers:* Religiosae; Dublin Archiepiscopal Archives. Letter dated: ' 88th Regiment. October, 1855.'
9. Archives: Convent of Mercy, Kinsale.
10. Colborne, Brine: *Memorials of the Brave, or the Resting Places of our Fallen Heroes in the Crimea and at Scutari*, p. 39.
11. *The Nightingale Papers.*
12. Carroll: *Leaves from the Annals of the Sisters of Mercy*, ii, 193.
13. Bridgeman: *Diary*, p. 93.
14. Carroll: *op. cit.*, ii, 195.
15. Volunteer: *Eastern Hospitals and English Nurses*, ii, 256, 263. Carroll: *op. cit.*, ii, 195.
16. Doyle: *Memories of the Crimea*, p. 68.
17. *The Tablet*, November 10, 1855.
18. Bridgeman: *Diary*, pp. 92-95. Doyle: *Memories of the Crimea*, p. 57. This is another incident misapplied by Grace Ramsay to the Bermondsey Sisters. *Vide, Thomas Grant, First Bishop of Southwark*, p. 134.
19. Bridgeman: *Diary*, p. 91.
20. Bridgeman: *Ibid.*, p. 94.
21. Archives: Convent of Mercy, Kinsale.
22. Bridgeman: *Diary*, p. 96.
23. Carroll: *Leaves from the Annals of the Sisters of Mercy*, ii, 189.
24. Williams: *Priscilla Lydia Sellon*, passim, pp. 9, 13, 16, 43, 54.
25. Dock: *A History of Nursing*, iii, 84.
26. Dock: *op. cit.*, iii, 86-96.
27. Bridgeman: *Diary*, p. 105.
28. Archives: Kinsale; letter from Mother Bridgeman to Dr. John Hall.
29. Mitra: *The Life and Letters of Sir John Hall*, p. 441 ff.
30. Archives: Kinsale; Supplementary Confidential Report; *ut infra.*
31. *The Nightingale Papers*, MS. 43,393.
32. Bridgeman: *Diary*, p. 118.
33. Bridgeman: *Ibid.*, p. 120.
34. Cook: *The Life of Florence Nightingale*, i, 294.

### Chapter 16.

1. *The Nightingale Papers.*
2. *The Nightingale Papers*, 43,403; 43,393.
3. Bridgeman: *The Bridgeman Diary*, p. 91.
4. Archives: Convent of Mercy, Kinsale. *The Confidential Report.*

5. Stanmore: *Memoir of Sidney Herbert*, i, 417.
6. Archives: Convent of Mercy, Kinsale. Letter of Sir John Hall to Mother Bridgeman.
7. Archives: Convent of Mercy, Kinsale. *The Confidential Report.*
8. W-Smith: *Florence Nightingale*, p. 192.
9. Archives: Convent of Mercy, Kinsale. Letter of Sir John Hall to Mother Bridgeman.
10. Archives: Convent of Mercy, Kinsale. *The Confidential Report.*
11. Bridgeman: *Diary*, p. 109.
12. Bridgeman: *Diary*, pp. 113-115.
13. Bridgeman: *Ibid.*, pp. 116-117.
14. Preston, Wise, Werner: *Men in Arms*. A History of warfare and its inter-relationships with western society. This work states that 206 out of 221 staff vacancies were given to outsiders, pp. 206-207.
15. Carroll: *Leaves from the Annals of the Sisters of Mercy*, ii, 202.
16. Archives: Convent of Mercy, Kinsale.
17. Cook: *The Life of Florence Nightingale*, i, 267.
18. Mitra: *The Life and Letters of Sir John Hall*, p. 448.
19. Cook: *op. cit.*, i, 273.
20. *The Lamp;* March 29, 1856.
21. Moran: *The Pastoral Letters and other Writings of Cardinal Paul Cullen, Archbishop of Dublin*, i, 408-409.
22. Doyle: *Memories of the Crimea*, pp. 106, 107.
23. This interpretation of Miss Nightingale's character is given by her first biographer, Sir Edward Cook. It is also seen in Lytton Strachey's *Eminent Victorians*; in Lord Stanmore's *Memoir of Sidney Herbert*; in S. Lane-Poole's *Life of Sir Stratford de Redcliffe*, etc.
24. Mitra: *The Life and Letters of Sir John Hall*, p. 418.
25. Bridgeman: *Diary*, p. 122.

## CHAPTER 17.

1. Russell: *The War in the Crimea*, ii, 380.
2. Mitra: *The Life and Letters of Sir John Hall*, p. 450.
3. Cope: *Florence Nightingale and the Doctors*, pp. 52-53. This letter is omitted in all current biographies of Florence Nightingale.
4. Bridgeman: *Diary*, p. 122; Mitra: *op. cit.*, p. 450; Cope, p. 54.
5. Bridgeman: *Diary*, pp. 122-123.
6. Bridgeman: *Diary*, pp. 123-124.
7. Mitra: *op. cit.*, p. 456.
8. Bridgeman: *Diary*, p. 125.
9. Bridgeman: *Diary*, p. 128.
10. Jackson: *The Inniskilling Dragoons*, p. 203 ff.
   Jourdain: *The Connaught Rangers*, ii, 183.
   Cunliffe: *The Royal Irish Fusiliers*, p. 215.
   Gretton: *The Campaigns and History of the Royal Irish Regiment*, p. 186.
   Steevens: *The Crimean Campaign with the Connaught Rangers*, p. 312 ff.
   Rousset: *Histoire de la Guerre de Crimeé*, ii, 455 ff.
   Russell: *The War in the Crimea*, ii, 428.
   Wood: *The Crimea in 1854 and 1894*, p. 385 ff.

Atkins: *The Life of Sir W. H. Russell, C.V.O., LL.D.*, i, 250 ff. Newspapers of the period corroborated this date. The date is also given in the general European histories listed in the Bibliography. In view of the foregoing proofs, the Woodham-Smith biography is therefore historically incorrect in citing *April* 29 as the date on which the Peace of Paris was signed.

11. *The Nightingale Papers*, MS. 43,402.
12. Bridgeman: *Ibid.*, pp. 130-131.
13. Archives: Convent of Mercy, Kinsale. Log-book of the General Hospital, Balaclava.
14. Croke: *The Croke Diary*, p. 10 ff.
15. Mitra: *The Life and Letters of Sir John Hall*, p. 478.
16. Archives: Convent of Mercy, Kinsale.
17. Archives: *Ibid.*
18. Archives: *Ibid.* War Office Document N. 155656/507.
19. *The Nightingale Papers*, MS. 43,402, British Museum.
20. Bridgeman: *Diary*, p. 138.
21. Russell: *The War in the Crimea*, ii, 437.
22. Mitra: *The Life and Letters of Sir John Hall* p. 459.
23. Mitra: *Ibid.*, pp. 460-461.
24. Archives: Convent of Mercy, Kinsale. Copy of *Statement No.* 10,020, made by Florence Nightingale to the War Office.
25. Archives: Convent of Mercy, Kinsale.
26. Archives: Convent of Mercy, Kinsale.
27. Archives: Convent of Mercy, Kinsale.
28. Archives: *Ibid.*

CHAPTER 18.

1. Croke: *The Croke Diary*, p. 20.
2. Bridgeman: *Diary*, p. 142.
3. Mitra: *The Life and Letters of Sir John Hall*, p. 470 ff.
4. Mooney: 'An Irish Bishop in a Moorish Kingdom,' published in *Assisi*, XII, 1940, pp. 142-144.
5. Croke: *The Croke Diary*, p. 26.
6. Bridgeman: *Diary*, p. 143.
7. Bridgeman: *Diary*, pp. 145-146.
8. Carroll: *Leaves from Annals of the Sisters of Mercy*. ii, 214. The rate of division worked out at £10 per head: Bermondsey, £80; Chelsea, £10; Liverpool, £30; Charleville, £20; Cork, £20; Dublin, £20 and Kinsale, £30.
9. Bridgeman: *Diary*, p. 144.
10. *The Nightingale-Herbert Papers; Additional MSS.* 43,393-43,395.
11. Bridgeman: *Diary*, p. 156.
12. Doyle: *Memories of the Crimea*, p. 101.
13. Carroll: *op. cit.*, ii, 212.
14. Bridgeman: *Diary*, pp. 148-149.
15. Archives: Kinsale. Letter from Fr. Gleeson, C.M., dated April 21, 1856.
16. Mitra: *The Life and Letters of Sir John Hall*, p. 460 ff.
17. Archives: Convent of Mercy, Kinsale; letter dated April 21, 1856.
18. *The Tablet*, May 8, 1954, Vol. 203, No. 5946.

19. *The Nightingale Papers.* MS. 43,393 p. 232 *et versa.*

20. *The Cullen Papers :* Ex Archivis Dubliniensis. Letter from Fr. Cuffe, dated April 21, 1856.

21. Croke: *Diary,* p. 40.

22. Archives, Convent of Mercy, Kinsale; letter dated April 21, 1856.

23. *History of the Great National Banquet for the Victorious Soldiers returned from the Crimean War and Stationed in the Irish Garrisons by the People of Ireland in the City of Dublin, October 22, 1856.*

24. Cope: *Florence Nightingale and the Doctors,* passim.

25. Cope: *Ibid.,* p. 122.

26. Joyce: *Red Cross International and the Strategy of Peace,* pp. 95-97.

27. Joyce: *Ibid.,* p. 21.

28. Fink: *Catholic Influences in the Life of Florence Nightingale,* p. 10.

29. Walsh: *These Splendid Sisters,* pp. 179, 183.

30. *The Lamp,* March 22, 1856.

## CHAPTER 19.

1. Archives, Convent of Mercy, Kinsale. According to my original data from these Archives, Sister M. Joseph Lynch went in 1858 on a foundation to Cincinnati, Ohio. A later Act of Chapter for 1859 states that Sister M. Joseph got permission to transfer to the Convent of Mercy, Brooklyn, where a brother of hers was pastor. A recent work—*The Way is Mercy*—(Evans) on the centenary of the Cincinnati foundation mentions a Sister M. Joseph *Leahy* of Kinsale as one of the pioneer foundresses. There possibly is some slip-up of annalists on this matter: there could not have been two Sister M. Josephs in the community in 1858 . . . Perhaps Miss Leahy was known in religion as Sister Joseph Mary . . .

2. Archives: Convent of Mercy, Charleville.

3. Cook: *The Life of Florence Nightingale,* passim, i, ii.

4. W-Smith: *Florence Nightingale,* p. 140.

5. Leslie: 'Forgotten Passages in the Life of Florence Nightingale.' *The Dublin Review,* 161, October, 1917, p. 179 ff.

6. Archives, Kinsale.

7. W-Smith: *Florence Nightingale,* pp. 424-425. This biography ignores the Sisters. It merely states that the Jubilee celebrations were " planned around Miss Nightingale."

8. Doyle: *Memories of the Crimea,* p. 127.

9. Doyle: *Ibid.,* p. 128.

10. Bridgeman: *Diary,* p. 32.

11. Walsh: *These Splendid Sisters,* p. 137.

12. Burton: *So Surely Anchored,* p. 259.

# BIBLIOGRAPHY

1. *PRIMARY SOURCES : UNPUBLISHED*

A. The Archives from the following Convents of Mercy:

*Kinsale :*    i. The Bridgeman Diary.
        ii. Letters of Florence Nightingale.
       iii. Letters of Medical Officers, Protestant Chaplains and Lady Nurses employed in Scutari and Koulali.
       iv. Letters of Archbishop Paul Cullen; Most Rev. William Delany, Bishop of Cork; Very Rev. Wm. Yore, V.G., Dublin; Henry Edward Manning; Rev. William Ronan, S.J.; Rev. Michael Duffy, S.J.; Rev. Michael Gleeson, C.M.; Mary Stanley.
        v. Letters of Sidney Herbert; Sir John Hall; Mr. David Fitzgerald.
       vi. Letters of Catholic Chaplains.
      vii. Confidential Report of Mr. David Fitzgerald on the nursing system in the Crimean Hospitals.
     viii. Log-book of the hospitals in Scutari, Koulali and Balaclava, with Florence Nightingale's comments on same.
      xi. General Order issued by Lord Panmure on November 5, 1855; Reference No. 071/35.
        x. War Office Document, 155656/507, issued on May 19, 1856, to Dr. Manning, *sub manu* Benjamin Hawes, Secretary to Lord Panmure.
      xi. Newspaper cuttings.

*Charleville:*    The Diary of Sister M. Joseph Croke; a detailed account of events in Scutari, Koulali and Balaclava.
      Rhymed Version of above.
      Extracts from Community Annals.

*Cork :*    Letters written from the Crimea by Sister M. Paula Rice and Sister M. Aloysia Hurley.
      Extracts from Community Annals.

*Dublin:*    Extracts from Community Archives.

*Carlow:*    The Community Annals: Letters from Sister M. Aloysius Doyle and Sister M. Stanislaus Heyfron.

*Gort :*    Extracts from Community Annals.

*Liverpool :*    The Community Annals: Letters from Sisters M. Elizabeth Butler, Magdalen Alcock and Winifred Sprey.

*Chelsea :*    Extracts from the Community Annals.

*Bermondsey :*    A compilation of letters from Mother M. Clare Moore and her Sisters in Scutari.
      Letters from Bishop Grant of Southwark and from several Army Chaplains.

*Limerick :*    The Community Annals referring to the early life of Joanna Bridgeman.
      The Community Register.

B. *THE DUBLIN ARCHIEPISCOPAL ARCHIVES.* (The Chancellery, Archbishop's House, Drumcondra).

The Cullen Papers: Religiosae; non-catalogued: a collection of documents relative to the mission of the Sisters of Mercy to the Crimea. Letters from Dr. Grant of Southwark; from Mother Bridgeman and from the Army Chaplains to Archbishop Cullen. Also included is a copy of the terms secured at the War Office by Manning, with a copy of the General Orders issued to Lord William Paulet by Lord Panmure on April 27, 1855, *sub manu* Benjamin Hawes.

C. *THE ARCHIVES, ST. MARY OF THE ANGELS, BAYSWATER, LONDON.*

The correspondence of Dr. Henry Edward Manning with Mary Stanley in the period dating, October, 1854-April, 1856.

D. *DOCUMENTS FROM THE PUBLIC RECORDS OFFICE, LONDON.*

W.O. 1/369.
W.O. 1/370.
W.O. 1/371.
W.O. 2.
W.O. 14.
W.O. 28.
W.O. 32.
W.O. 55.
W.O. 60.

Miscellaneous reports: Headquarters Records; Commissariat Department; Old Whitehall Papers 1855-; Registrar's Department, Scutari Depot; Ordnance Office; and a letter book of the Board of General Officers to enquire into statements respecting supplies for the British Army in the Crimea.
War Office Order Books.
The Admiralty Records.

W.O. 93.
W.O. 60/42.
W.O. 43/97/155656, No. 411: part of a letter written by Florence Nightingale to Sidney Herbert in March, 1856, with marginal comments by one " N. Prescott ". This, the only Nightingale document in the Public Records Office, is on display in the Museum Department, Chancery Lane, London.

### 2. *PUBLISHED SOURCES*

A. *THE NIGHTINGALE PAPERS, BRITISH MUSEUM.*

MSS. 43,402; 35,789; 43,393.
These papers cover Miss Nightingale's correspondence with her sister, Lady Verney, and with Sidney Herbert during the period of her superintendence in the Crimea.

B. *THE HERBERT PAPERS, BRITISH MUSEUM.*

Additional MSS. 43,393-43,395.
These papers incorporate the correspondence of Sidney Herbert with Florence Nightingale, 1854-1861.

C. *HANSARD'S PARLIAMENTARY DEBATES.*

D. *DOCUMENTS FROM THE WAR OFFICE LIBRARY.*
  i. *Report upon the State of the Hospitals of the British Army in the Crimea and Scutari, together with an Appendix.*
  Presented to both Houses of Parliament by command of Her Majesty, 1855. (The Hospitals Commission.)
  ii. *First, Second and Third Report from the Select Committee on the Army before Sebastopol; with the proceedings of the Committee.*
  Ordered by the House of Commons to be printed, March 1, 1855. (The Roebuck Committee.)
  iii. *Report of the Commission of Inquiry into the Supplies of the British Army in the Crimea, with the Evidence Annexed.*
  Presented to both Houses of Parliament by command of Her Majesty, 1856. (The McNeill-Tulloch Commission.)
  iv. *The Journal of the Royal Army Chaplains' Department;* vols. iv, v, vi.


3. *WORKS CONSULTED*

(Place of publication: London; unless otherwise stated.)

Arnold, Thomas.    *A Catholic Dictionary;* (Kegan Paul, Trench & Co.).
Addis, William E.    London 1917.
Atkins, John Black, *The Life of Sir W. H. Russell, C.V.C., LL.D.,* 2 vols. (John Murray) 1911.
Abel-Smith, Brian. *A History of the Nursing Profession.* (Heinemann & Co.) 1960.
Baker, Rachel. *The First Woman Doctor:* The Story of Elizabeth Blackwell, M.D. (Julian Messner Inc.), 1944.
Barry, Michael J. *Lays of the War.* Cork, 1855.
*Battersby's Directory for the Whole World.* Dublin, 1848.
Bridgeman, Mother M. Francis. *A Guide for the Religious called Sisters of Mercy,* 1866.
Bruun, Geoffrey. *Nineteenth Century European Civilization.* (Oxford University Press). 1959.
Bryant, Alexander. *English Saga, 1840-1940.* (Collins, Eyre & Spottiswode) 1940.
Burke-Savage, R. S.J. *Catherine McAuley,* (Gill & Co.) Dublin 1945.
Burton, Doris. *The Loveliest Flower;* Ten Foundresses of Religious Congregations. (Burns & Oates). 1957.
Carroll, Sr. M. T. Austin. *Leaves from the Annals of the Sisters of Mercy;* 3 vols. (H. J. Hewitt.) New York, 1881.
Carty, James. *Ireland from Grattan's Parliament to the Great Famine, 1783-1850.* (Fallon & Co.). Dublin, 1949.
Cecil, Algernon. *Queen Victoria and her Prime Ministers.* (Eyre and Spottiswode) 1953.
Charques, R. D. *A Short History of Russia.* (C. Tinling & Co.) 1961.

Chesney, Kellow. *Crimean War Reader*. (Muller & Co.) 1961.

Clifford, Henry, V.C. *Letters and Sketches from the Crimea;* with an introduction by General Sir Bernard Paget, G.C.B., D.S.O., M.C. (Michael Joseph Ltd). 1956.

Brine, Frederick, Colborne, John. *Memorials of the Brave;* or the Resting Places of our Fallen Heroes in the Crimea and at Scutari. 2nd Edition. 1858.

Concannon, Helena. *The Irish Sisters of Mercy in the Crimean War.* (Irish Messenger Office). Dublin, 1950.

Cook, Sir Edward. *The Life of Florence Nightingale.* 2 vols. (Macmillan & Co.) 1913.

Cook, Sir Edward. *Delane of 'The Times'.* (Constable & Co.) 1915.

Cope, Zachary. *Florence Nightingale and the Doctors.* (Museum Press.) 1958.

Cummins, N. Marshall, M.B., F.R.C.P.I. *Some Chapters of Cork Medical History.* (University Press.) Cork, 1957.

Cunliffe, Marcus. *The Royal Irish Fusiliers.* (Oxford University Press). 1952.

Curtis, Edmund. *A History of Ireland.* (Methuen & Co.) 1936.

D'Alton, A. E. *A History of Ireland.* 3rd Edition. (Gresham Publishing Co.) Dublin, 1925.

Dance, E. H. *The Victorian Illusion.* (Heinemann Ltd.) 1928.

Darnell, Lilian M. *Nursing.* (Robert Hale Ltd.) 1959.

Davis, Elizabeth. *The Autobiography of Elizabeth Davis, a Balaclava Nurse.* Edited by Jane Williams. 2 vols. (Hurst & Blackett). 1857.

Devas, Rev. F. C. *Mother Magdalen Taylor,* 1921.

Dock, Lavinia L. Nutting, Adelaide. *A History of Nursing.* The Evolution of Nursing Systems from the Earliest Times to the Foundation of the first English and American Training Schools for Nurses. (Putnam's Sons). 1907.

Doyle, Sr. M. Aloysius. *Memories of the Crimea.* (Burns & Oates Ltd.) 1897.

Edwards, William. *Notes on British History.* Part IV. From the Treaty of Versailles to the end of Queen Victoria's reign. (Rivingtons) 1948.

Evans, Mary E. *The Spirit is Mercy.* (Newman Press). Westminster, Maryland, 1959.

Fay, C. A. *Souvenirs de la Guerre de Crimée.* Paris, 1867.

Fink, Leo. *Catholic Influences in the Life of Florence Nightingale* (C.T.S. Pamphlet). New York, 1946.

Fleetwood, John, M.B., D.P.H. *A History of Medicine in Ireland.* (Browne & Nolan). Dublin, 1951.

Fortescue, Hon. J. W. *A History of the British Army.* Vol. xiii. (Macmillan & Co.) 1930.

Furneaux, Rupert. *The First War Correspondent;* William Howard Russell of 'The Times' (Cassell & Co.) 1944.

Gavan-Duffy, Charles. *The League of North and South.* (Chapman & Hall). 1886.

Gibbs, Peter. *Crimean Blunder.* (Muller & Co.) 1960.

Goodman, Margaret. *The Experiences of an English Sister of Mercy.* (Smith, Elder & Co.) 1862.

Grant, A. J. *Europe in the Nineteenth and Twentieth Centuries, 1789-1950.* 6th edition. (Longmans Green & Co.) 1952.

Gretton, G. le M. *The Campaigns and History of the Royal Irish Regiment, 18th Foot. 1684-1902.* (Wm. Blackwood & Sons.) 1911.

Gwynn, Denis. *Nicholas, Cardinal Wiseman.* (Browne & Nolan). Dublin 1950.

Gwynn, Stephen. *A History of Ireland.* (Macmillan & Co). 1923.

Halevy, Elie. *A History of the English People in the Nineteenth Century.* Part IV. Victorian Years, 1841-'95. (Ernest Benn). 1950.

Harcave, Sidney. *Russia, A History.* (Claver-Hume Press). 1954.

Hawthorn, Nathaniel. *English Notebooks.* (Kegan Paul, Trench & Co.) 1883.

Hayes, Carlton J. H. *A Political and Social History of Modern Europe.* Vol. ii. Revised Edition. 1815-1925. (Macmillan & Co.) 1926.

Hayden, Mary.     *A Short History of the Irish People.* Part II; 1603-1925.
Moonan, George.     (Educational Company of Ireland). Dublin, 1925.

Hibbert, Christopher. *The Destruction of Lord Raglan.* (Longmans Green & Co.) 1961.

*A History of the Times.* Vol. ii. Printed in London at Printinghouse Square. 1939.

*History of the Great National Banquet* given to the Victorious Soldiers returned from the Crimean War and stationed in Irish Garrisons, by the People of Ireland in the City of Dublin, October 22nd, 1856.

Horn, D. B. *A History of Europe. Vol. iv.* 1789-1930. (Harrap & Co.) 1931.

Jackson, E. S. *The Inniskilling Dragoons.* (Arthur L. Humphries). 1909.

Jourdain, Lt. Col. J. H. T. *The Connaught Rangers.* Vol. iii. (Royal United Services Institution, Whitehall). 1924.

Joyce, James A. *Red Cross International and the Strategy of Peace.* (Hodder & Stoughton). 1959.

Kinglake, A. W. *The Invasion of the Crimea.* 9 vols. Listing the origins of the Crimean War and its progress down to the death of Lord Raglan. 6th edition. (Wm. Blackwood & Sons). 1887.

Lady Volunteer. *Eastern Hospitals and English Nurses.* An account of Twelve Months' Experience in the Hospitals of Koulali and Scutari. (Hurst & Blackett). 2 vols. 1856.

Lane-Poole, Stanley. *The Life of Lord Stratford de Redcliffe, Viscount Canning :* from his Memoranda and Private and Official Papers. 2 vols. (Longmans Green & Co.). 1888.

Lammond, D. *Florence Nightingale.* (Duckworth & Co.) 1935.

Laver, James. *Victorian Vista.* (Hulton Press). 1954.

Lawrence, John. *Russia in the Making.* (Allen & Unwin). 1957.

Leslie, Sir Shane. *Cardinal Manning, His Life and Labours.* (Burns Oates.) New York, 1954.

Lindsay, Donald.     *A Portrait of Britain between the Two Exhibitions,*
Washington, E. S.     *1851-1951.* (Clarendon Press, Oxford.) 1952.

Lipson, E. *Europe in the Nineteenth Century.* (A. C. Black, Ltd.) 1928.

Lucas, E. *The Life of Frederick Lucas, M.P.* (Burns Oates). 1886.

Lysons, Daniel. *The Crimean War from First to Last.* 1895.

Major, Ralph H. *War and Disease.* (Hutchinson's Scientific and Technical Publications). 1945.

*Memoir of the Right Honourable Sir John McNeill, G.C.B., and of his Second Wife, Elizabeth Wilson.* (By their Grand-Daughter). (John Murray). 1910.

Millis, Walter. *Armies and Men.* (Jonathan Cape). 1958.

Mitra, S. M. *The Life and Letters of Sir John Hall, M.D., K.C.B., F.R.C.S.,* (Longmans Green & Co) 1911.

Mooney, Rev. Canice, O.F.M. *An Irish Bishop in a Moorish Prison. Assisi,* Vol. xii, No. 3. (Assisi Press). Dublin. March, 1940.

Moran, Patrick Francis, D.D. *The Pastoral Letters and other Writings of Cardinal Cullen, Archbishop of Dublin.* (Browne & Nolan). Dublin, 1882. vol. i.

Morley, John. *The Life of William Ewart Gladstone.* 3 vols. (Macmillan & Co.) 1903.

Morris, G. W. *Nineteenth-Century Britain—and After.* (Pitman & Co). 1935.

Murphy, Denis. *They Did Not Pass By.* (Longmans Green & Co.) 1957.

Nightingale, Florence. *Notes on Nursing;* what it is and what it is not. (Harrison & Sons.) 1860. 2nd edition.

Osborne, Hon. & Rev. S. G. *Scutari and its Hospitals.* (Dickinson Brothers). 1855.

*The Panmure Papers.* A selection from the correspondence of Fox Maule, Second Baron Panmure, afterwards Eleventh Earl of Dalhousie. edited by Sir George Douglas, Bart. M.A., and Sir George Dalhousie Ramsay, C.B., late of the War Office; with a supplementary chapter by the late Rev. Principal Rainey, D.D. (Hodder & Stoughton). 1908.

Pavey, A. E. *The Story of the Growth of Nursing as an Art, a Profession and a Vocation.* (Faber & Faber). 1938.

Pincoffs, Peter, M.D. *Experiences of a Civilian in Eastern Military Hospitals.* (Williams & Norgate). 1857.

Purcell, E. S. *The Life of Cardinal Manning.* 2 vols. 1905.

Preston, Richard A    *Men in Arms.* A History of Warfare and its Inter-
Wise, Sidney F.,    relationships with Western Society. (Atlantic Press).
Werner, Herman C.    1956.

Ramsay, Grace. (K. O'Meara). *Thomas Grant, First Bishop of Southwark.* (Smith, Elder & Co.). 1886.

Reid, T. Wemyss. *Richard Monckton Milnes;* the Life, Letters and Friendship of R. M. Milnes, First Lord Houghton. (Cassell & Co.). 1890.

Reid, Douglas A. *Memories of the Crimean War.* 1911.

Reynolds, A. E. *Three Cardinals.* (Burns Oates Ltd.). 1959.

Rousset, Camille. *Histoire de la Guerre de Crimée.* 2 vols. (Libraire Hachette et Cie). Paris, 1877.

Russell, William H. *The War in the Crimea.* 2 vols. (Routledge & Co.). 1856.

Russell, William H. *The British Expedition to the Crimea.* (Routledge & Co.). 1858.

Russell, William H. *The Great War with Russia.* (Routledge & Co.). 1895.

Ryan, Rev. E. A., S.J. *The Sisters of Mercy.* An Important Chapter in Church History. Dublin, 1957.

*Selection of Parochial Examinations relative to the Destitute Classes in Ireland;* from the Evidence received by His Majesty's Commissioners for Enquiring into the condition of the Poorer Classes in Ireland. Published by Authority; (Miliken & Co.). Dublin, 1835.

Simpson, Donald H. *Henry Press Wright, First Archdeacon of Columbia.* Published in *The British Columbia Historical Quarterly.* Vol. xix. Nos. 3 and 4. July-October, 1955.

Skene, J. H. *With Lord Stratford in the Crimean War*. (Richard Bentley & Sons). 1883.

Smith, Rev. Joseph, C.P. *Paul Mary Pakenham, Passionist*. 1915.

Stanley, Arthur P. *Memoirs of Edward and Catherine Stanley*. 3rd Edition (John Murray). 1880.

Stanley, Mary. *Hospitals and Sisterhoods* (John Murray). 1854.

Stanmore, Lord. *Memoir of Sidney Herbert, Lord Herbert of Lea*. 2 vols. (John Murray). 1906.

Steevens, Nathaniel. *The Crimean Campaign with the Connaught Rangers, 1854-'56*. (Griffith & Farran). 1878.

Steinberg, S. H. *A Short History of Germany*. (Cambridge University Press). 1944.

Strachey, Lytton. *Eminent Victorians*. (Chatto & Windus). 1918.

Taylor, A. J. P. *The Course of German History*. A Survey of the development of Germany since 1815. (H. Hamilton). 1945.

Thomas, Dana Lee. *Living Biographies of Famous Women*. (W. H. Allen & Co.). 1959.
Thomas, Henry.

de Toqueville, Alexis. *Journeys in England and Ireland*. (Faber & Faber). 1958.

Trevelyan, G. McAuley, *British History in the Nineteenth Century and After, 1782-1919*. (Longmans Green & Co.). 1937.

Tulloch, Alexander. *The Crimean Commission and the Chelsea Board*: being a Review of the Proceedings and Report of the Board. (Harrison & Sons). 1857.

Wadham, Juliana. *The Case of Cornelia Connelly*. (Collins & Co.). 1958.

Walpole, Spencer. *The Life of Lord John Russell*. 2 vols. (Longmans Green & Co.). 1889.

Walsh, James J. *These Splendid Sisters*. (Sears & Co.). New York, 1927.

Walsh, James J. *The World's Debt to the Irish*. (The Stratford Company) Boston, 1926.

Ward, Wilfrid. *The Life of John Henry, Cardinal Newman*. 2 vols. (Longmans Green & Co.). 1912.

Weymouth, Anthony. *This Century of Change*. (Harper & Co.). 1953.

Whyte, J. H. *The Independent Irish Party, 1850-'59*. (Oxford University Press). 1958.

Williams, T. J. *Priscilla Lydia Sellon*. (S.P.C.K.). 1950.

Wilson, P. H. *The Greville Diary*. 2 vols. (Pitman & Co.). 1927.

Wood, General Sir Evelyn, V.C., G.C.B., G.C.M.G. *The Crimea in 1854 and 1894* (Chapman & Hall). 1896.

Woodham-Smith, Cecil. *Florence Nightingale*. (Constable & Co). 1951.

Woodham-Smith, Cecil. *The Reason Why*. (Constable & Co.). 1953.

Wright, Henry Press. *England's Duty to England's Army*. (The Royal Empire Society). 1858.

## 4. *PERIODICALS.*

*The Dublin Review*, 161, October, 1917.

Crimean War special Centenary Issue of *The Tablet*, March 27, 1956.

*The Lamp;* an Illustrated Catholic Magazine, published in London by C. Dolman & Company. Circulation suspended after 1925.

*The British Columbia Historical Quarterly*. Vol. xix. Nos. 3 and 4. July-October, 1955.

## 5. *NEWSPAPERS.*

i. *The Cork Examiner.*
ii. *The Cork Constitution* or *The Daily Advertiser.*
iii. *The Freeman's Journal.*
iv. *The Tablet.*


Dates for which examined: All issues from June, 1854-July, 1856.

# INDEX

337